A. Einstein

B. KUZNETSOV

EINSTEIN

Phaedra

New York

Translated from the Russian by V. T A L M Y

Phaedra Inc.
First Printing March 1970   .

CONTENTS

INTRODUCTION

He was a man, take him for all in all.

S h a k e s p e a r e. *"Hamlet"*

Hamlet's ideal of a man was that of the Renaissance and the new times. His father, the late King, was to him a harmonious personification of thought embodied in action. Hamlet himself was a personification of thought seeking such embodiment. The 17th century adopted and gave concrete expression to the new ideal. The new man deserves his name when he is no longer satisfied with the harmony and subtlety of his own logical constructions, as was characteristic of the Middle Ages, but seeks the harmony of the real world and its assertion in life. Hamlet's remark—like the whole tragedy of the Prince of Denmark, like all of Shakespeare's work—is a programme for the new times. 17th-century rationalism departed from the scholastic tradition of self-contained ratiocination and turned to nature, to the natural sciences and practical experience. Its claims to independence were based on the conformation of mental constructions to reality.

The 18th century was an age of direct revolutionary intervention of rational thinking into public life.

The 19th-century science, having convinced itself of the infinite complexity of the universe, became more human. It was no longer canonised and scholars were busy pushing back its frontiers and verifying it.

In the 20th century science came closer still to the people. The unshakable classical laws which had nurtured the idea of apriority were found to be inexact, and new and more precise laws took their place. In spite of the complexity and incomprehensibility of the new concepts people felt that they were bringing science down to earth from the Olympus of *a priori* knowledge, echoing in a way the great feat of Prometheus. Great events were in the making on earth and a science which stopped short of nothing in the quest for truth and harmony appealed to people. Being children of an age destined to go down in history as an age of revolutions, they took to the new, paradoxical world picture.

The development of scientific thinking displays what seems to be a contradiction: as science departed from anthropomorphic positions it grew more human. This of course is not surprising because anthropomorphism, which is the attribution of human characteristics to things not human, leads to the idea of divine revelation as the source of true knowledge. The new science broke away from this idea. The less science is restricted by direct subjective observations, the deeper it penetrates into the objective laws of nature, the closer it is to man, and the more human it becomes. Strange as it may seem, but in the early 17th century the geocentric objectification of direct observation—the sun travelling around the earth—represented the standpoint of closed circles, while the most paradoxical heliocentric ideas of Galileo, which contradicted apparent observation, were debated with animation and sympathy in the streets of Italian towns.

In the 20th century a scientist can achieve the highest repute ("a man, take him for all in all") if he propounds a theory severing as drastically, if not more so, with dogmas and dogmatic "self-evidence". Even more than before, the antidogmatic paradoxicality of science conditions its appeal to man. The spirit and the people of the 20th century combine to draw science away from "self-evident" propositions. Characteristic of the age is a turn to generalised conceptions. The time has passed when the contributions of science to practical needs are restricted to specific findings. The fundamental scientific ideas, the notions of space and time, the universe and its evolution, the smallest particles of matter, in short, the world picture as a whole have become an immediate source of industrial and technological change as well as of changes in the mode of thinking and outlook of men.

The farther a scientist progresses from particular questions to the general picture of the universe the closer his work approaches the urgent problems of mankind as a whole. More, the most paradoxical general conceptions of the world, which break radically with the old way of thinking, present the straightest road to these problems. The theoretical foundations for far-reaching changes in human life are provided by conceptions lying far beyond the sphere of direct observation, conceptions involving velocities approaching that of light and spatial domains of millions of light years and trillionths of a centimetre, and revealing completely paradoxical (from the viewpoint of classical science) relationships.

Today "self-evidence" must be rejected even more emphatically than in the first half of the century. Niels Bohr once remarked in connection with Heisenberg's unified theory of elementary particles: "This is undoubtedly a mad theory. The only thing is whether it is mad enough to be true." This statement offers a good idea of the situation in science.

Modern science, and not only physics, is bound to advance "mad" ideas breaking completely with traditional views and therefore apparently paradoxical. On the order of the day is a repudiation of the classical fundaments of natural science, a repudiation even more sweeping than the one which, in the first quarter of the century, marked the beginnings of the contemporary views on space, time and the structure and motion of matter.

The history of science knows of many drastic turns to "mad", paradoxical notions. Usually they soon cease to be "mad", turn into trivial truths, and come to be regarded as natural, "the only possible", all but a priori qualities of knowledge, and in any case "self-evident". Once the road to the summit has been blazed, it seems so natural and obvious that one finds it hard to realise how paradoxical the original choice had seemed and what "mad" courage had been required to leave the beaten path which had once seemed the only possible one.

After a theory sheds its "paradoxicality" and becomes "self-evident" the nimbus of "madness" passes on to the man who had enunciated it. A scholar's biography records not the upshot of his scientific achievement but the gradient of scientific progress associated with it, the rate of increase in human knowledge, the derivative of knowledge with respect to time, the upsweep of the curve of knowledge. The difference between science and its history lies in that history deals not so much in knowledge and levels attained as in derivatives with respect to time, in transitions from ignorance to knowledge and from error to truth. Periods when reliable information about physical reality tends to accumulate at an unusually high rate become turning points in the history of science. In the historic aspect the results of a scientific discovery are correlated to the level of knowledge preceding it; the degree of escalation is not reduced by the fact that the new-fangled ideas may later become commonplace. Introducing an analogy with concepts to be discussed later on, we could say that an evaluation of a contribution to science, of the difference between two successive levels, is independent of the aspect from which it is undertaken, just as an addition to a Cartesian coordinate is independent of the point of origin of the coordinate system in which it is investigated. A contribution to knowledge retains its significance no matter how far we may have progressed since it was made. Thus, the transition from the idea of a flat earth to that of a globe is as remarkable today as it was in the days of Ancient Greece when the hypothesis was first enunciated. No great change in the scientific world picture, no crucial juncture in the history of science ever loses its portent, and the gulf between two successive stages in science never narrows, the abruptness, paradoxicality and "madness" of the leap to a higher level are as awe-inspiring as ever.

In the biography of a scientist such crucial junctures are viewed through the prism of his life and work in relation to his scientific temperament and inner world, in relation to the world around him. The measure of genius is to be found in the rate of scientific progress, the gradient of science, its derivative with respect to time.

A brainful of facts and figures does not yet make a genius. A genius contributes to previous knowledge, and it is this contribution which provides insight into both his intellectual and emotional worlds.

As Heine said, a dwarf standing on a giant's shoulders may see farther ahead, but "no giant heart beats in his chest".

The following trailing in the wake of a genius may possess a greater baggage of factual knowledge than their idol: but they contribute nothing, or almost nothing, to man's earlier knowledge because they lack the driving "spirit of Dr. Faust" in their thoughts, emotions and temperaments.

The measured beat of a giant heart is clearly heard in the story of Einstein's life. The true measure of his scientific achievement can be grasped only when one realises that never before had a more paradoxical and drastic transition to a new world picture been propounded than was the transition from Newtonian conceptions to the ideas of Einstein. It was a generalisation and completion of the work begun by Newton, but it caused a revolution in science.

For two centuries Newton's system had been regarded as the ultimate solution of the fundamental problems of science, as the final and preordained picture of the world. This estimation is reflected in Alexander Pope's verse:

> *Nature and Nature's law lay hid in night;*
> *God said, let Newton be! and all was light.*

Then came Einstein with his theory of relativity, and some wit added the lines:

> *But not for long. Let Einstein be! the Devil said,*
> *And lo, 'twas dark: the light had fled.*

The conclusion implicit in these two lines is a reflection of the widespread notion that rejection of the fundaments of Newtonian mechanics was tantamount to a rejection of a scientific understanding of the objective world. Dogmatic thinking identifies a given stage in scientific advance with science as a whole; it regards transition to a new stage as nothing short of the total collapse of science; it may pull science back to the old position or it may deny science the objective credibility of its findings; but it can never comprehend that the essence of science lies in a continuous evolution towards a more and more faithful description of the real world.

Viewed in this perspective, every revolution in science is an apotheosis of progress.

Like Newton's mechanics, relativity theory is more than just another milestone in the history of science. It has changed the very mode of thinking of men, it is a milestone in the history of man's spiritual development. Applications of relativity theory have served to change the material conditions of human society.

Einstein enunciated his theory in an age which will forever be seen as the great era in which man spanned the distance from the kingdom of necessity to the kingdom of freedom, when he opened a new chapter in his history. The advent of relativity theory meant that science had come of age. It had at long last shed its puerile anthropocentrism, the idea of man as the centre of the universe, the absolutised picture of the world lying before the terrestrial observer.

In ancient times anthropocentrism found expression in the absolute notion of up and down, incompatible with the idea of a spherical world. According to this world picture antipodes "down under" would necessarily "fall off the earth".

The image of a round earth developed in Ancient Greece required acceptance of the notion of the relative nature of "up" and "down", the notion that every direction in space is as good as the other, that space is, in short, isotropic. The globe, however, remained the centre of the universe, and from this standpoint motion relative to the earth was absolute motion. Thus the statements "this body is in motion relative to the earth" and "the earth is in motion relative to this body" describe different processes, the former being absolutely true, and the latter absolutely false.

Copernicus destroyed the geocentric system. But the new centre of the universe, the sun, did not occupy its exalted position for very long: the universe of Giordano Bruno and Galileo had no centre, no fixed reference point.

The concept of absolute motion of a given body not referred to other bodies remained, however. Up to the end of the 19th century, it was assumed that optical processes in moving bodies proceeded in some way differently than in bodies at rest; this difference gave meaning to the word "motion" without reference to another body relative to which the given body could be said to be moving. All of space was assumed to be pervaded by an absolutely fixed stationary ether; a moving body was thought to create an "ether wind" just as a running man feels the wind flowing around his body.

This view was thrown overboard by Albert Einstein in 1905 in a paper entitled "On the Electrodynamics of Moving Bodies" ("Elektrodynamik bewegter Körper") published in the September issue of the German scientific journal *Annalen der Physik*. In this article Einstein postulated the constancy of the velocity of light in all bodies moving with respect to one another without acceleration.

Shortly after that the theory of relativity was clothed in the mathematical formalism of four-dimensional geometry. In conventional three-dimensional space the position of any point is determined by three numbers. Addition of a fourth number, time, gives geometrical meaning to the concept of an *event* as a localisation of a material particle at a given point at a given instant. Four-dimensional geometry and the concept of four-dimensional space-time were used to develop the laws governing such *events*, i.e., the locations of material particles at different points and times (in other words, the laws of motion of particles and bodies comprising them).

The special theory of relativity outlined by Einstein in 1905 lays down that internal processes take place in bodies in the same manner irrespective of their uniform motion in a straight line. Internal effects of motion are not present in the case of *inertia, or coasting motion*. Later on, in 1916, Einstein extended the principle of relativity to accelerated motion. The rest of his life was devoted to the elaboration of a unified field theory which would include the laws of gravitation and electromagnetic field as special cases.

Why did these highly abstract problems arouse such great interest in such wide circles? Why did this interest extend to the man who tackled them more than has ever been the case with other new theories? Why do men see Einstein as a personification of 20th-century science with all its unprecedented opportunities and hazards?

It is the answers to these questions that define the basic features of our century. Man today is concerned with channelling science to sane applications and removing the threat of annihilation that it carries. In this quest of his he must reckon not only with the content of various scientific theories, he must also reckon with the sanity and the conscience of science. Einstein personified the latter two qualities. It is this aspect of the man that appeals most to the non-scientific community. The idea of the objective "extra-personal" world and its cognisability and paradoxicalness, the driving force behind the never ending pursuit for new, more precise and more general concepts gradually crystallised throughout his life. It is a record of the eternal struggle of reason against all forms of mystic anti-intellectualism. It also shows a growing realisation of the public responsibility of science.

The meaning and purport of Einstein's life can be traced through his scientific works, public pronouncements and letters to friends and colleagues. It is presented in his two autobiographical articles, one written in 1955, a month before his death,[1] and the more comprehensive *Autobiographical Notes*.[2] The latter is hardly an autobiography in the conventional sense, though this is probably hardly surprising.

"Here I sit," Einstein begins, "in order to write, at the age of 68, something like my own obituary." He goes on to describe how the desire gradually grew in him to discover the rational laws of the universe. He sets forth his epistemological credo and goes "back to the obituary" and the origins of his mathematical interests. The bulk of the article is devoted to an analysis of the main physical ideas from the 17th to the 19th century—Newtonian mechanics, thermodynamics, electrodynamics—and finally the physical ideas that emerged in our century. After reviewing Newton's mechanics Einstein writes:

" 'Is this supposed to be an obituary?' the astonished reader will likely ask. I would like to reply: essentially, yes. For the essential in the being of a man of my type lies precisely in *what* he thinks and *how* he thinks, not in what he does or suffers. Consequently, the obituary can limit itself in the main to the communicating of thoughts which have played a considerable role in my endeavours."

We shall refer to Einstein's autobiography on many occasions in discussing his world outlook and the sources of his great discoveries.

Einstein called his autobiography an "obituary" because it sums up his work and his views. It is presented in historical perspective. He singles out from the kaleidoscope of life the events which make it a part of the intellectual history of mankind. Never before has scientific history merged more completely with a scientist's life. This is a sure sign of a genius. For only the life of a genius merges so completely with the life of the human race as a whole. The interests of such a man are in unison with the requirements of develop-

---

[1] Printed in *Helle Zeit—Dunkle Zeit. In Memoriam Albert Einstein*, edited by Carl Seelig, Europa Verlag, Zurich 1956, S. 9-17. (Afterwards referred to as *Helle Zeit*.)

Translator's note: Quotations from all non-English sources have been translated into English from the Russian, as quoted in the Russian original.

[2] *Albert Einstein: Philosopher-Scientist*, edited by Paul A. Schilpp, Tudor, New York, 1951, pp. 3-95. (Afterwards referred to as *Philosopher-Scientist*.)

ing science, his quest follows the ways of science, his accomplishments advance science to new and higher levels. In Einstein the fusion with science was probably greater than in any physicist before him.

It is not surprising, therefore, that ideas of personal greatness were completely alien to Einstein and he always brushed aside with his frank, hearty, childlike laughter any attempts to attach the epithet of genius to his name. Contemplation of the self is a part of the "merely personal" from which a genius disengages when he achieves "the mental grasp of the extrapersonal world".

The contrasting of the "merely personal" and the "extrapersonal" with which Einstein begins his *Autobiographical Notes* determines the composition of the "obituary". Emphasis is laid on the retrospective nature of Einstein's life story, with attention focused on its major, truly historic milestones. Later on we shall discuss this important aspect of the autobiography in greater detail. Here we shall only note that an account of Einstein's life should follow, to some extent at least, the fabric of his autobiography. Accordingly, we shall detract frequently from chronological order in tracing Einstein's philosophical evolution and undertake to form generalisations designed to show how his life fused with the development of science. If we achieve this we shall have a biography of a genius. For a story of Einstein's life must necessarily proceed from generalisations of the advance of history as embodied in the life-work of the creator of relativity theory. Yet historical generalisations alone are not enough to a biography of Einstein. The three generations of Einstein's contemporaries cherish the smallest details of his life, his looks, his habits, his manner of speech. People remember him not only for his mighty intellect, but also for his humanism, kindness and charm.

Despite the abstract nature of his ideas, despite his constant flight from the "merely personal", which constituted the meaning of his life, Einstein is not seen by ordinary people as a featureless prophet, a bearer of "tablets of the Law" from the summits of abstract thought. The reason can be found in an analysis of his world outlook and in the purport of his scientific exploit. Einstein knew—in fact he proceeded from the consideration—that speculative reasoning, even if its logical structure is beyond reproach, cannot by itself unravel the laws of nature. We can say that Einstein did discover the new "tablets of the Law", the new world equations, confirmed by experiment, which invalidated the old tablets, but it was not a case of bringing the Law from Mount Sinai. On the contrary, he elevated principles discovered here on earth to the status of world equations.

The disciples of founders of dogmatic doctrines are prone to elevate their masters to divine status. Einstein is not threatened with such a fate. The non-dogmatic nature of relativity theory, with its absence of *a priori* concepts, is in complete harmony with the image of its founder. Einstein was still a boy when he began his quest for a rational world system. Yet even then he eschewed the idea of some *a priori* skeleton as being responsible for the general *ratio* governing the turbulent flow of physical reality. As he saw it, *ratio*, order, harmony are characteristics of the "extra-personal" world, which is independent of the conscience.

Great ideas embracing the universe spring from the external well of empirical knowledge; they find confirmation in it, they change, evolve towards greater generalisations and body forth in concrete form. Viewed from this aspect, scientific ideas do not appear as revelations, nor their propounders as prophets, neither in their own eyes nor in the eyes of mankind.

Einstein concludes his *Autobiographical Notes* with the words: "This exposition has fulfilled its purpose if it shows the reader how the efforts of a life hang together and why they have led to expectations of a definite form."[1]

He presents the principal tendencies in his scientific work, and the quoted conclusion can be regarded as a statement of the connection between them. Einstein's life-work displays a remarkable logical harmony of the same order as the orderly, rational and unified world which he sought in the maze of random observations and experiments. This is not just a figure of speech. The life of every great scholar is, in the final analysis, found to be subordinated to a single mental exploit. Einstein, however, stands out among the explorers of nature in respect of the harmony of his scientific interests and mode of thinking. One could even speak of the music of his work, for the succession of Einstein's ideas in time makes such a natural series that his biographer need

[1] *Philosopher-Scientist*, p. 95.

hardly waste his time seeking the inner logic of the events in Einstein's work, so apparent it is. More, his intimate life was in complete accord with the logic of his scientific exploit. In his autobiography Einstein sought to detract from the fortuitous and personal in order to present the "extra-personal" evolution of his ideas. And this is also true of his own being. Reading Einstein's biography is like listening to a musical piece in which every note is uniquely determined by the dominant theme.

There are formulas in the autobiography which link Einstein's own career as a scientist with the progress of science as a whole. I had thought of applying these formulas and calling this book *Flight From Wonder*, as Einstein defines the overcoming of the "wondering" which occurs in the face of a paradoxical fact and the inclusion of that fact in a rational system of the world.

I had also thought of calling this book *Flight From Self-Evidence*. It is the customary and habitual that seem "self-evident", and the duty of science, as Einstein saw it, is to develop new concepts which, though clashing with "obvious" logical schemes and observations, are in agreement with more precise experiments and more precise, strict and orderly logical patterns.

Finally, I had thought of calling my book about Einstein *Flight From the Merely Personal*. Einstein writes in his auto-biography: "In a man of my type the turning point of the development lies in the fact that gradually the main interest disengages itself to a far-reaching degree from the momentary and merely personal and turns towards the striving for a mental grasp of things."[1]

These formulas give an insight into the remarkable whole-ness of Einstein's character, the harmony of the mental and the emotional in his character.

The Einstein absorbed in computations designed to answer the question of the finality or infinity of the universe, and the Einstein spending his time copying off in his own hand the text of his original paper on relativity to sponsor a public fund raising campaign (the recopied manuscript was purchased for several million dollars and handed over to the Library of Congress): these are two facets of the same image,

[1] *Philosopher-Scientist*, p. 7.

and one feels that Einstein could not act otherwise. Only a man who never thought of himself could disengage so completely from the "merely personal" and pursue so doggedly a theory clashing with the evidence of observation, the evidence of logic and millennium-old tradition, a veritably "mad" theory, in the best sense of the word. In this respect Einstein's absolute moral integrity is inseparable from the titanic power of his mind.

In his *First Recollections,* Lev Tolstoi tells a fable of a green wand with the secret of human happiness engraved on it together with other secrets that can be discovered if the owner of the wand can keep his mind off certain trivialities for the duration of one hour. In science, possession of such a green wand can be gained only by dint of supreme concentration of the mind, unswerving in the face of any obstacles whatsoever, a concentration which leaves no room for unrelated thoughts in a mind completely disengaged from the momentary and merely personal.

Presented as the story of a concerted, purposeful quest for the increasingly more universal and exact world laws, Einstein's life history can be divided into three periods.

In the first, with adolescence came the initial striving for the "extra-personal", the search for the meaning of life which led to interest in natural science and the desire to probe the laws governing the objective world. Einstein's student days marked the maturing of his world outlook and the acquisition of the mathematical and physical knowledge whose synthesis later led to the development of the special theory of relativity.

The second period embraces his generalisation of relativity theory for accelerated motion. This work was crowned by the enunciation of the general theory of relativity and the emergence of the new cosmology based on it. The period ended with the confirmation of special relativity by direct observation in a solar eclipse and universal acclaim of the theory.

The third period passed, retrospectively speaking, under the sign of the approaching atomic age. In the twenties the microcosmic theory of quantum mechanics was developed. Einstein was critical of some of its propositions. He himself was busy elaborating (or rather attempting to elaborate) a unified field theory.

Einstein and his contemporaries are in general disagreement, more or less, as to their evaluation of this period of his life, from the late 1920s to the end. To Einstein the ideas which he pursued over the latter thirty years of his life represented the ultimate of the "extra-personal" towards which he strove. All those years he devoted himself largely to the search for a new theory capable of explaining, on the basis of unified propositions, the totality of phenomena associated with gravity, electromagnetic field and other fields of force.

Most appraisals of Einstein's work, including biographical studies, proceed from the apparent fruitlessness of his quest. Yet today, in the 1960s, trends are appearing which already call for a reassessment of earlier appraisals. They offer new insight into the tremendous mental effort which had consumed a good half of Einstein's life. An analysis of these trends and some forecasts concerning the future of the theory of elementary particles are therefore essential before final judgement can be pronounced on the outcome of Einstein's life-work.

Chapter 1
ADOLESCENCE

His truthfulness and sense of justice, which earned him the nickname Biedermeier (Honest John), verged on the morbid. What had then seemed morbid is seen today as an expression of inborn, indestructible instinct. Those who know Einstein, the man and the scientist, know that that childish morbidity was but a forerunner of his unshakable moral integrity.

M o s z k o w s k i

The environment into which Albert Einstein was born brought him very early in life into contact with two diametrically opposed historical traditions. They confronted him many times afterwards, all his life, in fact. One was the rationalist tradition. It was firmly rooted in Swabia, the land of his birth, its roots reaching out to Alsace and France. The other was the tradition of blind faith in the infallibility of the police state, depicted in such bold relief by Heinrich Mann in his *Untertan*. Its heralds were the Prussian officers and bureaucrats who were swarming into Southern Germany to enforce the law and order of the newly founded Empire. Einstein personified the rationalist tradition. The purpose of his life was cognition of the great rational world harmony. His world of paradoxes, to be sure, is a far cry from the ossified world picture from which the disciples of 18th-century classical rationalism proceeded. But the accompaniments of the rationalist outlook inherited from the 18th century—belief in the independence of reason, Voltaire's irony and tolerance, defence of man's natural aspirations against the encroachments of tyranny as proclaimed by Rousseau—remained to a greater or lesser degree in the customs and ideas of Einstein's environment and, associated with early impressions, lived on in him. The hostile tradition also persisted in the environment, acquiring during Einstein's lifetime dimensions and forms which made it a menace to the very existence of civilisation.

Albert Einstein was born on March 14, 1879, at Ulm, an old German town on the left bank of the Danube River, at the foothills of the Swabian Alps. Its history dates back to the 9th century. Once an eminent and thriving member of the Swabian union of towns, it became a big fortress in the 16th century and took part in the struggle of the Protestant princes against the Catholic Church and the Emperor. Ulm has gone down in the history of the Napoleonic wars as the place where the Austrian army under Mack suffered a terrible defeat.

By the Vienna peace treaty of 1809, which sealed Austria's defeat, Ulm became part of the Kingdom of Württemberg. In 1842 the old fortifications were restored and reconstructed by Prussian engineers, and its twelve forts and turrets straddled the Danube. This time they faced against France.

In the 1870s Ulm continued to preserve the external features of a medieval Swabian community: narrow, winding streets lined with gabled houses and dominated by a massive 15th-century Gothic cathedral with a five-hundred-foot tower. The tower offered a splendid view to anyone caring to climb it: undulating country stretching to the hills of the Tirol and Switzerland, the Swabian Alps, the fields of Bavaria and Württemberg in the distance, and at one's feet, the rugged outline of the Wilhelmsburg citadel and the surrounding forts, the town hall, market place, a small foundry works, and several textile mills. Thirty thousand inhabitants: cloth and leather merchants, labourers, artisans, foundrymen, weavers, masons, cabinetmakers, makers of the famous Ulm pipes, furniture makers, brewers—most of them native Swabs, two-thirds Catholic and one-third Lutheran, with a sprinkling of several hundred Jews whose way of life hardly differed from that of the rest of the populace.

The spoken language was the melodius Swabian idiom, which persisted for quite a time in Einstein's speech, and the whole life in the speech of his second wife, Elsa. To her he was always "Albertle", the land was "Ländle", the city (Stadt) "Städtle".[1] Clashing with this soft emotional dialect

---

[1] Philipp Frank, *Einstein. His Life and Times*, Jonathan Cape, London, 1950, p. 4.

was the harsh, clipped speech of the Prussian newcomers. The resulting dissonance was an expression and a symbol of the gulf between the two ideological and cultural traditions mentioned at the beginning of the chapter. The petty-bourgeois circles of Württemberg could boast a degree of broadmindedness and religious and national tolerance, as opposed to the extreme nationalism, bigotry and haughty intolerance commonly associated with the notion of "Prussianism".

In the circle to which the Einstein family belonged, Heine, Lessing and Schiller were honoured by Jews and Christians alike and their works stood on the shelves side by side with the Bible or the Gospel, as the case might be. Schiller, in particular, was extremely popular, not least for the frequent occurrence of the dear Swabian idiom in his books.

Hermann Einstein, Albert's father, who was good at mathematics, had once dreamed of entering a university after completing his course at a Stuttgart gymnasium. Instead, however, he was forced to go into business. In 1878 he married Pauline Koch, daughter of a rich Stuttgart grain merchant, and settled in Ulm where Hermann Einstein's parents had been living since 1868 and where there were many relatives. In Ulm, Hermann Einstein opened up an electrical goods shop. Fifteen miles from Ulm, in Hechingen, lived Hermann's cousin Rudolf with his daughter Elsa, Albert's coeval and future wife. The kinship was even closer on the maternal side, for Elsa's mother was Pauline Koch's sister.

In 1880, a year after Albert's birth, the family moved to Munich where Hermann and his brother Jakob set up an electrical workshop. When Albert was five they moved to Sendling, a suburb of Munich, where they built a house and a small factory for manufacturing dynamos, arc lamps and measuring instruments. All that remained of Pauline's dowry was invested in the project.

In 1881 a girl, Maja, was born into the family. Almost the same age, the two children, Maja and Albert, became great friends and the garden surrounding their home in Sendling was their playground.

Hermann Einstein imbued his children with a love of nature. Excursions in the picturesque country around Munich were a family custom in which numerous relatives took part.

Sometimes Rudolf Einstein would come from Hechingen with Elsa.

Pauline Einstein was a great lover of music. She played the piano and sang. Her favourite composer was Beethoven, and above all she loved his sonatas. The family loved music and classical German literature.

Hermann Einstein's brother Jakob lived with the family. He was a good engineer and it was he who developed in Albert a liking for mathematics. The brothers handled the affairs of their electrical factory together, Hermann looking after the commercial and Jakob the engineering aspects of the business. They were not successful businessmen, however, and the family was never well-off.

Albert was a quiet, reserved child. He shunned friends and took no part in the boisterous games of other children. Playing soldiers was especially distasteful to him. The strains of military brass bands sounded up and down the country, troops marched through the streets of towns with crowds of enthusiastic boys keeping step at their heels while the burghers lined the pavements and viewed with pride the marching young empire, pleased at the new opportunities opening up to their offspring. Poor little Albert, however, clung to his father's hand and cried and begged to take him home. The din and racket frightened him and got on his nerves.

In due course the time for school came. Elementary education in Germany was conducted on a denominational basis and the schools were controlled by the clergy of different religious groups. The Jewish school was far from home, and besides, the fee was beyond the Einsteins' circumstances. Albert was placed in a nearby Catholic school. It was there that his schoolmates first noted his "morbid sense" of justice, to use the expression of Alexander Moszkowski, one of Einstein's first biographers, who interviewed him in 1920.[1] It was probably there, in the elementary school, that Einstein got his first taste of anti-semitism. "There were not many Jewish children in the school and it was here that the first drops from the wave of anti-semitism which threatened to engulf the school from outside spattered little Albert. For

[1] A. Moszkowski, *Einstein. Einblicke in seine Gedankenwelt,* Entwickelt aus Gesprächen mit Einstein von Alexander Moszkowski, Hamburg-Berlin, 1921, S. 220.

the first time a hostile dissonance rushed in to jar the simple and harmonic world of his soul."[1]

This may not have been the first dissonance of its kind in his life, for there was also the subconsciously felt dissonance of Prussian fifes and drums against the background of classical music, and the dissonance of gutteral peremptory shouts against the background of the soft, emotionally coloured speech of the natives of Southern Germany. Many years had to pass, of course, before Einstein could observe the common features inherent in the different manifestations of the evil, irrational force opposed to the reason and harmony for which his soul had always craved. At the time the spatter of anti-semitism had hurt the little boy, not because he was its victim, but because it ran contrary to the ideals of reason and justice which had already taken root in his mind. In any case, it should be said that never, then or subsequently, had it aroused in Einstein a feeling of national isolation; on the contrary, it planted in his soul the germs of international solidarity of men of like mind.

At the age of ten Albert entered the Luitpold gymnasium in Munich. The atmosphere there had nothing in common with the boy's inclinations and disposition. The "classical education" had degenerated into a cramming of Latin and Greek grammar, and history into a tedious chronology of events. The teachers were more like army officers, with the pupils as the "other ranks". Recalling the time, Einstein once commented: "The teachers in the elementary school appeared to me like sergeants, and in the gymnasium the teachers were like lieutenants." The general dreary background was not, however, without its bright spots. There was in the gymnasium a teacher by the name of Ruess who really tried to reveal to his pupils the spirit of ancient civilisation, its influences on classical and contemporary German culture, and the continuity of the cultural life of epochs and generations. The delight he derived during readings of *Herman and Dorothea*, that masterpiece of romantic sentimentalism, remained deeply engraved in Einstein's memory. He would seek every opportunity to speak with Ruess and gladly submitted to the punishment of staying on after school, without lunch, whenever Ruess was there to

[1] A. Moszkowski, op. cit., S. 220.

22

conduct the extra period. Years later, when Einstein was a professor at Zurich, he passed through Munich and decided to call on Ruess. But the name of the young man in the worn suit meant nothing to the old teacher. Ruess imagined that his caller wanted to approach him for money and received him very coldly. There was nothing left for Einstein but to depart in all haste.

The years went by and Albert passed duly from form to form. A reticent, quiet boy, he showed no brilliance in his studies. As a matter of fact the precision and depth of his answers escaped the shallow minds of the teachers, who were exasperated by his slow manner of speech.

Meanwhile brainstorms were brewing in the boy's head. He sought in the greater world and the social environment the harmony which would be in tune with his inner world. Albert's initial religiousness soon collapsed under the impact of natural science. The textbooks at school could not reveal the world harmony to his inquiring mind. This he found in some popular scientific books recommended to him by Max Talmey, a medical student from Poland who visited the Einsteins. It was a tradition to invite every Friday a poor emigrant student to dinner. Talmey called Albert's attention to a series *Popular Books on Natural Science* (*Naturwissenschaftliche Volksbücher*), compiled by Aaron Bernstein. The books discussed zoology, botany, astronomy and geography. More important, they dealt with the subject matter from the standpoint of the general universal causal interdependence of natural phenomena. After that Albert was an enthusiastic reader of Büchner's *Force and Matter* (*Kraft und Stoff*), a very popular book among young Germans at the close of the 19th century. Despite its superficiality and the author's utter incomprehension of the infinite complexity of the world revealed by the great discoveries of the 19th century, Büchner's book was instrumental in drawing many young men from religion. It made a great impression on Einstein. Instruction in the elementary school and the gymnasium followed the biblical interpretation of the origin of the world and life, whereas Büchner's interpretation of modern knowledge was a negation of the religious principle and an assertion of the material nature of the world.

In the elementary school Einstein had received Catholic instruction. At the gymnasium he received instruction in the

Jewish religion, which was provided for Jewish pupils. Einstein was stirred by the historical and artistic values of the Old Testament, but this could not counter the impact of natural science on his mind. He soon developed a definite aversion for religion of any kind and made up his mind to abandon the Jewish religious community and not to become a member of any religious group.

Einstein displayed an interest in mathematics at an early age. This may have been due to his uncle Jakob who liked to say: "Algebra is a jolly science. We go hunting for a little animal whose name we don't know, so we call it x. When we bag our game we pounce on it and give it its right name." The subject fascinated the boy, and he soon joined the hunt, frequently abandoning conventional methods to seek new ways of solving simple problems.

When Albert was twelve years old algebra and geometry were due to commence in the forthcoming school year. He was already familiar with algebra but knew nothing as yet of geometry. He got himself a textbook on the subject and, like any schoolboy, began leafing through it. The book proved so exciting that he was unable to tear himself away from it.

In the meantime Albert had begun taking violin lessons at the age of six. He was unfortunate in the choice of tutors, who, like his school teachers, were unable to inspire him. He dutifully stuck to his guns for seven years, but it took Mozart's sonatas to awaken him to the beauty of music. He was carried away by their grace and emotion and wanted to give them expression with his violin. He lacked the skill, however, so he proceeded to perfect his technique until Mozart finally sounded forth. Music became his favourite pastime. From the age of fourteen he took part in all domestic concerts. Mozart and his music played the same part in Einstein's life as Euclidean geometry did in his scientific development.

Hermann Einstein

Pauline Einstein

Six-year-old Albert and his sister Maja

Einstein in Aarau

Chapter 2

STUDENT DAYS

Joy in looking and comprehending is nature's most beautiful gift.

Einstein

Hermann Einstein was not a successful businessman. The electrical factory yielded no profit and eventually he was reduced to the verge of bankruptcy and decided to seek his fortune elsewhere. Italy seemed best suited because of both the business prospects it offered and the colourful life which appealed to him so much. Besides, some rich relatives of Pauline's (grain merchants in Genoa) promised their support. So in 1894 the family, together with uncle Jakob, moved to Milan, leaving Albert behind in Munich to finish the gymnasium. The Einstein brothers first undertook to set up business in Milan, but things fared poorly and they moved to Pavia, where they were no better off, so they returned to Milan and opened their factory *Per la construzione di dinamo e motori elettrici a correnti continue e alternate.* They were kept in business mainly thanks to the support of the Italian and German branches of the Koch family.

Alone in Munich, fifteen-year-old Albert was having a hard time at the gymnasium. He was far in advance of his classmates in mathematics and physics, but he found it increasingly difficult to keep going. His critical attitude towards the pedagogical methods of the gymnasium was further enhanced by the books he read. The endless cramming of Latin and Greek, the rote and abundance of useless information in other subjects, the military type atmosphere, and the self-confident ignorance of the teachers and authorities were unbearable. The serious-minded boy, indifferent to schoolboy pranks, had acquired no close friends at school, and now his family was far away. Albert decided to leave the gymnasium and join his parents in Italy. He obtained a doctor's certificate stating that because of a nervous breakdown he was in need of a six-month holiday.

The school authorities, however, anticipated his intention. They had long been looking askance at Einstein's scepticism and free-thinking. He was offered to leave the gymnasium as his presence undermined the other pupils' respect for the school. This was one year before graduation.

Einstein's first act on rejoining his family in Milan was to renounce his German citizenship and his adherence to the Jewish religious community.

Italy charmed Einstein. He fell in love with its ancient temples, museums and art galleries, its palaces and picturesque hovels, its merry, hospitable and easy-going people, who worked or idled, made merry or brawled with the same effusiveness and expressive gesticulation. The music and singing and animated melodious speech was in sharp contrast with the cold, rigid spirit of rules, norms of behaviour, precedence and nomenclature that had oppressed him in Germany. He travelled to Genoa and other places, and wherever he went he experienced an inner freedom never felt before.

This could not last forever, however, and the time came for Albert to think of his future. His father's affairs were going from bad to worse. The establishment of the electrical factories in Milan and Pavia had swallowed up all of the family's savings, with no appreciable dividends. At last Hermann Einstein was compelled to tell his son that he found it very difficult to support him and he would have to take up some profession as soon as possible. By then it was clear to Albert that his prime interests lay in mathematics and theoretical physics. The difficulty, however, was of combining the two interests with a practical profession. His father and uncle insisted on an engineering career. Their advice was all the more worth heeding as without a gymnasium diploma it would be hard to get into a university. A technical institution was agreed upon, and the only thing was to choose a suitable one with instruction conducted in German. Studying in Germany was out of the question. Outside of Germany the most famous institute was the Swiss Federal Polytechnic of Zurich, to which Albert applied for admission. At the entrance examinations he made a brilliant showing in mathematics, but his knowledge of foreign languages, botany and zoology proved lacking. The absence of a gymnasium diploma was also taken into account and he was not accepted. The director of the Polytechnic, however, who had been impressed by Einstein's knowledge of mathematics, advised him to finish a Swiss secondary school and apply again the following year. He recommended the Cantonal school at the small town of Aarau where the staff and the pedagogical methods were very progressive.

With the memory of Munich fresh in his mind Einstein hated the idea of returning to secondary school, but then, there was nothing else to do. The Aarau school, however, turned out to be a pleasant surprise. The teachers were as friends to the students, the lessons were interesting, and the students were able to work independently in the physical and chemical laboratories; there was a zoology museum with microscopes, and a garden for practical botany classes. The senior pupils frequently discussed social problems. Many young revolutionary emigrants lived in Switzerland, and such questions were constantly being debated.

Einstein lived in the home of one of the school's teachers, Professor Winteler. He spent much of his time with Winteler's children, who were of his own age, and they often took long walks in the hills. He also made some friends among his fellow students.

The year at Aarau revealed to Einstein that in a school not shackled by scholastic routine and conducted by progressive-minded people teaching could be an interesting profession which, furthermore, combined well with research work.

Einstein finished the Aarau school in 1896 and was accepted to the Zurich Polytechnic without examinations. He studied there from October 1896 to August 1900, at a department which trained teachers in physics and mathematics.

The teacher-training department was, for all practical purposes, a physico-mathematical faculty. Besides the courses in mathematics and physics, Einstein listed himself for several special courses in philosophy, history, economics and literature.[1] However, he rarely attended the main physics and

[1] These are the classes to which Einstein enrolled and the teachers who conducted them: differential and integral calculus (Adolf Hurwitz); descriptive geometry (Wilhelm Fiedler); analytical geometry, theory of invariants, theory of determinants (Carl Friedrich Geiser); theory of definite integrals, theory of linear equations (Arthur Hirsch); geometric theory of numbers, function theory, elliptical functions, differential

mathematics classes. Heinrich Weber, who conducted the physics course, was an expert in electrical engineering but in theoretical physics he added nothing to what Einstein did not already know. Einstein appealed directly to the works of Maxwell, Kirchoff, Boltzmann and Hertz. It was then that his initial interests, which had been divided equally between physics and pure mathematics, centred on a few fundamental problems of theoretical physics. Among his mathematics instructors were such outstanding men as Adolf Hurwitz and Hermann Minkowski, but their lectures, too, failed to interest Einstein. Minkowski, who later developed the mathematical apparatus of relativity theory, never saw its future propounder at his lectures. When the theory was enunciated Minkowski remarked that it was the last thing he could have expected of his student at the Zurich Polytechnic.

Minkowski's lectures and the lectures of other professors in the various branches of higher mathematics were regularly attended by Marcell Grossmann, who took careful notes at all of them. Grossmann became a good friend of Einstein's and years later he took part in developing the mathematical apparatus of general relativity. Grossmann's notes enabled Einstein to pass his examinations. This gave him a freedom in attending lectures which he enjoyed greatly. The need to study for the sole purpose of an examination had always oppressed him.

"This coercion," he writes in his *Autobiographical Notes*, "had such a deterring effect [upon me] that, after I had passed the final examination, I found the consideration of any scientific problems distasteful to me for an entire year. In justice I must add, moreover, that in Switzerland we had to suffer far less under such coercion, which smothers every

equations in partial derivatives, variation calculus, analytical mechanics (Hermann Minkowski); general mechanics (Albin Herzog); applications of analytical mechanics (Ferdinand Rudio); physics, electrical engineering (Heinrich Friedrich Weber); practical physics (Johann Pernet); astrophysics, astronomy (Alfred Wolfer); theory of scientific thinking, Kantian philosophy (August Stadler); and in the optional subjects: designing (Ernst Fiedler); external ballistics (Geiser); ancient history, geology (Albert Heim); Swiss history (Wilhelm Echsli); economics (Julius Platter); statistics, insurance (Jacob Rebstein); the works and views of Goethe (Robert Saitschik).

truly scientific impulse, than is the case in many other localities. There were altogether only two examinations; aside from these one could just about do as one pleased. This was especially the case if one had a friend, as did I, who attended the lectures regularly and who worked over their content conscientiously. This gave one freedom of choice of pursuits until a few months before the examination, a freedom which I enjoyed to a great extent and have gladly taken into the bargain, the bad conscience connected with it, as by far the lesser evil. It is, in fact, nothing short of a miracle that the modern methods of instruction have not yet entirely strangled the holy curiosity of inquiry; for this delicate little plant, aside from stimulation, stands mainly in need of freedom; without this it goes to wreck and ruin."[1]

Zurich, like other Swiss university towns, was a haven to which flocked a cosmopolitan host of students, revolutionary emigrants, and young people who had fled from national or social oppression in their countries. Not all the students were revolutionaries, but most of them were democratically minded. It was a social milieu of great political and scientific temperament. Even those whose interests were restricted to pure science could not help being influenced by it.

Einstein made many friends among emigrant students. Among them was Mileva Maritsch, a Serbian girl from Austria-Hungary. She was a serious, taciturn girl, neither quick-witted nor very attractive, but she and Einstein found a common interest in studying the works of great physicists. Einstein always felt the need of a friend and companion to whom he could voice his ideas. Mileva was a rather unresponsive listener, but she suited him. There was no one in Zurich who could equal him in intellect (in fact he never did have a friend who could be his equal in all respects), nor did he meet a girl capable of attracting him by beauty alone, without the benefit of a scholarly background.

Einstein's closest friends were Marcel Grossmann, Louis Kollros and Jakob Ehrat, all of them, like Mileva, of the 1896 term at the Polytechnic. Grossmann lived with his

[1] *Philosopher-Scientist*, p. 17.

parents in the village of Thalwil on the Lake of Zurich. Jakob Ehrat, with whom Einstein usually sat at lectures, lived with his mother, who was very fond of Albert. She frequently recalled the time when Einstein once came to their house suffering from a bad cold. He had wrapped around his neck a scarf which later turned out to be a runner from the chest of drawers in the room he rented. Incidentally, his landlady earned a living by ironing laundry, and she liked to listen to music while she worked. To oblige her Einstein would often miss his lectures and (what mattered more to him) meetings with his friends at the café Metropole, and play the violin to the good woman.

Einstein also visited the family of Gustav Maier, a friend of his father's back from Ulm. Years later Einstein wrote to the Maiers on the occasion of their golden wedding anniversary:

"You were my parents' best friends in Ulm at a time when the stork was just preparing to deliver me from his inexhaustible storehouse. You helped me liberally when I came to Zurich in the autumn of 1895 and flunked my examinations. The doors of your hospitable house were open to me all through my student days, even though I would come down from Uetliberg in dirty boots."[1]

Once in a while Albert would visit a distant relative, Albert Karr, who represented the firm of the Genoan Kochs in Zurich. They used to hold domestic concerts at which Einstein accompanied Mrs. Karr who had a fine voice.

Einstein spent his vacations with his parents in Pavia or Milan.

He did not have much to live on. Hermann Einstein's business affairs were as bad as ever and Albert's only income was a monthly allowance of 100 francs contributed by his rich Genoan relatives. Out of this sum he set aside 20 francs towards the fee necessary for the acquisition of Swiss citizenship.

In the autumn of 1900 Einstein passed his state examinations and received his diploma. His friends also graduated, except for Mileva, who continued for another

---

[1] C. Seelig, *Albert Einstein. Leben und Werk eines Genies unserer Zeit*, Zürich, 1960, S. 70.

year, though she could not hope for a diploma: women were merely issued a certificate of graduation.

Despite earlier promises, a reputation of a talented young man, and a good showing (his marks by the six-point scale were: theoretical physics, 5; practical physics, 5; theory of functions, 5.5; astronomy, 5; graduation thesis, 4.5; over all mark, 4.91), Einstein was not retained at the Polytechnic. His more fortunate friends were given positions, Grossmann under Fiedler, Ehrat under Rudio, and Kollros under Hurwitz. The road to work in theoretical or experimental physics at the Polytechnic was barred to Albert: he had never attended Weber's lectures, as he already knew all the professor had to say, and in Pernet's laboratory he set aside the instructions for the experiments and conducted them as he saw best. Moreover he had once had the impudence to address his teacher as "Herr Weber" instead of "Herr Professor", an extremely grave violation of etiquette.

Einstein was forced to seek a job outside the Polytechnic. He earned a little by doing some computations for the Swiss Federal Observatory in Zurich. The rest of the time he spent plodding the streets of Zurich in search of a steady job. This, he hoped, would become easier as soon as he became a Swiss citizen. He received his citizenship papers in February 1901, after paying up all his savings and submitting to an interrogation during which he was asked questions about his health, the character of his grandfather, and many others, including whether he was inclined to drink. The new-baked Swiss citizen was duly relieved of military service when a medical examination revealed that he suffered from flatfoot and varicose veins.

The search for work continued. In May Einstein obtained a temporary position as teacher in a technical school at Winterthur. From Milan (whither he had gone to await the results of his job-hunting) he wrote to a professor in Zurich:

"I have been offered a position in a technical school at Winterthur, to last from 15 May to 15 July, to teach mathematics while the regular professor serves a term in the army. I have just received news that the question is settled and am beside myself with joy. I haven't the least idea who the compassionate person was who recommended me: I was never in the good books of my former professors, and yet the position was offered me without my having asked for it. I also have hopes of getting a permanent job at the Swiss Patent Office. . . . I should add that I am a gay finch whose spirits can be dampened only by a stomach ache or something of that kind. . . . In a few days I will cross the Splügen on foot and thus combine a pleasant duty with pleasure."[1]

One can imagine the "gay finch" with no means of subsistence and no permanent job being "beside himself with joy" at the prospect of a two-month position and a trek across the hills of Splügen to his place of work. Einstein belonged to the happy category of people who are not easily discouraged by setbacks and are quick to rejoice at the slightest glimmer of success. Not that he was so easy-going and light-hearted as to have no room for internal dramatic collisions. On the contrary, in a mind rid of the daily cares and concerns of life there was more room than ever for violent "extra-personal" storms and conflicts.

In the autumn of 1901 Einstein was out of work again. He found another short-term haven in Schaffhausen, a small town on the Rhine known for its waterfalls and frequented by tourists who came to see them. There lived the family of one Conrad Habicht, a fellow student from the Polytechnic. On Habicht's recommendation Einstein secured a position as tutor at a boarding-school for students. His job was to prepare them for their school-leaving examinations. Einstein enjoyed his work and tried to make the lessons lively and interesting, discarding the scholastic routine which had oppressed him so greatly at school. However, his ideas about the methods and purpose of education clashed with those of his employer, Jakob Nüesch. Einstein proved too independently minded, and Nüesch soon discharged him.

In Schaffhausen, Einstein and Habicht were together a great deal, they talked a lot and played violin duets. A friendship sprang up between them which later continued and grew stronger in Bern.

Again Einstein was out of work. Teaching seemed completely barred to him. He could not comprehend the reason for this: was it because of the general unemployment in the country, or because he was a naturalised Swiss,

[1] C. Seelig, op. cit., S. 80.

or because he was a Jew, or simply because he was no good?

The spring of 1902 found Einstein in Milan again. From there he continued to write to universities inquiring about available vacancies. Meanwhile Marcel Grossmann was finally able to land the job at the Patent Office in Bern mentioned in the letter quoted above. The director of the Patent Office, Friedrich Haller, was a friend of Marcel's father, and he agreed to take Einstein.

"Dear Marcel," Einstein wrote in a letter to Grossmann in April 1902. "When I found your letter yesterday I was deeply moved by your devotion and compassion which do not let you forget an old, unlucky friend. I could hardly find better friends than you and Ehrat. Needless to say I would be delighted to get the job. I would spare no effort to live up to your recommendation. I have spent three weeks at my parents' home looking for a position of assistant lecturer at some university. I am sure I would have found one long ago if not for Weber's intrigues against me. In spite of all this I don't let a single opportunity pass unheeded, nor have I lost my sense of humour. . . . When God created the ass he gave him a thick skin.

"Spring has come here and it is beautiful. The world looks at you with such a happy smile that you can't help brushing away the blues. Besides, musical gatherings prevent me from turning sour. As for science, I have some excellent ideas, but they will take some time to hatch."[1]

The "excellent ideas" concerned questions of molecular attraction, and the epithet had nothing personal in it. Einstein was not the man to admire his own accomplishments. His admiration was for the harmony of nature. He writes in connection with his work on molecular attraction: "How wonderful the realisation of unity in the complex of phenomena which had at first glance seemed isolated."[2]

Today we know that this statement embodied the programme which was to fill the whole of Einstein's life.

In Bern Einstein had a long interview with Haller, the director of the Patent Office, who decided that the quiet young man was suited for the job even though he lacked

---

[1] C. Seelig, op. cit., S. 85-86.
[2] Ibid., S. 86-87.

previous experience. The position of technical expert, third class, drew Einstein a yearly salary of 3,500 francs. Einstein moved to Bern and in July 1902 took up his new job.

Albert and Mileva's wedding was delayed by the illness of Hermann Einstein. Like his wife, he was opposed to the marriage and Albert did not like the idea of going against his father's will at a time when the latter was on his death-bed. Just before the end, however, Hermann Einstein agreed to his son's marriage. The wedding was celebrated on January 6, 1903, at a local restaurant, where Albert entertained his new Bern friends. The wedding trip of the newly-weds was no longer than their walk from the restaurant home, where Einstein found that he had mislaid the key of their flat.

Chapter 3

BERN

*The formulation of patent statements was a
blessing. It gave me the opportunity to think
about physics. Moreover, a practical profession
is a salvation for a man of my type: an
academic career compels a young man to
scientific production, and only strong characters
can resist the temptations of superficial
analysis.*

E i n s t e i n

W as Einstein's position at the Patent Office such a
blessing for research as it seemed to him? The passage in
the epigraph from his autobiographical essay written a
month before his death favours this judgement. A retrospective review offered Einstein the opportunity to analyse and
judge the nature of physical ideas and the logical,
psychological and cultural foundations on which they
developed. In the present case it was not just a matter of joy
and relief at being finally established in life. In summing
up his life Einstein lays stress on the things that constituted
the groundwork of his scientific exploit.

Einstein's life in Bern can be compared with Isaac
Newton's Woolsthorpe period during the plague of 1665-1667,
when he had to go away from Cambridge. It was in
Woolsthorpe that Newton developed his ideas on differential
calculus, universal gravitation and the breaking-down of light
into monochromatic rays. It was in Bern that Einstein
developed the theory of Brownian movement, the photon
theory, and the special theory of relativity. What better
confirmation of his assessment of the salutary conditions for
scientific research in Bern?

It should be said, however, that the history of science
generally contradicts such an estimation of the value of a
practical profession for scientific research. In fact, most
physical discoveries in modern times have been made by

professional researchers who had gone through the usual stages of the scientific profession: college, scientific school, an independent work on a problem in harmony with the school.

Possibly then, Einstein's appreciation of conditions in Bern as being so conducive to the development of the theory of relativity applies only to himself and does not fit into the history of science. This might be the case if Einstein's life were not so greatly interwoven with the history of science, though it stands out as a special case and analogies are not easily applied to it.

In effect Einstein continued the Bern tradition all his life. He took up problems for investigation without apparently ever considering the possible assessment of their results. This, however, was permissible for a professional research worker, a professor at Prague, Zurich, Berlin and Princeton, and *subsequently* to the enunciation of the theory of relativity. At the beginning of the road a practical job not connected with science facilitated the complete concentration of the mind on the problems at hand.

The lucid, exhaustive initial formulation of the relativity theory, the immediate possibilities for further generalisations which it presented, and its impact on all spheres of learning and culture required an unparalleled ability to overcome all human frailties, including the "temptations of superficial analysis".

The relationships of relativity theory were evolved out of a revision of the basic concepts of space and time, a revision which was not motivated by any extraneous requirements. Einstein would probably have arrived at relativity theory in other circumstances, but freedom from academic restraints was most conducive to the discovery. The image of the freedom of life in Bern, life free from the shackles of academic authority and authoritarianism, is ample confirmation of Einstein's appreciation of his work at the Patent Office.

His work there also undoubtedly helped to stimulate his interest in physics. It is not easy to arrive at new physical ideas radically affecting both the content and the very mode of theoretical physics without the benefit of associations and analogies from more or less related sources. Unfortunately, none of Einstein's early notes, which could reveal the

The "Olympian Academy" (Habicht, Solovine, Einstein)

Einstein and Mileva

evolution of his thoughts and ideas up to the formulation of the special theory of relativity, are extant. All we know is that, in his own words (in the passage quoted in the epigraph and elsewhere), he was greatly assisted in his ratiocinations by the contact with engineering and technology offered by the Patent Office: the endless variety of new and often ingenious kinematic principles, technological recipes, modifications of old ideas, transpositions of patterns and designs from one sphere to another, the bold application of old methods to the solution of new problems.

The extent of Einstein's interest in engineering technology is seen in his work on scientific apparatus. Conrad Habicht had a younger brother, Paul, who lived in Bern at the time, where he attended a gymnasium. He was interested in electrical engineering, and after finishing school he moved to Schaffhausen where he established an electrical measuring instruments factory. In 1908, Einstein in collaboration with Paul Habicht built an instrument for measuring potentials of as small as 0.0005 volt. In 1910 they designed the "Einstein-Habicht potential multiplier". Einstein continued to design various instruments and devices in his later years.

In the first months of his Bern sojourn Einstein decided to give private lessons. He placed an advertisement in the local newspaper to the effect that Albert Einstein, Ph. D., of the Zurich Polytechnic, gave lessons in physics at three francs an hour. Among the few persons who responded to the ad. was a Maurice Solovine, a Rumanian university student interested in physics. The two young men were immediately drawn to each other and a close and lasting friendship developed between them. In 1956, Solovine published a book of reminiscences and letters from Einstein to him.[1]

At the university Solovine studied philosophy, literature, Greek, mathematics, physics and geology, and he attended lectures at the medical faculty. He was interested in theoretical physics as a means for developing a comprehensive picture of nature.

The first thing that struck Solovine in the semi-dark corridor leading to Einstein's room were the remarkably

[1] A. Einstein, *Lettres à Maurice Solovine*, Paris, 1956. (Afterwards referred to as *Solovine*.)

large, luminous eyes of the man who ushered him in. Their first interview immediately revealed an identity of views and interests. Very soon the lessons turned into long discussions of topics of mutual interest. A little later they were joined by Conrad Habicht, who had come to Bern to continue his studies in mathematics.

The trio gathered after work and study hours and took long walks or went to one of their flats, where they conversed and read books. They perused the philosophical works of Spinoza and Hume, new books by Mach, Avenarius and Pearson, Ampère's old *Essai sur la Philosophie de Science*, papers by Helmholtz, Riemann's famous lecture *Sur les Hypothèses qui servent de base à la géométry*, Dedekind's and Clifford's mathematical treatises, Poincaré's *La Science et l'hypothèse*, and many other works. They also read together Sophocles's *Antigone*, Racine's *Andromache*, Dickens's *Christmas Carols*, Cervantes' *Don Quixote*, and other world masterpieces.

Although Einstein and his friends had read many of these books before, they enjoyed discussing them. Often a single page or passage would spark an argument lasting far into the night or even several days. Before Mileva's arrival in Bern the friends had their meals together. A usual dinner consisted of sausage, cheese, fruit, and tea with honey. Einstein's lessons were few, they paid poorly, and he joked that he could probably earn more by playing the violin in the streets. Nevertheless they were all happy. Recalling those years, Solovine quotes Epicurus: "What better fate than cheerful poverty."

The three young men named their fraternity, which lasted three years, the "Olympian Academy". Those youthful days left a lasting imprint in Einstein's memory. In 1953 he wrote to Solovine:

"Immortal Olympian Academy.

"In your short lifetime you took childish joy in clarity and reason. Your members founded you to make fun of your cumbrous, pompous old sisters. How right we were has been made clear to me in the course of many years of direct observation.

"Your three members stand fast as ever. They have faded somewhat, but your pure, vivifying light continues to illumine them in their solitude, for you have not aged like overgrown lettuce together with them.

"To you our fidelity and devotion to the last highly enlightened breath!

"Your now only corresponding member, A. E.
"Princeton, 3.IV.53"[1]

One finds in this comparison between the "Olympian Academy" and its "cumbrous, pompous old sisters" a rather melancholy summing up. After years of association with scholastic circles Einstein's thoughts turned to the carefree independence of the Bern period, their youthful disregard for the pompous respectability of those circles and, most important, the atmosphere of "childish joy in clarity and reason".

The optimistic rationalism of the Bern environment had, as we shall see, a direct bearing on the scientific ideals which led Einstein to his discoveries.

The three "Olympians" were later joined by Michele Angelo Besso, an Italian engineer whose wife, Anna, was a daughter of Professor Winteler of the Aarau school. Incidentally, another Bern resident was Paul Winteler, Anna's brother and future husband of Einstein's sister Maja. When Besso came to work at the Bern Patent Office in 1904, it was Einstein who helped him get the job. They usually walked home from work together.

Besso possessed an encyclopaedic knowledge of philosophy, sociology, technology, mathematics and physics, which made him an excellent companion for Einstein, who discussed a wide range of ideas with him. As Einstein remarked many years later, he could have found "no better sounding board for new ideas in the whole of Europe". Besso had a remarkable capacity for grasping new ideas and giving them important finishing touches. In his own words, "Einstein, the eagle, carried me, the sparrow, to lofty heights. Up there the sparrow could flutter a little higher".[2]

Besso's comment refers to the first oral exposition of the idea of relativity. He immediately realised that this was nothing short of a new era in science. At the same time he

[1] *Solovine*, p. 125.
[2] C. Seelig, op. cit., S. 120.

drew Einstein's attention to several new **points**. They discussed relativity at great length. The value of these discussions is seen in the final paragraph of Einstein's celebrated paper, "On the Electrodynamics of Moving Bodies":

"I should like to note in conclusion that my friend and colleague M. Besso was my devoted assistant in the elaboration of the questions herein and I am indebted to him for a number of valuable suggestions."

Another friend of Einstein's was Lucien Chavan who, like Solovine, was brought to his flat by the advertisement of lessons. A native of French Switzerland, he worked at the Bern postal and telegraph department whose offices were on the ground floor of the same building as the Patent Office (Chavan had tried to get Einstein a job in the postal department). Chavan had an interest in physics, and he attended lectures at the university, and also took lessons from Einstein. We have today his thorough notes on physics and a verbal portrait of Einstein written on the back of an old snapshot: "Einstein is 1.76 metres tall, broad-shouldered, with a slight stoop. His short skull seems remarkably broad. His complexion is swarthy. He has a narrow moustache above a large, sensitive mouth, an acquiline nose. His brown eyes have a deep, benign lustre. He has a fine voice, like the vibrant tones of a cello. Einstein speaks a good French with a slight foreign accent."[1]

With Mileva's arrival in Bern, Einstein settled down to the life of a family man. The friends, however, continued to get together and air their views. Mileva was an attentive, if taciturn, listener.

Solovine relates how, having argued and smoked to their hearts' content, the friends would listen to Einstein's violin or go out for a walk during which they continued their discussion. One midnight they climbed to the top of Mount Gurten, on the southern outskirts of Bern. The star-speckled sky diverted their thoughts to astronomy, and the conversation flared up with renewed force. They remained there until dawn and watched the sunrise. The sun's rays came from behind the horizon, gradually painting the barely visible silhouettes of the Alps a delicate pink. A vast mountain

[1] C. Seelig, op. cit., S. 94-95.

country opened up to their eyes. Morning came. The young men went to a small restaurant where they had coffee, and around nine o'clock they descended into the valley, tired and happy. Sometimes they walked 18 miles to the town of Tun, starting out at 6 a.m. and arriving at noon. With the Alps around them, they discussed the history of the earth, the formation of mountains and geology. At Tun they had lunch, then they camped for the day on the shore of the lake, returning to Bern by the evening train.[1]

Describing their discussions, Solovine says that Einstein spoke slowly, in an even tone, at times lapsing into thoughtful silence. He wrapped himself completely in his thoughts, to the point of utter oblivion of everything around him. Solovine presents some intimate episodes which illustrate Einstein's life in Bern.

Once on Einstein's birthday, Solovine and Habicht brought some caviar, which Einstein had never tasted before. They began discussing the inertia principle, and by the time they sat down to the table Einstein was so engrossed in the subject that he swallowed the caviar without even realising what it was. When his friends broke into laughter he looked at them incomprehensibly with his large eyes. After a moment's silence he said: "It's not worth treating such a rustic to delicacies: I wouldn't appreciate them anyhow."[2]

Here is another episode described by Solovine. Many famous musicians played in Bern, and the friends usually attended the concerts. Once, when a Czech symphony orchestra was in town, Solovine suggested that they all go to the concert. They happened to be deeply engrossed in a discussion of Hume, however, and Einstein suggested that they gather at Solovine's place instead. The next day Solovine was offered a ticket and he decided to go to the concert after all. He prepared a supper which included hard-boiled eggs, which his friends liked very much, leaving them a note in Latin: *Amicis carissimis ova dura et salutem* ("For good friends, hard-boiled eggs and salutations"). Einstein and Habicht did justice to the meal, smoked their pipes until the air in the room grew hazy, and departed, leaving a note of

[1] *Solovine*, xii-xiii.
[2] Ibid., ix-x.

their own: *Amica carissimo fumum spissum et salutem* ("For a good friend, much smoke and salutations"). Next morning Einstein greeted Solovine with a stern frown and the words: "Miserable person! How dare you trade our academic meeting for fiddles? Barbarian and blockhead! One more escapade of this kind and you will be expelled from the academy!" Then they got down to Hume, parting company long after midnight.[1]

In 1905, first Habicht and then Solovine left Bern. In May of the following year Einstein wrote to Solovine: "I have associated with no one since you left. Even our usual talks with Besso on the way home have terminated."[2]

Einstein writes of the response to his paper on relativity, published in 1905. Then the twenty-six-year-old scholar goes on: "I am approaching the age when one deplores the revolutionary spirit of youth."

In his letters to Habicht and Solovine written in 1906 Einstein mentions his papers on Brownian movement, photons and relativity. In May he wrote to Habicht, asking him to come to Bern: "I hereby call upon you to attend several meetings of our most glorious academy, thereby increasing its membership by fifty per cent."[3] Shortly afterwards, while waiting for the fateful issues of the *Annalen der Physik*, Einstein sent Habicht the following letter:

"Dear Habicht,

"A reverent silence reigns amongst us, and that I break it with such trivial chatter may seem a profanation. But is this not always the fate of the exalted in our world? What is engaging you, you petrified whale, you insipid pickled piece of a soul, you.... I know not what else filled seventy per cent with anger and thirty per cent with pity I could hurl at your head. You can thank the latter thirty per cent for my not sending you a tin of sliced onions and garlic for your failure to appear on Easter. Why haven't you sent me your papers yet? Don't you know, you miserable man, that I am one of the one-and-a-half young men who will read them with satisfaction and interest? I promise you in return four works, the first one very soon as I am expecting my author's

[1] *Solovine*, xi-xii.
[2] Ibid., pp. 5-7.
[3] C. Seelig, op. cit., S. 124.

copies. It is on the radiation and energy of light, and it is very revolutionary, as you will see for yourself, provided you send me your work first. The second work discusses the methods of determining the real dimensions of atoms by investigating the diffusion and internal friction of liquid solutions. The third proves that, according to the molecular theory of heat, bodies of dimensions of the order of 1/1000th mm suspended in liquid experience apparent random movement due to the thermal motion of molecules. Such movement of suspended bodies has actually been observed by biologists, who call it Brownian molecular movement. The fourth work is based on the concepts of the electrodynamics of moving bodies and modifies the theory of space and time; the purely kinematic part of this work should interest you.... Your Albert Einstein hails you. Friendly regards from my wife and yearling squealer."[1]

Several months later Einstein wrote to Habicht advising him to try to get a position at the Patent Office. This is followed by some extremely interesting remarks concerning corollaries of the theory of relativity and other physical problems.

"You have grown awfully serious," Einstein writes. "This is what solitude does in your terrible manger. What if I suggest your candidacy to Haller and smuggle you into the Patent Office? Would you come in that case? Consider this, for besides eight hours of work there remain eight hours of daily idleness, plus a whole Sunday. I would be delighted to have you here. In friendly company you would speedily regain your old cheerfulness."

The papers heralding a revolution in physics had already been published and acclaimed by such physicists as Planck and Wien, but still no thought of his own career entered Einstein's head. He was concerned with Habicht. On the threshold of fame Einstein remained completely satisfied with his position: eight hours at the Patent Office plus eight hours of "idleness" which could be devoted to scientific pursuits.

In his letter Einstein mentions the problems which might interest Habicht, among them that of spectra. "But I think," he writes, "that there are no simple links between these

[1] C. Seelig, op. cit., S. 125-26.

phenomena and others that have already been studied, therefore the problem of spectra is as yet not very promising."[1] Ten years later it was found that the problem of spectra, that is, the emission of electromagnetic radiation of different length by the atoms of matter, cannot in fact be simply and directly associated with known laws.

Finally, Einstein writes of the remarkable conclusion arising out of the special theory of relativity that the mass of a body must be proportional to its energy. His letter to Habicht is not dated but it was probably posted in September 1905, when Einstein had sent to the *Annalen der Physik* his paper on the proportionality between the energy and mass of a body, the point of departure for the corollaries of relativity theory which have had the greatest impact of all on human life and affairs.

Two years after Solovine's and Habicht's departure from Bern Einstein finally acquired a companion with whom he could discuss theoretical physics. This marked the beginning of a new period in his life, for Jakob Johann Laub had come to Bern at the request of the eminent scientist Wilhelm Wien with the specific purpose of meeting the famous founder of the theory of relativity. (Laub himself had presented a review of relativity theory at a seminar conducted by Wien.) The discussions between Laub and Einstein resulted in the publication of a number of joint papers. Nothing had changed in the simple, cordial bearing of Einstein, whom Laub found in a cold flat busy kindling a fire in a stove. Daily for several weeks Laub met Einstein at the Patent Office at the end of the day and accompanied him home, discussing points of interest on the way. Laub recalls their attending a performance of Wagner's *Götterdämmerung* at the Bern Opera and Einstein's enthusiastic whispering: "Wagner is not, God forgive me, in my taste, but in the scene of Siegfried's death his recapitulation of the hero's undaunted spirit is sublime."[2]

During the years 1907-1909, Einstein spent many winter evenings playing the violin in a quintet which included, besides him, a lawyer, a mathematician, a bookbinder and a jail warden. They played Haydn, Mozart and Beethoven.

[1] C. Seelig, op. cit., S. 126.
[2] Ibid., S. 121.

And none of the musicians ever suspected who their companion was.

To conclude this chapter, a few words about Einstein's family life in Bern. In 1904, Mileva gave birth to a boy, Hans Albert (Albert Einstein, Jr., later studied in Zurich, eventually moving to the United States in 1937 to become a professor of hydraulics at the University of California). Expenses grew with the family, but this did not worry Einstein. When his salary was raised to 4,500 francs he even remarked, "What will we do with all this money?" Mileva, on the other hand, could hardly make ends meet. But this was not her greatest concern. The main thing was the great difference in their dispositions. She was content to have Solovine and Habicht visit them, but she did not care for their walks, dining out of home, domestic concerts and big company. Einstein's scientific interests became gradually more and more remote to her. Her frame of mind was in no way improved by tuberculosis of the joints and neurasthenia from which she suffered. To these were added a steadily growing pathological jealousy and suspicion. The time came when even Einstein's easy ways and absent-minded kindness began to irritate her. Their estrangement grew, though it came out into the open much later on, some time after their departure from Bern.

Chapter 4

THE "EXTRA-PERSONAL"

In this world, if one hopes to keep to the right road one must sacrifice oneself to the end. Man's destiny is not happiness alone. . . . He must discover something great for the benefit of humanity.

Renan

The true value of a human being is determined primarily by the measure and the sense in which he has attained liberation from the self.

Einstein

Einstein's flight from the daily commonplace of the "merely personal" began when he was still a boy. But it took time for him to pin down the specific idea capable of transcending the "merely personal" interests which would be worthy of intellectual pursuit. For a brief period he found relief in religion. This was followed by "an orgy of free-thinking" and subsequently by devotion to an "extra-personal", but real and rational idea. The immediate stimulus for this was, as we have seen, the reading of popular scientific books. The consequence was more than just non-acceptance of religious dogma, as being incapable of standing up to comparison with the scientific picture of the world: the long-term result was social protest and a complete rupture with the convictions of the social environment. As Einstein wrote in his *Autobiographical Notes*, the collapse of Biblical legends under the blows of science bred in his mind the impression that by fostering religion, the state is intentionally deceiving the youth through lies. "It was a crushing impression," he writes. "Suspicion against every kind of authority grew out of this experience, a sceptical attitude towards the convictions which were alive in any specific social environment—an attitude which has never again left me. . . ."[1]

Einstein did not lapse into religious or social indifferentism, although indifferentism was one of the traditions of the environment which he had broken with in his early youth. Having rejected religion, Einstein accepted the idea which became the mainstay of his life and work. The basic, dominant purpose of his life became cognition of the objective "extra-personal" world.

"Out yonder there was this huge world, which exists independently of us human beings and which stands before us like a great, eternal riddle, at least partially accessible to our inspection and thinking. The contemplation of this world beckoned like a liberation, and I soon noticed that many a man whom I had learned to esteem and to admire had found inner freedom and security in devoted occupation with it. The mental grasp of this extra-personal world within the frame of the given possibilities swam as the highest aim, half consciously and unconsciously before my mind's eye. Similarly motivated men of the present and of the past, as well as the insights which they had achieved, were the friends which could not be lost. The road to this paradise was not as comfortable and alluring as the road to the religious paradise; but it has proved itself as trustworthy, and I have never regretted having chosen it."[2]

The idea of the objective nature of the world—the cornerstone of Einstein's outlook—which grew out of his boyhood quest for the "extra-personal" had an additional emotional and moral aspect. When Einstein later came up against notions of the world as a complex of sense elements, of subjective experience, he immediately opposed them. This was due to more than a scientist's spontaneous conviction of the reality of the world which, we know from history, is not enough for a rationally conscious choice of philosophical position. Einstein was still hardly more than a boy when "this huge world, which exists independently of us human beings" became to him an object of scrutiny capable of taking a person beyond the limits imposed by his sensations and beliefs. The conception of the world as an ordered system

---

[1] *Philosopher-Scientist*, p. 5.
[2] Ibid., p. 5.

of sense-impressions could not but be alien to Einstein. Similarly, the idea of the possibility of *a priori* logical knowledge of the world was also unacceptable. In the final analysis from this stand, there emerged the positive physical idea of the necessity of finding the quantities which do not change in any system of reference applied in the investigation of the laws of nature.

The quoted passage from Einstein's autobiography points to the sources of yet another fundamental idea. The "great, eternal riddle" of the world does not coincide with either our sense-impressions or our logical constructions. It stands opposed to them as an independent reality. Hence cognition of the world is a process of approximation to the truth. The anti-dogmatic tendency of science is linked with recognition of the independence of the objects of its investigation.

Although Einstein specifically defined his epistemological views only subsequently to his fundamental physical discoveries, they were not conclusions drawn from past actions. The relativity theory went beyond anything that could have been achieved in physics on the basis of a purely spontaneous conviction of the unity and cognisability of the world. This conviction gained in consistency and consciousness from boyhood on. Least of all can one speak of "influences" in the sense of borrowing the initial ideas from the philosophical and scientific books which Einstein perused in Munich, Zurich and Bern. Even in his youth he was no one's pupil and his views did not fit the pattern of any specific philosophical school.

Spinoza was probably the only philosopher congenial to Einstein. On the whole, however, notions and terms taken from books entered his arsenal of ideas which contributed actively to the development of relativity theory greatly transformed. They were further perfected in the process of application to physical problems, in the elaboration of new physical theories. In this process passing fancies disappeared together with the contradictions which usually crop up in the initial stages of the elaboration of a philosophical outlook.

Einstein writes in his 1949 *Autobiographical Notes* that the schematic picture presented by them does not convey the complexity and confusion of real spiritual evolution. In

retrospect an individual sees a uniformly systematic development; the actual experience, however, takes place in particular kaleidoscopic situations. Einstein was possessed with the idea of a unified scheme embracing all the laws of physical reality. In writing of his youth he quite naturally presents it in the light of the mature, advanced ideas which crystallised later. Taking into account this inevitable aberration, the reconstruction of his ideological development presented in the autobiography, which ignores the "atomistic structure" of man's conscious activity, correctly conveys the purport of Einstein's youthful ideas.

"In a man of my type the turning-point of the development lies in the fact that gradually the major interest disengages itself to a far-reaching degree from the momentary and the merely personal and turns towards the striving for a mental grasp of things. Looked at from this point of view the above schematic remarks contain as much truth as can be uttered in such brevity."[1]

A retrospective evaluation of early stages of mental development from the point of view of later opinions is essential in a biography of every scholar. In Einstein's case this is especially true, as evidenced by the cited passage: disengagement of the major interest from the momentary and merely personal subsequently forces a scholarly mind to seek a unified, integrated pattern in the realities of a complex and contradictory inner life. This is true not only of the kaleidoscopic influx of direct sense-impressions but also of the influx of philosophical and scientific ideas absorbed from the books of Einstein's youth. When, towards the end of his life, Einstein expounded on his stand in respect of the ideas of Hume, Kant and other philosophers, he was not amending the past: his purpose was to single out the ideas which had created a lasting impression, the philosophical influences which were not only episodes in his personal life but which also contributed to his scientific exploit and thereby became episodes in the history of science.

Einstein's attitude towards his own ideological evolution was the same as towards everything else: his striving was for the "extra-personal". In this case the "extra-personal" comprises the philosophical concepts and ideas which sank

---

[1] *Philosopher-Scientist*, p. 7.

into his mind and became, to some degree or other, the basis of new scientific conceptions. The differentiation between the "personal" biography and "extra-personal" history of science is characteristic of Einstein's memoirs. He reviews facts and thoughts, setting aside the merely personal and purely biographical and leaving the contributions to his creative endeavour. This differentiation makes for a better understanding of Einstein's thoughts and appraisals of the past. Thus, the appeal of Mach's philosophical views remains purely a biographical episode, while the initially spontaneous and later conscious suspicion for and non-acceptance of Mach's philosophy developed into an important premise of his "extra-personal" world outlook from which derived his revision of classical physics.

Let us dwell on the epistemological digressions in Einstein's 1949 autobiography. Einstein proceeds from the essential idea that the real world is independent of knowledge. In fact, this is the departing point of the autobiography. It presents in bold relief the evolution from youthful strivings for the "extra-personal" to the theory of relativity, which established explicitly and universally the physical relationships describing the world structure.

Einstein examines the sense-impressions, on the one hand, and the concepts, on the other, which can be derived from each other by purely speculative reasoning according to the strict rules of logic. The initial concepts, however, may be arbitrary. Logical thinking guarantees only that the relationships between concepts are deduced according to the accepted logical rules. In this sense a logically deduced proposition is true.

But logic cannot substantiate the truth of propositions in the sense of their agreement with objective reality. The guarantee of this lies in the connection between logically deduced propositions and the totality of sense-impressions provided by our organs of sense. By themselves sense-impressions offer no idea of the nature of things: science resorts to the logical deduction of concepts which, however, get "meaning", viz., "content", only through their connection with sense-impressions. It is impossible to gain an idea of the actual relationships in nature by logical reasoning alone. Einstein illustrates this point when he writes of the "wondering" that "seems to occur when an experience comes into conflict with a world of concepts which is already sufficiently fixed in us". He writes of the wonder he experienced when he was a child of four or five years at the sight of a compass. The image of the little boy impressed by the movement of the magnetic needle exemplifies the uninhibited perception, the childish ability to view the world, as if for the first time, without the burden of conventional notions and associations, which genuine scientists, like genuine artists, retain all their lives and which develops into the creative power of genius presenting a new explanation or image of the world.

Einstein writes of the deep and lasting impression left by the sight of the compass. It was, in fact, an impression extending into the "extra-personal" sphere. What is the meaning of this "wondering" of the kind prompted by the sight of the compass? A certain body of experience tells us that motion is caused by impact. From this statement a number of propositions and concepts can be deduced by logical thinking. The logical validity of the deduction, however, does not by itself guarantee their universal truth. Nor does it guarantee the truth of the initial premises, which are valid only insofar as the concept of impact as the cause of motion is in agreement with a certain body of facts. The behaviour of the compass gives rise to a new series of logical constructions as it comes into conflict with the former reasoning.

"Whenever such a conflict is experienced hard and intensively it reacts back upon our thought world in a decisive way. The development of this thought world is in a certain sense a continuous flight from 'wonder'."[1]

This conception of scientific development is directed against apriority of all kinds. Our interest, however, lies in the positive aspects of the conception. Einstein saw in the development of science a "flight from 'wonder'", that is to say, a transition to new series of concepts and logical constructions which do not contradict the "wonder" and proceed from it, from new experimental data. This should not be understood to mean a rejection of the criterion of truth with respect to logical constructions. Far from it. It is only that, by themselves, the logical constructions cannot guarantee

[1] *Philosopher-Scientist*, p. 9.

and uniquely determine their ontological content. They become ontologically meaningful when correlated to observations and sense-impressions. Such ontological verification takes place continually. Without it, logical consistency does not yet guarantee the truth of judgements.

"A proposition is correct," Einstein writes, "if, within a logical system, it is deduced according to the accepted logical rules. A system has truth content according to the certainty and completeness of its coordination-possibility to the totality of experience."[1]

If we take into account the endless complexity of the universe, it follows then that no logically consistent theory, which is in agreement with certain sense-impressions, is immune from a "wondering" and subsequent evolution towards new theories.

[1] Ibid., p. 13.

Chapter 5

RATIONALISM

Causa seu ratio, ratio seu causa.

Spinoza

*A body in motion or at rest must be brought
into that state of motion or rest by the action
of another body, which in turn is brought into
its state of motion or rest by a third body, and
so on ad infinitum.*

Spinoza

As a boy Albert Einstein was, of course, ignorant of the philosophy which proclaimed the sovereignty of reason. He did, however, come in touch with the cultural trends accompanying the liberation of reason from the authority of the Church. In his student days and in the "Olympian Academy" he got to know the classics of rationalist philosophy, their precursors, disciples, followers and fellow-travellers.

Viewed retrospectively, from the standpoint of the physical ideas of the mid-twentieth century and reasonable forecasts for the future, Einstein's work presents itself as a sequel to a great period in the cultural advance of mankind which began with the emergence of rationalism in philosophy and science, of which Newtonian mechanics was one of the expressions. One cannot read Einstein's writings without thinking of Galileo, Descartes, Spinoza, Hobbes and Newton. This is due to a remarkable similarity in ideas, made all the more remarkable by the fact that it is in no way intentional. In Einstein, the vague conjectures and searchings of 17th-century rationalist thinking acquire positive, orderly features which were impossible at the time. The logical connection is indisputable. Less apparent are the inroads which brought Einstein to problems and ideas of the 17th and 18th centuries. Initially he did not have the benefit of detailed first-hand knowledge: Spinoza was probably the only 17th-century philosopher whose works he had read. Acquaintance with the other great rationalists came through latter-day interpretations that have rendered all but anonymous the ideas of 17th-century thinkers which contributed to the treasure trove of philosophy and science. Apart from this Einstein's perception of the heritage of the 17th century had other, indirect, sources.

The rationalism of Descartes and Spinoza had a profound effect on the mode of thinking of people, on culture and art: the imprint of rationalism remained, and in some ways grew deeper, throughout the 18th and 19th centuries. Like other young people at the turn of the century, the students of the Zurich Polytechnic and the members of the "Olympian Academy", who may or may not have been aware of the historical sources of the ideas they drew from contemporary lectures, articles and books, were the heirs of rationalism. But the critical mind of the greatest physicist of that generation was so acute and profound that he was able to discern conflicts of the 17th century, when rationalist schemes had not yet solidified in final form, in the systematised and well-ordered treatises of the 19th century. 17th-century rationalism bequeathed to the future both positive answers and living contradictions. (We shall see at the end of the book that in the second half of our century, Einstein's conceptions of nature have also left such contradictions.) These contradictions were recorded in invisible ink, as it were, and only a genius capable of an unusually profound analysis of the positive results of science could make the records legible. Einstein's thoughts turned to the initial, general ideas lying at the roots of rationalist science. The ideal of rationalism—a world picture comprising only matter in reciprocal motion and interaction—was later supplemented by notions alien to, and independent of, this ideal. Among these was the concept of absolute motion referred to vacuum. Einstein returned from latter-day conceptions to the initial ideas of classical rationalist science. This was only possible on the basis of facts which could not have been known in the 17th, 18th and first half of the 19th centuries.

The point of departure of modern science is the idea of inertia and the relativity of inertial motion expressed by Galileo. We will discuss its historic role and its significance in Einstein's world later on. Here we will note the significance of Galileo's more general ideas for 17th-century rationalism.

Unlike rationalist ideas of earlier epochs, 17th-century rationalism was connected with a definite epistemological and ontological platform. The sovereignty of reason lies not in evolving streamlined, consistent constructions, but in its ability to present a true picture of nature. In other words, the harmony and consistency of mental constructions is an indication of their objective nature, their agreement with objective reality. This view is based on the ontological proposition that the world is a well-ordered, integrated entity. With Galileo this idea had not yet acquired its subsequent dogmatic flavour (a given mental construction is in complete and final agreement with the truth, it contains the ultimate truth). Galileo spoke of the infinity of knowledge. A modern student of his work, Leonardo Olschki, writes:

"For those who are used to getting at the root of things Galileo discovered an unsolvable world problem and a science extending infinitely through space and time, the boundlessness of which could give rise only to a feeling of bitterness and a realisation of the loneliness of man."

But this is a projection of much later attitudes into the past. Galileo derived a buoyant optimism from the thought of the infinity of knowledge. He wrote that "extensively", in volume of information, our knowledge is negligible in comparison with what is yet to be learned; "intensively" our knowledge of nature is absolutely trustworthy. Ignoring the "intensive" trustworthiness of knowledge can lead, and has led, to pessimism concerning the possibilities of science, and consequently to a rejection of the value of science. This has opened up the doors to various forms of reaction against reason and science which we shall discuss later on.

In Einstein, as in Galileo, the infinity of knowledge bred an optimistic outlook. The matter is not reduced to concepts covering a number of specific well-established truths. Both Galileo and Einstein were convinced that science had obtained a reliable principle embracing the whole of nature. Galileo wrote that mathematics reveals the necessity of phenomena and that "there is no such thing as ultimate trustworthiness". As Einstein saw it, the principle of causality embodies no *a priori* content; nor is it restricted to phenomena alone. To him causality is the objective *ratio* of the world. The cognisability of this *ratio* is not the trivial cognisability from which dogmatic philosophy proceeds and which implies exact agreement between objective reality and the scientific conceptions absolutised by the given dogmatic school. To Einstein the cognisability of a law governing physical reality is in itself a reality which exists in spite of the infinity of the world, the paradoxes and riddles which it poses to the researcher and the relative, restricted and faulty nature of any given stage in the advance of knowledge. Einstein even sees something paradoxical in the cognisability of the world: it is infinite, knowledge of it is limited at every given moment, and yet it is cognisable. This is the true meaning of Einstein's observation, "The most incomprehensible thing about the world is that it is comprehensible." The comprehensibility of physical reality appears as a "wonder" because it finds expression not in logical verbal constructions but in the history of science, in the history of technology, which reveals the way in which man cognises and comprehends the world in all its complexity.

Descartes's rationalism (if we speak of his physics) was essentially ontological, that is why it marked the beginning of a new era in science, culture, and mode of thinking. Reason dealt a crushing blow against authority by removing God from nature and explaining the totality of known facts by the laws of motion and interaction of bodies. As a result, according to Descartes, the world picture logically deduced on the basis of a small number of initial postulates is a unique, exact—and in this sense an ultimate—representation of the real world.

In Descartes's *physics* the primary reality is nature consisting of nothing but moving matter. From the point of view of Cartesian physics the efficacy of the intellect and its claims to sovereignty are based on its ability to create a picture corresponding to physical reality.

In Spinoza's philosophy, Cartesian physics triumphed over Cartesian metaphysics. It became a monistic philosophy no longer restricted by alien constructions. Being is substance consisting of infinite attributes, each expressing eternal and infinite essence. Spinoza calls it nature, and also God: *Deus sive natura*. In the 17th century such word usage represented a purely superficial window-dressing for an atheistic outlook. In the following century social and philosophical thinking could no longer tolerate such window-dressing, and men called a spade a spade. As a matter of fact, already in the 17th century people realised that Spinoza's philosophy makes short work of both traditional religion and deism.

The ontological tendency is probably more apparent in Spinoza than in other 17th-century rationalists: the intellect seeks to grasp the intrinsic harmony of cause and effect in nature. This harmony can be perceived when the intellect does not rely on direct sense-impressions (e.g., the apparent motion of the sun around the earth: heliocentrism is the point of departure of 17th-century rationalism), and builds up a new picture which, in the final analysis, explains the *totality of experience* in the most natural way. The epitaph on Galileo's tombstone reads: *Proprios impendit oculos, cum iam nil amplius haberet nature, quod ipse videret.* (He lost his sight because there was nothing left for him to see in nature.) Galileo did not have to see the moving sun, his mind was free and not restrained by sense-impressions. But he had to prove that the picture based on a negation of the motionless earth concept was in agreement with sense-impressions and determined the inevitability of the observed phenomena. He had to show that the new system explained the facts which failed to fit into the old one. Sightless though he was, in his mind's eye Galileo saw the tides in Venice, which, he thought, could not be explained from the geocentric standpoint. 17th-century rationalism challenged not the totality of sense-impressions but a given limited sphere of impressions, and stood opposed, not to *empeiria*, but to empiricism.

It is important to note that, according to Spinoza and other 17th-century rationalists, ideas should be independent of the observer's position, of what Pascal called the "hateful self". Only then will they be true. True ideas, Spinoza says, in his *Ethics*, always agree with those things of which they are ideas.

This thought, which is characteristic of Spinoza and 17th-century rationalism as a whole, is found in Einstein in the same simple, general and categorical form. Einstein, however, did not merely seek a true theory in which judgements would be independent of the individual observer's position (and therefore paradoxical and contradicting direct sense-impressions). He greatly advanced the application in physics of invariants, which do not change in going over from the sense-impressions of one observer to those of another. The steady increase of the number of invariants in the science of nature is essentially the main line of scientific development, an expression of the liberation of science from anthropocentric fetishes. Heliocentrism, the infinite and homogeneous universe of Bruno and Galileo, the concept of inertia, and classical relativity meant that truths valid only for terrestrial observers (and therefore in agreement with direct observation) were giving place to truths valid for any observer, and therefore expressing nature's independence of observation. Einstein freed this initial 17th-century conception of the restrictions later imposed upon it.

What conception of nature, according to Spinoza, is authentic and free of subjective features? The answer is Galileo's and Descartes's conception of homogeneous matter devoid of any properties. "Bodies differ among themselves according to their motion or rest, their speed or sluggishness, not according to their substance." Hence geometry (not arithmetic!) is the basis of science. It enables the causal links of nature to be revealed. These links are reduced to the interactions of bodies. The quotation from Spinoza's *Ethics* in the epigraph to this chapter speaks of such interactions. In the *Ethics*, that ideological zenith of 17th-century rationalism, all causes that could not be reduced to interactions between bodies were excluded from the universal causal relationship. For many years this idea played a prominent part in Einstein's researches. In Spinoza it was linked with the idea of a single world substance. All reality is the reality of infinite substance whose attributes (bodies) depend in their motions on the substance alone.

Nature's freedom from transcendental effects of any kind finds expression in the conservation of states. We shall see that the idea of the conservation of states led Spinoza to a very broad and general concept close to that of the inertia of Galileo and Descartes.

The dependence of every body on the behaviour of all bodies in the universe makes the latter a mechanical entity. In a mechanical entity the same laws govern throughout. Therefore the world harmony is a simple pattern. Galileo, Kepler, Newton and the 17th-century rationalist philosophers, all spoke of the simplicity of the universe. Spinoza and other rationalists regarded this simple world, which consists only of bodies in reciprocal interactions, as the prototype and the basis of moral and aesthetic harmony. The 17th century sensed the beauty of this simple, objective world made orderly by causal relationships which could be grasped by the mind. "Here we are in a world of mentally perceivable beauty," as Malebranche wrote.

18th-century rationalism proceeded to dot the i's and cross the t's that had remained undotted and uncrossed. It carried the idea of the sovereignty of reason beyond the limits of speculative reasoning and injected it into the public conscience. The 18th century was an age of Reason—not rationalist scientific and philosophical thinking, but Reason bodied forth in action. The ideas of Rousseau, Voltaire, and the encyclopaedists reached Einstein on the wings of the spirit of free-thinking which pervaded Europe and was more prominent in Southern Germany than in other parts of the country. As for 18th-century scientific thinking, the strict logic and beauty of Lagrange's *Mechanique analytique*, for example, made a greater impression on Einstein than the masterpieces of socio-philosophical thought. 18th-century science entertained the conception of reason which had finally found the exact and ultimate solution to the problems posed by nature.

Conversely, the findings and style of 19th-century science convinced Einstein of the infinite complexity of physical reality. Thus he was confronted with two forms of rationalism, two forms of the apotheosis of reason, viz., 1) reason has achieved exact and ultimate knowledge of nature, and 2) reason infinitely approaches the true picture of nature. Einstein inclined to the latter formula, which is why his philosophical adherences passed on from the 18th century to Spinoza, whose rationalism had not yet come to the idea of ultimate solutions for the riddles of reality. Einstein's rationalism included the idea of the contradictory, complex and paradoxical nature of reality; cognition of the world, as he saw it, consists in successively tackling more and more difficult riddles. He was convinced that their solution would reveal the essentially simple harmony of the universe. In spite of the complexity of the laws of physical reality, they are not chaotic and they constitute an orderly system ascending to the most comprehensive and general unified laws governing the world.

What name could one give to this objective harmony of the world? Einstein knew its rational name. He spoke of the uniform causal relationship embracing the universe. However, he was too far removed from the militant anti-clerical traditions of 18th-century rationalism for the words "God" and "religion" to seem offensive to him, and they appear in his works and his letters. But his use of these words is not an expression of a departure from atheism.

When Einstein spoke of "God" he usually put a touch of familiarity or even irony into the word. While in Prague, Einstein was compelled, against his will, to send his children to a school where they received religious instruction. "Eventually," he remarked jokingly, "the children believe that God is some kind of gaseous vertebrate."[1] Once in Princeton Einstein complained about the diet he had been prescribed, remarking, "The Devil has seen to it that we are punished for any pleasure we ever get." When his companion asked why he did not ascribe this to God, Einstein replied: "The only difference between them is in sign: one comes with a plus, the other with a minus."[2] Leopold Infeld recalls that, when asked whether they would work on a Sunday, Einstein replied, laughing, "God does not rest on Sunday either."[3]

In the Institute for Advanced Study at Princeton, N. J., where Einstein worked during the last twenty years of his life, there is a small hall with a fireplace over which are carved Einstein's words: *"Raffiniert ist der Herr Gott, aber boshaft ist er nicht"* ("God is sophisticated, but He is not mean"). The objective harmony of the universe may find expression in paradoxical relationships ("God is sophisticated"), but it exists. Einstein's "God" is an alias for the objective, material laws of physical reality, an alias for the objective *ratio* embracing the universe. "This sense of the materiality of the outside world," Infeld writes, "is so powerful in Einstein that it frequently falls into its opposite. When Einstein speaks of God he means the intrinsic relationships and logical simplicity of the laws of nature. I would call it a 'materialistic approach to God'."[4]

[1] Ph. Frank, op. cit., p. 336.
[2] C. Seelig, op. cit., S. 426.
[3] L. Infeld, *Quest*, Doubleday, Doran, New York, 1941, p. 271.
[4] Ibid., p. 271.

To Einstein religiosity meant the realisation of being, which stems from an understanding of the world harmony. He writes in "The Meaning of Life":

"To know an answer to this question [on the meaning of life] means to be religious. You ask: Does it make any sense, then, to pose this question? I answer: the man who regards his own life and that of his fellow creatures as meaningless is not merely unhappy but hardly fit to live."[1]

The word "religious", as employed by Einstein, does not imply any affinity between the feeling of the meaningfulness of life and the harmony of physical reality, on the one hand, and religiosity in the literal sense of the word, on the other. Einstein proceeded from a purely psychological affinity. A scientist consumed by a realisation of the world harmony is oblivious of his "self". As concerns the nature of the universal *ratio*, the scientist's position is diametrically opposed to that of the believer. The latter seeks in the world an intelligent being who controls it. The scientist rejects this idea and sees the world as completely dominated by material causality.

"But the scientist is possessed by the sense of universal causation. The future, to him, is every whit as necessary and determined as the past. There is nothing divine about morality; it is a purely human affair. His religious feeling takes the form of a rapturous amazement at the harmony of natural law.... This feeling is the guiding principle of his life and work, insofar as he succeeds in keeping himself from the shackles of selfish desire."[2]

In "Religion and Science"[3] he contraposes scientific conceptions of the world to belief in a "personal God". Einstein speaks of the deep conviction of the rationality of the universe and the yearning to understand it Kepler and Newton must have felt to enable them to spend years of solitary labour in disentangling the principles of celestial mechanics.[4] It is this conviction which urges the scientist on towards the objective truth even in the face of the conceptions prevailing in his age.

[1] A. Einstein, *Ideas and Opinions*, Alvin Redman, London, 1956, p. 11. (Afterwards referred to as *Ideas and Opinions*.)
[2] Ibid., p. 40.
[3] Ibid., pp. 36-40.
[4] Ibid., p. 39.

The conviction of the rationality of the universe has nothing in common with the idea of a personal God or immortality of the soul. Einstein rejected this idea most emphatically. "I cannot conceive of a God who rewards and punishes his creatures," he writes. "Neither can I, nor would I, want to conceive of an individual that survives his physical death; let feeble souls, from fear or absurd egoism, cherish such thoughts."[1]

The nature Einstein venerated had no place for a God, for in it the objective *ratio* of causality reigned supreme. He venerated the eternal nature which dissolves the individual, and the knowledge of which gives freedom from fear and egoism. "I am satisfied," he goes on, "with the mystery of the eternity of life and with the awareness and a glimpse of the marvelous structure of the existing world, together with the devoted striving to comprehend a portion, be it ever so tiny, of the Reason that manifests itself in nature."[2] In a letter to Einstein, Solovine protested against the likening of this feeling to "religion". To this Einstein replied:

"I can understand your dislike for the term 'religion' in relation to the emotional and psychological attitude so apparent in Spinoza. But I have no better expression to denote the conviction of the rationality of reality and its accessibility to the human mind. Without this conviction science degenerates into soulless empiricism. I do not care if the clerics capitalise on this. There is no remedy against such capitalisation, in any case."[3]

This is a characteristic conclusion. Einstein was aloof from public movements fighting for social justice under the banner of militant free-thinking, and he saw no real ways of overcoming religion. From this stems his indifference to terminology—which is so important in demarcating ideological positions. Einstein's attention is focused on a different aspect of the matter: recognition of the fact that physical reality is rational and can be cognised, recognition of the paradoxical and unexpected quality of its laws. Later in a letter to Solovine he again writes of the "wonder" and "eternal riddle" of nature. In his words, he had to clarify this point "so that

[1] *Ideas and Opinions*, p. 11.
[2] Ibid., p. 11.
[3] *Solovine*, p. 103.

you would not imagine that, enfeebled by age, I have become the prey of *curés*".

Einstein lays stress on the idea of a rational and cognisable objective world, as opposed to the conception of a chaotic universe and the subjective nature of the laws governing it. One could expect, Einstein says, that we ourselves bring order into the world, like the alphabetic listing of words in a dictionary. But this conception is opposed by Newton's law of gravitation, which agrees with the objective causal order of nature. Knowledge penetrates deeper and deeper into this order, and its existence represents the "wonder" which grows with the increase of knowledge. This wonder, Einstein continues, undermines positivism and the dogmatic conception of a world without wonder.[1]

The fallacy of likening this feeling of "wonder" to religion even in a purely psychological plane is evident. Equally evident is the logical incompatibility of such a likening with the true meaning of Einstein's ideas. Science derives inspiration, emotion and romance from a knowledge of the laws of nature. Such knowledge leaves nothing of the feeling that nature is governed by non-causal relationships, which underlies every religiosity, even when it is not connected with the idea of a personal God.

With Einstein the vagueness of the ideological division between the conviction of the causal harmony of physical reality and the religious conviction of the non-causal "wisdom" of the universe, is due only to inconsistency in terminology. Actually, though, Einstein's world is unequivocally a world of causal relationships. This is borne out not only by numerous verbal statements but, more important, by his attitude towards modern physical theories.

In Einstein's own words, he believed in "Spinoza's God". Hence, in order to establish his position with regard to religion we must return to an analysis of the meaning which Spinoza put into the concept of "God".

Already in the 17th century it was apparent to many that there was nothing more divine in Spinoza's God than the name. The "prince of atheists", as he was called, was equally denounced by the defenders of orthodox religion—Catholic, Protestant and Judaic alike—and the exponents of deism.

---

[1] Ibid., p. 115.

According to Jacobi, Spinoza was neither a pantheist nor a cosmotheist (Einstein, incidentally, employs the terms "cosmic religion"), but an out-and-out atheist.

And Voltaire sums up Spinoza's stand in the lines:

> *"Pardon me," he whispered in [God's] ear,*
> *"But, between us, I think you don't exist."*

"It is remarkable," Heine wrote, "that the most diverse parties have attacked Spinoza. They constitute an army whose motley ranks present an amusing sight. Marching alongside a crowd of black and white cassocks carrying crosses and smoking censers is a phalanx of encyclopaedists incensed by this *penseur téméraire*. Next to a rabbi from the Amsterdam synagogue sounding the attack on the horn of faith comes Arouet de Voltaire piping the flute of ridicule in favour of deism, and every now and then one hears the howling of the old witch Jacobi, sutler to that religious army."

Despite "terminological" concessions to religion in speaking of himself as "the most religious of all non-believers" and of "cosmic religious feeling" and "Spinoza's God", Einstein conceded nothing of essence, and his "God" was even more formal and nominal than Spinoza's. Essentially Einstein progressed from Spinoza to Feuerbach, who substituted for the identification *deus sive natura* the contraposition *aut deus aut natura*.

Feuerbach was the real heir of Spinoza's essentially atheistic rationalism and the real continuator of the most essential, specific and promising trends in 17th- and 18th-century rationalism. He interpreted the objective reason, the "extra-personal" *ratio* of physical reality, in terms of universal causal relationships, thereby ridding science of the fiction of a purposeful will. "That which man calls the purposiveness of nature and conceives as such," Feuerbach writes, "is in reality nothing but the unity of the world, the harmony of cause and effect, the interconnection in general in which everything in nature exists and acts."

This universal harmony gives rise to the idea of a supreme, "extra-personal" being. Feuerbach retains the emotional colouring of his attitude towards the harmony of nature which is so characteristic of Spinoza: "One of the most common dirges of religious and scholastic mourners concerning atheism is that atheism destroys or ignores an essential human requirement, namely the requirement to recognise and venerate authority, and that is what makes man egoistic and proud. Atheism, however, while it abolishes the theological eminence above man, does not necessarily abolish the moral eminence above him. Moral eminence is the ideal which every man must set himself if he hopes to achieve anything; but this ideal is—and should be—a human ideal and purpose. The natural eminence above man is nature itself." Against this passage Lenin made the following note in his conspectus of Feuerbach's *Lectures on the Essence of Religion*: "Atheism abolishes neither *das moralische Über* (=das Ideal), nor *das natürliche Über* (=die Natur)."

Einstein's veneration of the natural harmony of the universe would not have acquired the irrational name of "cosmic religion" had he gone through the school of Feuerbach. For a number of reasons his direct acquaintance with philosophical doctrines was confined to Spinoza's rationalism.

Let us see what Einstein could gain from Spinoza's doctrines, or rather, from their inner meaning which characterises 17th-century rationalism as a whole. How, in particular, does the idea of the objective harmony of the universe affect the notions of *a priori* or empirical origins of scientific concepts? The problem is connected with fundamental, essentially epistemological questions, on the one hand, and with the pattern of Einstein's physical theories and his critique of classical physics, on the other.

The deepest and most specific distinction of 18th-century rationalism lies in its ontological conclusions. The sovereignty of reason is proved by its ability to present an authentic world picture. The world is governed by an objective *ratio*, the universal causality of all processes. This ontological conclusion already opposes the idea of *a priori* knowledge of the world as a whole. But if nature is governed by a universal causality, then science can deduce concepts on the basis of the unified laws of being without proceeding from direct observation. It should seek deeper relationships which are independent of individual, possibly subjective, observations. The search may take the form of geometrical theorems, which extract a wealth of content from a few propositions. This road, however, does not mean recognition of *a priori* sources in science. It means merely the primacy of the general results of observations over specific sense-impressions, and it leads to the "cruel experiment" which enables the researcher to deduce new laws of physical reality.

This is the purport of the ideas which Einstein borrowed from Spinoza. If harmony rules nature, then the concepts which express it cannot constitute an *a priori* framework into which the results of concrete observations can be fitted.

If there exists a hierarchy of more and more general laws establishing the universal harmony and embracing all processes, then each concrete empirical observation cannot reveal the nature of things. It must be correlated to a scheme of logically interconnected concepts.

If the world harmony is not a uniformity of processes, and if it does not preclude the complexity and contradictory nature of physical reality, then the logical deduction of concepts based on certain facts may come into contradiction with other, paradoxical, facts and a new general pattern, paradoxical in comparison with the old one, may be required to explain them.

Thus Einstein's rationalism rules out both the idea of the *a priori* origin of scientific concepts and the idea of science as an orderly record of direct observations.

We shall first discuss Einstein's stand with regard to certain philosophical schools deriving from this, then his conclusions concerning classical mechanics, thermodynamics and electrodynamics, and finally the genesis of his physical discoveries. These discoveries could not have been made without a deliberate and consistent rejection of the ideas of an "orderly record" or *a priori* sources of science.

Chapter 6

EINSTEIN AND POSITIVISM

> *To him the veils of Maya conceal not a vanishing phantom, but a core that can be understood and which becomes more and more apparent as he removes one veil after another.*
>
> *Moszkowski*

> *Conviction that the external world exists independently of the observer investigating it constitutes the basis of the whole science of nature.*
>
> *Einstein*

> *What I dislike... is the basic positivistic attitude, which from my point of view is untenable, and which seems to me to come to the same thing as Berkeley's principle,* esse est percipi.
>
> *Einstein*

In speaking of Einstein's philosophical sympathies the characteristic differentiation between the impressions which remain episodes in his personal life and those which prepared the way for his discoveries becomes of special importance.

Also to be noted is Einstein's characteristic attitude towards philosophical literature. Thus, he ascribed purely aesthetic value to many philosophical works and, at the same time, great philosophical and scientific value to works of fiction. His attitude was that of a sympathetic listener accepting the philosopher's point of view with an indulgent (or ironical, as the case might be) smile. He might admire the formal refinement and clarity of exposition of a work or note a useful negative effect—the overthrow of some fetish or other—but he rarely accepted affirmative statements and never took the attitude of a pupil. In many natural scientists such a stand stemmed from "extra-philosophical" pretensions, that is, from a repetition of very old philosophical errors, from a muddled and eclectic—and only in this sense "new" and "independent"—formalism. Einstein never claimed to be above philosophy. His attitude towards 18th- and 19th-century philosophy can be summed up in the following way.

For scholars who had witnessed the advance of science in the 19th century and accepted the idea of the infinite complexity of nature, even Spinoza's system was too closely linked with the illusion of ultimate solutions for the riddles of the world. By the turn of the century, scholars had come to regard as practically self-evident the idea expressed by Goethe that the solution of any problem contains a new problem. The 17th century, though it hoped that ultimate solutions would be found for all problems, did not pretend to be in a position to find them, and it retained a sufficiently clear perspective for further advance. When Newton spoke of himself as of a boy "finding a smoother pebble or prettier shell than the ordinary" on the shore of "the great ocean of truth that lay all undiscovered" before him, he spoke as a man of the 17th century; his pupils and followers belonged to the 18th century, an age of rationalism tending towards an ossified picture of the world. In some philosophical systems opposition to this view soon evolved from the legitimate contention that no knowledge can be regarded as final to a groundless scepticism concerning the value of science as a whole.

At the time when Einstein was making his first inroads into philosophical literature there already existed a philosophical school which drew its generalisations not from a world picture treated as final or *a priori*, but from the idea of a continuously changing and evolving conception of the world. This school, however, was not known to Einstein. In other philosophical schools criticism of dogmatic formalism frequently takes the shape of equally dogmatic agnosticism. This type of criticism proceeds from valid propositions, which are then elevated to the status of absolutes, and a critique of a specific, historically transient world picture turns into a dogmatic negation of objective truth.

The picture of the world drawn by Newton in his *Principia* provided sufficient scope for criticism. Thanks to the efforts of many philosophers, starting with Bishop Berkeley, who linked his critique of Newton's absolute space with his own *esse est percipi*, this criticism was canonised and extended from Newtonian propositions to science as a whole. For the most part it did not develop into consistent solipsism and fell into some form or another of inconclusive negation of the existence of an objective external world and the possibility of understanding it.

Some natural scientists responded only to the negative and partial aspects of such criticism, challenging only certain specific, concrete physical notions and concepts.

In the 18th century, English agnosticism was dominated by Hume. Einstein read Hume's fundamental work, *An Enquiry Concerning Human Understanding,* in Bern. (This was the volume the "Olympian Academy" had been studying at the time of Solovine's defection to the concert.) Einstein highly valued Hume's works. What did he glean from them? We have his own testimony and can answer this question quite definitely.

Einstein's problem was whether or not it was possible to deduce from observations of physical phenomena the causal relationships between them. Hume's answer is negative; from this he concluded that it was impossible to penetrate into the causality of observable phenomena and that human understanding was restricted to the phenomena themselves. Subsequently Kant, following in Hume's footsteps, arrived at the notion of the *a priori* nature of causality, as well as of space and time. However, Einstein's conception of the real world of matter as the cause of sense-impressions and of the cognisability of the objective laws of motion were not in the least shaken by reading Hume. Einstein proceeds from the idea that a series of observable phenomena does not determine unequivocally the nature of the causal relationships between them. Hence the picture of causal relationships is to some degree deduced independently of direct observations. Einstein speaks of the *free* construction of concepts expressing causal relationships. Does this mean that such concepts are *a priori* or conceptual, or that causal concepts are arbitrary as a whole? The answer is No. The causal connection of processes may be expressed by means of different kinds of constructions, and in this sense their choice is arbitrary. But they must be in agreement with observation, and it is our duty to select the construction which agrees best.

We will deal with all this in greater detail later on, for Einstein presents his views on the origin of causal concepts not so much in connection with his perusal and evaluation of philosophical works, as in the elaboration of new physical concepts. Accordingly, his views should be judged, not by their formalism, but by their heuristic effect, by the part they have played in the revolution in physics. From this aspect the effect of Hume's philosophy on Einstein was purely negative.

As to Kant, Einstein's rejection of his epistemology is expressed in unequivocal terms. Kant raised Hume's agnosticism to the level of an elaborate system and added a number of ideas involving such problems of classical physics as space and time which interested young Einstein. What was said before of Einstein's purely aesthetic evaluation of philosophical works applies in full to Kant. Einstein did not accept Kant's philosophy and he rejected Kantian epistemology, especially the *a priori* conception of space and time. At the same time he enjoyed Kant and derived great aesthetic satisfaction from his works. He was also drawn to Kant by the cultural and historical content of classical German philosophy. One feels in Kant's works the spirit of the Germany of Lessing, Schiller and Mozart, which contrasts so sharply with the spirit of Bismarck, his forerunners and disciples. 18th-century German culture appealed to Einstein because of its affinity to the spirit of rationalism and free-thinking that penetrated into Germany from beyond the Rhine.

Einstein, we know, was brought up on this spirit in his native Swabia, where it enjoyed freedom of expression, and it was instrumental in the formation of his world outlook. Classical philosophy belonged to the age of Reason, and this historical flavour appealed to men more than its content. A good example is Heine, by no means an adherent of Kantian philosophy, with his fine historical comparison between the law-abiding German professor and Robespierre and his humorous, yet serious, description of Kant's evolution from his *Critique of Pure Reason* to his *Critique of Practical Reason*. The Germans, it should be said, generally *ratiocinated* on what the French *did*, and the rumblings of revolution were clearly heard in German philosophy, literature and art. The atmosphere of classical philosophy, literature and music appealed to Einstein. Not so the new philosophy, for here (as in his attitude towards Wagner's music) his criticism of content was not mitigated by the almost intrinsic appeal of Kant's writings. We shall speak of Einstein's stand with regard to Kant's philosophy later on, in connection with his interpretation of the fundamental concepts of geometry. In the whole history of science it would be hard to find a more decisive refutation of Kantian apriority, as expressed in his conception of the *a priori* nature of space, than that presented by the theory of relativity.

From Hume, Einstein took an idea which the former had not in fact expressed in so many words, that is, Hume questioned the validity of human understanding as a whole whereas Einstein questioned the validity of a specific domain, Newtonian mechanics. These two approaches are poles apart and in order to challenge the validity of a concrete historically limited theory, one must be convinced of the objective truth of science, of its approach to absolute truth; the criterion of evaluation in challenging a specific theory is its agreement with objective reality. Therefore, Einstein could not follow the road of classical philosophy in its advance from Hume to Kant. He could have repeated Schiller's words, addressed to natural scientists and transcendental philosophers:

Be ye opponents! The time is not ripe to join hands:
Only on different roads will you come to the truth.

Classical philosophy and natural science did in fact seek the truth along different roads. Natural science advanced from Newton, through the accumulation of empirical data and 18th-century mathematical natural science, to the ideas of energy conservation, irreversibility, and evolution. Classical philosophy advanced through Hegel and Feuerbach towards an essential merger of philosophy and natural science, which developed in the 19th century. It was effected in the works of Marx and Engels. This road, however, lay outside of Einstein's field of vision.

For this reason Einstein could find no positive programme in classical philosophy subsequent to Spinoza for perceiving the "extra-personal". He found it in the classical science of the 19th century. The centre of gravity of his interests shifted to the domain of theoretical physics. Here happened something analogous to Einstein's attitude towards mathematics. In his youth he was unable to find the mathematical problems or inroads which would correspond directly to his physical ideas, he did find them later. In philosophy he never went beyond Spinoza's rationalism.

Einstein's attitude towards the positivism of the 1890s and 1900s can be formulated very simply in terms of final judgement and its effect on his physical works. Viewed from the purely biographical aspect, this problem is a bit more complicated, though never approaching either the complexity or the importance of the question of Einstein's attitude towards Spinoza. For our purpose, a brief review of the two positivistic conceptions of the time will suffice. The one is linked with the name of Ernst Mach and, placed in a nutshell, it declares that science "studies summaries of observations" and there exists no objective causality independent of observation; scientific concepts and laws are organised, "economical" records of observations. The second, known as "conventionalism", is associated with Henri Poincaré, and it states that scientific concepts are arbitrarily stipulated conventions and whether they agree with reality or not is no concern of science.

Although initially sympathetic to Mach's philosophy, Einstein later came to reject it, and he made his attitude clear in no equivocal terms on a number of occasions. In all of his statements on questions of philosophy and science there is probably no more deprecatory epithet than the one given in his address to the French Philosophical Society: "Mach is a poor philosopher."

At the same time, Einstein was for many years guided by the far from philsophical thesis advanced by Mach in his *Mechanics* in connection with his criticism of the concept of absolute space. A few words must be said of the connection between Mach's thesis and his criticism of the Newtonian conception, on the one hand, and his philosophy, on the other.

In the most general terms, Mach's thesis says that all events in nature can be explained by the interaction of material bodies. This is hardly a new idea, and it essentially coincides with Spinoza's conception of reality. Mach, however, opposed his thesis to Newtonian mechanics. This is what Einstein called "Mach's principle". In Newtonian mechanics inertia forces (such as those which make the passengers of a bus pitch forward when the driver brakes suddenly) are explained not by the interaction of bodies, but by the change in a body's velocity referred to space. Mach regarded this interpretation as untenable. As mentioned before, this is purely a mechanical thesis offering a certain picture of the world. Does it stem in any way from Mach's philosophical views?

Not uniquely. More, the image of interacting bodies as a scientific picture of the objective world is incompatible with positivism of any brand. The connection here is the same as between criticism of *classical* science and scepticism with regard to *every* science. In his work on the history of mechanics Mach came to the conclusion that Newton's absolute space contradicted the general premise of classical science: interactions between bodies as the cause of all natural phenomena. He could not, however, formulate a mechanical conception capable of interpreting observable facts without reference to absolute motion and absolute space. Apart from his qualities as a scholar (he did not possess the magnitude required for the task), in comparison with Newtonian concepts Mach was nowhere near the sources of a new world picture. From criticism of Newton's conception of *absolute* space, Mach turned to criticism of his conception of *objective* space. This is an example of the transformation of a segment of the curve of knowledge into a straight line which Lenin spoke of.

Einstein never doubted the objective nature of space. Criticism of Newtonian concepts was for him the point of departure in the quest for new concepts of space as an objective form of the existence of matter. It was this aspect that drew him to Mach's views. But he was quick to discern the faults in Mach's epistemological conclusions from the criticism of Newtonian mechanics, as well as the difference between "Mach's principle" in mechanics and the Machian philosophical school.

"Mach's principle" figured in Einstein's work for many years. Only towards the end of his life did he realise its limited nature. His interest in Mach's philosophy was a fleeting one, and it ended before the enunciation of the theory of relativity (possibly due to his work on the theory). It was succeeded by a sharply negative attitude towards "Machism".

Within the Machian school there were no unanimous views concerning Einstein's ideas. Mach himself rejected the relativity theory. Some Machists attempted to present Einstein's views as an example of the positivistic approach to science. When Einstein in a series of articles and lectures drove home the purport of relativity theory, many of Mach's followers realised the need for a qualified revision of their teacher's ideas. The result was so-called "logical positivism". Its adherents saw together with Mach in the main question: to them "experience" was a purely subjective notion and objective reality did not exist, to say nothing of the possibility of understanding it. They only shifted the centre of gravity of subjective "experience" to the sphere of experimental verification of logical constructions. Subject to verification, however, was not the agreement of a construction with objective reality but its subjective value. The core of "logical positivism" was the "Vienna Circle", a group of physicists and philosophers to which also belonged Philipp Frank, author of an Einstein biography referred to in this book.

Poincaré's philosophical ideas were never sympathetic to Einstein. Some scholars find that in the 1930s Einstein came closer to Poincaré's idea of scientific laws and concepts as being free, arbitrary conventions, chosen by agreement among scientists. As a matter of fact, throughout his work on the unified field theory, Einstein frequently stressed the criteria of logical clarity and universality of a physical theory; this could be interpreted as meaning choice of a theory without regard to its agreement with objective reality.

In his early works expounding the special theory of relativity, Einstein gave prominence to the role of direct observation and the importance of dealing with essentially observable quantities and concepts. But then, when two men say the same thing they do not necessarily mean the same thing, especially if one of them is Einstein. Mach and Einstein both spoke of "experience", "observation", etc. But to Mach these words were not associated with objective processes. To Einstein "experience" and "observation" were manifestations of objective reality. Poincaré and Einstein both spoke of the "free creation" of physical theories. But with Einstein this meant only that out of a number of more or less freely created theories ("free" insofar as they do not follow uniquely from the experimental data that has to be explained) the scholar must choose those which agree best with physical reality.

74

The idea of "free creation of physical theories" is worth analysing. In a lecture at Oxford, in 1920, Einstein spoke of the "correct way" of science as lying through human inventiveness in the free creation of logical constructions. This idea of "free creation", which appears in many of Einstein's writings, has given rise to quite a few misunderstandings. Philipp Frank, who is generally impartial in presenting Einstein's statements against Mach's philosophy and positivism as a whole, nevertheless attempts somewhat to reconcile Einstein's views with the neo-Machian epistemology of the "Vienna Circle". He proceeds in his reasoning from Einstein's thesis of the "free creation of logical constructions".[1]

Some materialist philosophers regarded Einstein's "free imagination" as more than just subjective terminology; they regarded it as a concession to subjectivistic epistemology in essence, and this in spite of Einstein's explicit opposition to the idea of *a priori* knowledge independent of experience and conventionalism. The meaning which Einstein put into the idea of "free creation" in science is apparent from the following passage in his Oxford lecture:

"It is my conviction that pure mathematical construction enables us to discover the concepts and the laws connecting them, which give us the key to the understanding of the phenomena of nature. Experience can, of course, guide us in our choice of serviceable mathematical concepts; it cannot possibly be the source from which they are derived.

"In a certain sense, therefore, I hold it to be true that pure thought is competent to comprehend the real as the ancients dreamed."[2]

This declaration of the rights of "free thought" was directed against Mach's empiricism, against "pure description" and the confinement of scientific construction to phenomenological statements of fact. But doesn't Einstein go over to the positions of Kantian apriority, does he not in fact declare that the mind freely deduces the world picture from *a priori* forms of understanding inherent in that understanding or from arbitrary "conventions"?

We have an excellent criterion for answering this question. The dividing line lies along the recognition of the objective

---

[1] Ph. Frank, op. cit., pp. 338-39.
[2] Ibid., p. 283.

nature of physical reality. The answer, therefore, is negative: Einstein stands on the positions of objective reality and objective knowledge of that reality: he sees knowledge as a reflection of reality, and his own physical ideas derive from this epistemological position. What, then, is meant by "free creation of the human mind"?

The mind develops hypothetical constructions not necessarily ordered by experience. Observations—our sense-impressions—guide us in our choice of construction, which does not necessarily follow uniquely from experience. It is deduced from general principles which are not of an *a priori* nature and are in turn derived from the *general* idea of the world based on the totality of observations, on the accumulated knowledge of the world.

To Einstein the fact that conclusions deriving from the general idea of the world, and not from direct observation (such as the prediction of Neptune, which did not follow uniquely from observations of the motion of Uranus and was "freely" deduced from the causal conception of the universe), agree with subsequent observations, is a refutation of subjectivism in its most consistent form, i.e., solipsism. In his "Reply to Criticism" (which concludes the *Philosopher-Scientist* volume) Einstein says that the basic positivist attitude comes essentially to the same thing as Berkeley's principe, *esse est percipi.* The best argument against positivism is the continuous confirmation of the general conception of the world, the confirmation of its being and its unity. If conclusions based on this conception, but not deriving directly from phenomena, are confirmed by experience, then knowledge is not restricted to phenomena, it can penetrate beyond phenomena and uncover their objective causes. Thus, the "free creation of the mind" was, in Einstein's eyes, an argument against Berkeley and his disciples.

Why does "pure mathematical construction" enable us "to discover the concepts and the laws connecting them which give us the key to the understanding of the phenomena of nature"? Why is "pure thought competent to comprehend the real as the ancients dreamed"?

These epistemological assertions rest on an ontological postulate: the world is not a chaos of isolated processes, it is an entity in which the processes of nature are connected by a universal causal relationship which determines their course. We perceive this connection, thereby penetrating beyond phenomena; the existence of the objective cause underlying them is proved by the agreement of "free" (i.e., deriving from the general conception of the world, but not predetermined by a specific observation) construction with the results of experiment.

Such an ontological and epistemological scheme presumes that mathematical constructs may or may not agree with the results of a physical experiment, and this immediately rules out the primitive concept which declares geometrical theorems to be simple descriptions of observable bodies, or the concept according to which the fundaments of geometry are arbitrary conventions or *a priori* possessions of the human mind.

Einstein presents an extremely lucid exposition of what he means by "free creation of the human mind" in his article, "Maxwell's Influence on the Evolution of the Idea of Physical Reality". He begins with stating his belief in the objective nature of physical reality.

"The belief in the existence of an external world independent of the perceiving subject is the basis of all natural science," he writes. "Since, however, sense perception only gives information of this external world or of 'physical reality' indirectly, we can only grasp the latter by speculative means. It follows therefore that our notions of physical reality can never be final. We must always be ready to change these notions—that is to say, the axiomatic basis of physics —in order to do justice to perceived facts in the most logically perfect way."[1]

Einstein does not oppose speculative reasoning to sense perception. The source of speculative thought lies in experience, not in *a priori* concepts, as Kant says, or in conventions, according to Poincaré. It does, however, stand opposed to individual sense-impressions, insofar as they do not present a picture identically corresponding to physical reality. The non-*a priori* and non-conventionalist nature of speculative constructs is seen in the fact that they can never be accepted as final, even the fundamental axioms of physics. They depend on the totality of observations, that is to say, on the never ending series of experiments which steadily

[1] *Ideas and Opinions*, p. 266.

advance physics towards an increasingly true description of reality. The axioms of physics are never final, and the time inevitably comes when they must be revised. But the independence of physical reality of the observer is not subject to revision. It is the overall premise of all physical theories.

Thus, "free creation" means freedom from specific, partial results of observation and dependence on the general conception of the universe, on the *totality* of sense-impressions, experiments and practical experience. From this follows the value of scientific concepts which do not derive uniquely from observations (although suggested by them) and are creations of the human mind. They are called hypotheses and are advanced "on credit", subject to subsequent verification, which may refute them or elevate them to the status of an unambiguous theory.

The atomistic theory of the ancients was to Einstein a model of a hypothesis deriving from general principles. In connection with a book by Solovine on Democritus's system Einstein wrote in 1930 that he regarded Democritus not in historical perspective but as a contemporary (this, incidentally, is a characteristic trait of Einstein's which we shall discuss later on). What appealed to Einstein most of all was Democritus's firm belief in the omnipotence of physical causality.

"One cannot help marvelling at this firm belief in physical causality, which cannot be dispelled at the will of *homo sapiens*. As far as I know, only Spinoza was as radical and as consistent."[1]

A world picture comprising only atoms and their motions and interactions was for a long time Einstein's ideal of a scientific representation of nature. His works on Brownian movement demonstrated that behind specific macroscopic processes lay the moving and colliding molecules. His radiation theory treats light as an aggregate of moving particles. Relativity theory rid classical notions of nature of absolutes alien to the picture of material particles in reciprocal motion. True, ultimately Einstein's ideas led to the concept of particle *transmutation*, which does not fit into this ideal scheme. This

[1] *Solovine*, p. 55.

finale, however, concerns not so much Einstein's biography as the biography of his ideas.

Einstein considered that, within certain limits, a scientific theory could develop on the basis of general tendencies: it links certain facts with the initial premises of the world picture in the most natural way and gradually sheds arbitrary supplementary postulates. The experimental verification of such a theory is a matter for the future. This, as we shall see later on, was the pattern which Einstein's physical ideas followed. We shall also see that they could not have evolved merely on the basis of a spontaneous recognition of the objective reality of the world; they required a conscious epistemological and ontological credo. The "extra-personal" world, Spinoza's philosophy, and a generalisation of scientific development, brought Einstein to a definite philosophical platform. It was an important prerequisite for his physical discoveries. These, in turn, gave clarity to his epistemological views. The Brownian movement theory led Einstein to a clearer realisation of the epistemological roots of the rejection of the reality of atoms in Mach's works. Reflection on the relativity of inertial, and later accelerated, motion revealed with greater clarity the fact that reality is independent of our knowledge.

During the great debate on problems of the microcosm, Einstein continued to come out against positivism sharper than ever. Not content with new arguments in support of the objective nature of physical reality and man's ability to understand it, Einstein developed new angles of approach to the past; his assessment of the present state of affairs in science and forecasts for the future blended with retrospective evaluations. Worthy of note in this connection is his essay, "Remarks on Bertrand Russell's Theory of Knowledge", written in 1944 for the "Russell" volume of the *Library of Lving Philosophers*.[1] It is prof to Einstein's non-acceptance of either Mach's phenomenalistic empiricism or the *a priori* and conventionalist notion that pure logical thinking is independent of experience. It also reveals that Einstein's opposition to these epistemological schemes stemmed from his philosophical platform and was based on his interpretation of the history of scientific thinking.

[1] Printed in *Ideas and Opinions*, pp. 18-24.

"During philosophy's childhood," Einstein writes, "it was rather generally believed that it is possible to find everything which can be known by means of a mere reflection." This illusion was a lasting one, and Einstein found it even in Spinoza. This "more aristocratic" illusion of *a priori* knowledge, he goes on, has as its counterpart the "more plebeian illusion of naive realism, according to which things 'are' as they are perceived by us through our senses". This illusion is the point of departure in the understanding of things by individuals as well as by science as a whole. But, like the notion of *a priori* perception of physical reality, it also belongs to the childhood of science. Already in antiquity men discovered that there was a gulf between the objective causes of sensations and phenomena. Modern sciences had their point of departure in the difference between subjective sense-impressions and objective reality. Hume derived from it his scepticism concerning empirical methods of knowledge: as he saw it, they were unable to get down to the objective world hidden behind apparent phenomena.

Then, Einstein goes on, Kant took the stage. He declared that definitely assured knowledge must be grounded in reason itself and need not necessarily agree with our sensory experience of the independent objective world. This in effect concluded the evolution of agnosticism. According to Hume, whatever in knowledge is of empirical origin is never certain, and it can give no indication as to the causal connection of events. Kant denied objective existence to such concepts as space, time and causality; they are creations of the human mind, not of the outside world, he said. Subsequently the philosophy of agnosticism merely repeated Hume and Kant.

Thus, historically there developed two mutually complementary and interconnected schools of agnosticism. One sees knowledge as a systematised record of empirical observations. The other, following Kant, sees it as a result of the development of *a priori* ideas inherent in the human mind. Later, when science began to alter concepts which Kant had regarded as *a priori*, agnosticism declared them the result of a convention and ascribed to them pragmatic, but not ontological, value.

Einstein was a direct heir of the rationalism of Spinoza and the 18th-century materialists; as such he held that the human mind is capable of developing a trustworthy knowledge of nature; therefore constructs of the mind possess objective ontological value. In its "free creation", however, the mind derives a trustworthy picture of the real world through concepts from which experimentally verifiable conclusions can be deduced.

This is Einstein's fundamental epistemological thesis; it is a development of the general premise of Spinoza's rationalism and it stands opposed to all schools of positivism. Einstein reaffirmed it on many occasions and, most important, it was the guiding principle in the development of his physical theories.

From this standpoint Einstein levels his criticism of positivism. As far as the positivist is concerned, "all those concepts and propositions which cannot be deduced from the sensory raw material are, on account of their 'metaphysical' character, to be removed from thinking". But, "this claim—if carried through consistently—absolutely excludes thinking of any kind as 'metaphysical'. In order that thinking might not degenerate into 'metaphysics', or into empty talk, it is only necessary that enough propositions of the conceptual system be firmly enough connected with sensory experiences...."[1]

This thesis, which was tried and tested in Einstein's work on relativity, quantum mechanics and the unified field theory, enabled him, in spite of a lingering sympathy for Hume's philosophy, to see that the tradition of identifying the search for objective truth with "metaphysics" begins with Hume. In fact, he writes, it was Hume who "created a danger for philosophy in that, following his critique, a fatal 'fear of metaphysics' arose which has come to be a malady of contemporary empiristic philosophising; this malady is the counterpart to that earlier philosophising in the clouds, which thought it could neglect and dispense with what was given by the senses".[2]

Einstein finds this positivistic "fear of metaphysics" in some of Bertrand Russell's constructions, notably in his conception of the thing as a "bundle of qualities".

[1] *Ideas and Opinions*, p. 23.
[2] Ibid., p. 24.

Einstein's epistemological views evolved throughout the world of his life. He never clung to established solutions which could be subsequently applied unchanged to specific physical problems. The development and elaboration of his epistemological ideas merged with their application, sometimes running ahead of the physical conceptions, at times trailing in their wake. Einstein's epistemological principles never achieved the harmony and integrity of his physical theories.

At the same time, it should be noted that the *foundation* of his epistemological credo was layed before the enunciation of the relativity theory. It was still vague, and his anti-positivistic stand found expression rather in his conviction of the objective and cognisable harmony of the universe. This deep-rooted conviction had a profound influence on his life, it determined his interests, ethical views and aesthetic affiliations.

Chapter 7

DOSTOYEVSKY AND MOZART

> Dostoyevsky gives me more than any thinker,
> more than Gauss!
>
> *Einstein*
>
> One day Einstein and I met in the dining room
> of the Aarau school, where we always had
> such a good time playing Mozart's sonatas.
> When Einstein's violin began to sing the walls
> of the room seemed to recede and for the first
> time the real Mozart appeared before me in a
> halo of Hellenic beauty with his pure lines,
> gracefully playful or mighty and exalted. "This
> is divine, we must repeat it!" Einstein
> exclaimed.
>
> *Hans Byland*

Einstein presented a rare example of a physicist in whom aesthetic interests and inclinations were closely linked with his scientific ideas. Not that he applied aesthetic principles in expounding physical views. This kind of exposition has gone down in the history of literature as a poetic canon in Lucretius's didactic poem. Galileo's works became a canon of Italian prose writing. Here we shall deal with something of a different nature.

Einstein spoke of the paradoxical facts which make one depart from a conventional, logical construction in favour of a new one. Initially the departure takes place intuitively. The paradoxical fact induces a series of vague associations in the scientist's mind. It is as if he sees the whole of the chain of deductions and conclusions which would strip the observed fact of its paradoxical nature by virtue of the paradoxical nature and novelty of the whole chain. Mozart spoke of the supreme moment of creation when the composer momentarily hears the whole of a still unwritten symphony. As Einstein saw it, intuition is essential to scientific creation, it is the element which links scientific creation with artistic creativity. He also attached importance to moral intuition. He wrote, in 1953, to one of his old friends:

"Dogs and little children immediately recognise a kind person from a bad one; guided by their first impression, they confide in the former and keep away from the latter. As a rule they are not mistaken, even though they do not apply scientific methods or systematic physiognomic studies in accumulating their small experience."[1]

Trust in moral intuition appealed to Einstein in the image of Don Quixote, and he reread Cervantes's great novel many times, especially in his latter years. Could the poor head of the knight-errant of La Mancha, befuddled with illusions, be in any way congenial to the genius of rationalist thinking?

Einstein's rationalism was an "escape from self-evidence"; *Don Quixote* is unrivaled in world literature in the portrayal of a man whose intense, though illusory, emotional life overshadows all everyday interests. Don Quixote, that symbol of intuitive discrimination between good and evil, is the purest soul in world literature; small wonder that the purest soul in 20th-century science was drawn to him. An insight into this attraction can be found in the following passage from a letter to Max Born: "It is every man's duty to be a model of integrity and have the courage seriously to uphold one's ethical convictions in the company of cynics. For many years I have striven to act accordingly—with varying success."

Complete mental immersion in the fundamental problems of science and morality is what makes Einstein akin to Dostoyevsky, although with Einstein the centre of gravity lies in the domain of science while with Dostoyevsky it was in the domain of morality. In Dostoyevsky's *The Idiot* there is a scene in which Prince Myshkin speaks of the emotions of a man condemned to death. He expounds his views in a conversation with General Yepanchin's doorman in the most trivial circumstances. But through this triviality there emerge the contours of cardinal problems. Einstein, too, could introduce major questions of outlook in any situation, on any occasion. In doing so he could break with habitual notions in the most unexpected way.

In tracing the logical and psychological inroads which brought Einstein to the theory of relativity, one is struck by

[1] *Helle Zeit*, S. 55.

his remarkable ability to view the world as if for the first time, through newly opened eyes, without being burdened down by conventional associations. In literature probably no one possessed this gift to a greater extent than Lev Tolstoi. This alone is already an expression of the unity of scientific and artistic perception of the world. "In scientific thinking," Einstein says, "there is always the poetic element. The appreciation of good science and the appreciation of good music demand, in part, similar mental processes."

Then comes the second aspect of scientific and artistic creation. Old, habitual associations are severed and reality, stripped of conventions, sparkles with fresh, striking, paradoxical colours. Dostoyevsky achieves this affect by subjecting his characters to "cruel experiments". He places them in difficult, unbearable situations, thereby seeking to bring out aspects of the mind and character which would have remained hidden in ordinary circumstances.

The scientist, too, subjects nature to such "cruel experiments" when he aims at results which otherwise remain hidden. How does a moving body behave in the conditions of a "cruel experiment" when it travels at velocities comparable with the speed of light? Most paradoxically.

The next step is pure thinking, in which the body's paradoxical behaviour is deduced from the most general properties of space and time. What was initially a paradox, finds its natural place in the world harmony.

Artistic perception of the world passes through similar stages. "Pure description", like *a priori* constructs, remains outside the pale of creativity. The integrity of an image, the harmony of the details which simultaneously characterise it, the music of the narrative (which may include dissonances, but never arbitrary elements), and the necessity of every detail correspond to the natural uniqueness of a scientific picture.

In Dostoyevsky the music of the narrative is sometimes extremely harsh. It is quite impossible to predict the next action or remark, the approaching turn in the events or the new torments of somebody's ailing soul. But when all has been said and done, one feels that only thus could it have been. It is this paradoxicalness coupled with a singleness of purpose and a compelling truth in character development that is responsible for the tremendous impact of Dostoyevsky's books. This compelling truth of paradoxical events is what contributes to the intellectual and emotional tension which they arouse in the reader.

This feature of Dostoyevsky's work (essentially common to all art, but brought to a fine point) was in tune with the paradoxicalness of physical reality, the compelling credibility of bizarre paradoxes which are represented so vividly in Einstein's work.

"Harmony" and "musicality" are two words which link Einstein and Dostoyevsky. They are associated with some of Einstein's innermost thoughts and emotions, and he used them many times in essays, articles, lectures, letters and interviews. We shall mention here an address which Einstein delivered in May 1918 at a celebration of Max Planck's sixtieth birthday.[1] It is in some respects autobiographical, for the two men shared in common the very traits of Planck's which appealed most to Einstein.

Einstein begins by defining the inner psychological motives that lead men to the temple of science. Many, he says, take to science out of a joyful sense of superior intellectual power; science is their own special sport to which they look for vivid experience and the satisfaction of ambition. Many others have come to science for purely utilitarian purposes. But there is a third category of men: those who find in science or art a refuge from everyday life. They are oppressed by its painful crudity and hopeless dreariness; they long to escape from personal life into the world of objective perception and thought. "This desire," Einstein says, "may be compared with the townsman's irresistible longing to escape from his noisy, cramped surroundings into the silence of high mountains, where the eye ranges freely through the still, pure air and fondly traces out the restful contours apparently built for eternity."[2]

A few words about the social motives of this "escape from everyday life".

Einstein knew *whither* these desires led a scientist, but he did not care to analyse from *whence* they sprang. Their sources lay in the inevitable agonising gulf that separated the chaos, contradictions and dreariness of everyday life and

[1] *Ideas and Opinions*, pp. 224-27.
[2] Ibid., p. 227.

the harmonious ideal. Everyday life is dreary because it is not filled with devotion to the "extra-personal" ideal; it is chaotic because it is not subordinated to the "extra-personal" goal. In his quest for harmony man creates works of science and art. But man is not restricted to an idealistic representation of the harmony which life lacks. He seeks and finds the ways and means of bringing harmony into everyday life. In the course of this quest public thought comes to realise that the chaos of everyday life is a result of the chaos in the social existence of men. It discovers the objective forces of social development which inevitably lead to a transition from chaos to harmony.

All roads lead to Rome, and in the 20th century they have become clearer than ever before. Dostoyevsky, whose soul was literally torn by his thirst for harmony, saw no positive social programme, and he achieved harmony not in his world outlook but in his creative work. Einstein was well aware of the forces guiding man to social harmony and the forces dragging him into the abyss of an all-destructive chaos. But it was not in the social sphere that his thinking came to be a model of clarity and precision, and he was more aware of the scientific results of the "escape from everyday life" than its social sources.

Hinging on what has been said is Einstein's view on scientific utilitarianism. Although he concedes that the "utilitarian" scientists may have contributed a major share to the building of the temple of science, he nevertheless does not rank them among the true *élite* of science. All his life Einstein saw that the utilitarian requirements imposed on science served to draw it away from its ideals, usually in the opposite direction. Einstein's antipathy towards the utilitarian motivations of science is in effect an expression of his ideal of the harmonious society in which utilitarian interests would coincide with the intrinsic ideals of science.

What are these ideals? As Einstein sees it, they are the same in science and in creative art. The artist and the scientist both seek to create a picture in which harmony prevails.

Dostoyevsky's affinity to Einstein lies, we might say, in that the harmony of his narration, his world in which the most unexpected twists receive logical justification, is a kind of "non-Euclidean" world.

In fact, Ivan Karamazov, of the *Karamazov Brothers*, actually speaks of a "non-Euclidean reality" as of a kind of universal harmony. "I am as confident as a new-born babe," he says, "that sufferings will heal and mitigate. The petty comedy of human contradictions will vanish like a bad dream, like a dirty concoction of a little, mean Euclidean mind. Ultimately, in the world finale, at the moment of supreme harmony, there will occur or appear something so precious that it will suffice for all hearts, it will cure all wrongs and redeem all the evil deeds of men and the blood shed by them."

Dostoyevsky longed for a "non-Euclidean" harmony. It is a longing that captivates the readers of his books. He knew that the moral harmony was attainable only beyond the confines of the "Euclidean world", that his very longing for it left him without the straw of traditional faith to which he clung; but the mischief is done, the stream of doubt is swift and the straws of tradition are of no avail.

To be sure, there is no direct connection between Dostoyevsky's "non-Euclidean world" and the non-Euclidean world of the general theory of relativity. Dostoyevsky's influence upon Einstein was of a purely psychological nature. The search for a harmonious picture in which unusual facts of life shed their paradoxical features is more intense and fruitful when the scientist comes fully to realise the infinite complexity of the world and, at the same time, the causal nature of the contradictory, paradoxical phenomena one observes in it.

When science is ripe for a "madness" of the kind Bohr spoke of, it is good for habitual associations and notions to be shaken by a powerful psychological stimulus such as can be provided by an artist of Dostoyevsky's stature. An analogy in genetics is offered by the Russian biologist Timiryazev. Genetists, he writes, have a system of acting on organisms in order to break down their hereditary basis and cause many deviations from the original type, out of which useful traits can then be chosen and perpetuated. The procedure is described by the French verb *affoler*, which means "to drive mad".

Literature sometimes has a similar effect on scientific thinking. It stimulates the development of new associations of ideas. In Einstein's case its impact could be especially great if the writer displayed a paradoxical "non-Euclidean" harmony in his works. I think that Einstein must have been greatly impressed by this frequently overlooked and rarely analysed facet of Dostoyevsky's genius. In the case of most readers the greatest impact of Dostoyevsky lays in the unusual situations he presents. Not many people are capable of grasping the rational nature of laws which govern the agonising paroxysms of mind and soul which Dostoyevsky describes in his books. Einstein was probably keenly aware of Dostoyevsky's musicality. This would explain the seemingly strange companionship of Dostoyevsky's tragic "Beethovian" mode of expression and the bright genius of Mozart in Einstein's heart.

Einstein was no virtuoso on the violin, but his playing was distinguished by a purity, confidence and sincerity of expression. Moszkowski says that Einstein greatly admired the violinist Josef Joachim, especially his performance of Beethoven's Sonata No. 10 and Bach's Chaconne. When Einstein played the violin he was more interested in giving a faithful rendering of the architectonics of the piece than in asserting his own individuality as a performer. His manner of playing was in accord with this approach.

Einstein also liked very much to improvise on the piano. He used to say that when away from home he always longed to get his fingers on the keys.

It would seem that what appealed most to Einstein in music was the objective logic of its images and moods, which dominates the personality of both composer and performer, just as the objective logic of physical reality dominates the mind of the researcher. He would probably have subscribed to Leibniz's profound observation (though it hardly exhausts the essence of music), that *profession de foi* of rationalist aesthetics: "Music is the joy of a mind engaged in calculation without being aware of it."

Einstein's favourite composers were Bach, Haydn, Schubert and Mozart. Bach attracted him by the Gothic architectonics of his music. As Moszkowski writes, he associated the soaring quality of Bach's music with both the architectural image of a Gothic cathedral lifting its spire to the sky and the orderly logic of mathematical constructs.[1]

---

[1] A. Moszkowski, op. cit., S. 201.

Einstein's attitude towards Beethoven was rather complicated. He understood where the man's greatness lay, but his heart did not respond to the tense dramatism of Beethoven's symphonies. More to his liking was the limpid clarity of Beethoven's chamber music. He saw the symphonies as an expression of the restless, surging personality of their author; the personal content in them drowned the objective harmony of reality. In Handel Einstein admired the perfection of musical form, but as a thinker he failed to find a deep penetration into the essence of nature. He found Schumann original, exquisite and melodious, but he did not feel the grandeur of generalisation in Schumann's works. Schubert was closer to him.

When Einstein listened to Wagner he seemed to see a universe organised by the composer's genius but not the extra-personal universe whose harmony is rendered with the greatest devotion and sincerity. In part this may have been due to the composer's personality, but in any case, Einstein failed to find in Wagner's works the detachment from the author's self which makes for the objective truth of reality. Neither did he find this truth in the works of Richard Strauss; he found that Strauss's music disclosed only the superficial rhythms of reality.

Einstein could be carried away by the sounds of Debussy, just as in science he might admire a mathematically exquisite, but hardly important, problem. It was the structure of a piece that attracted him. Einstein had an extremely "architectural" perception of music. This may be why he did not understand Brahms. The complexity of counterpoint was unable to give the feeling of simplicity, purity and sincerity which he prized above all else. As in science, purity and simplicity were to him the earnest of a trustworthy reflection of physical reality. Mozart was the composer he loved most, the master of his mind.

He was probably drawn to Mozart by the following congenial trait. Einstein frequently took a quizzical stand towards the facts of life as a shield against too painful impressions. He opposed them with irony—sometimes merry, sometimes caustic. Frank writes that "the use of such caustic words was for Einstein an artistic way of coming to terms with the world, like the playing of a Mozart sonata, which also represents the evil of the world in a playful manner."[1]

Einstein's humour derived from the very essence of his world outlook. He wrote in "The World as I See It":

"Schopenhauer's saying, 'a man can do what he wants, but not want what he wants', has been a very real inspiration to me since my youth; it has been a continual consolation in the face of life's hardships, my own and others, and an unfailing wellspring of tolerance. This realisation mercifully mitigates the easily paralysing sense of responsibility and prevents us from taking ourselves and other people all too seriously; it is conducive to a view of life which, in particular, gives humour its due."[2]

These sentiments are by no means to be taken as a fatalistic reconciliation with reality. At the basis of Einstein's world outlook there lay a deep-rooted belief in the objective harmony of the universe, coupled with an equally deep-rooted desire for social harmony. His scientific temperament was bent on creating a physical picture expressive of nature's harmony. Anything that fitted into the groundwork of this picture was of immense value to him, and he worked with tremendous zeal on the special physical and mathematical problems whose solution was necessary for the generalisation of the fundamental concepts of space, time and motion. Whatever seemed incidental and not directly connected with the unified world picture was of little or no interest. The subsequent generalisations of physical concepts carried Einstein on and on; each new problem (special relativity in 1905, general relativity in 1908-1916, the unified field theory in the second quarter of the century) seemed to him immeasurably more important than any thing previously achieved. This explains why he could speak jestingly when appraising past achievements, but never concerning work at hand.

Where social problems were concerned Einstein could be humorous and tolerant with regard to many facts of life, but he had an intense, unmitigated loathing for war, poverty and obscurantism. However, in spite of the public repercussions and social impact of many of his statements, Einstein

---

[1] Ph. Frank, op. cit., p. 338.
[2] *Ideas and Opinions*, p. 8.

was not a social fighter. One doubts whether he could ever have reconciled himself with the daily facts of life had it not been for a realisation of the general causality of existence, a firm belief in the triumph of human ideals, and a sense of confluence with the world harmony. These were fundamental traits of Einstein's inner world which paved the way for his escape from the everyday commonplace and enabled him to view the life around him and his own existence with composure and humour. Later on we shall hear of Einstein's need for solitude, of which he himself and many of those who knew him have frequently spoken. His well-known aloofness was in no way a manifestation of egoism. His escape was from daily contacts with other people as much as from his own everyday "self" in the name of the "extra-personal". It was not so much the distance as the isolation that he sought.

Humour was Einstein's means of escape into the "extra-personal". Never indifferent to the basic sores of society, militarism and exploitation, Einstein was unruffled by scholastic snobbishness and narrow-mindedness, incomprehension and indifference, vilification of himself and his ideas. These things could not move him because they concerned him personally; they were isolated, partial pinpricks of reality which could in no way affect his vision of the universe and humanity as a whole, and he shrugged them off with humorous composure.

Einstein's "Mozartian" approach to life was another form of his escape into the "extra-personal". But the playful embellishments of Mozart's music did not hide from him the purity and harmony of the basic themes.

In Einstein's own work the main road to the "extra-personal" lay through the elaboration of general (and ever more general!) conceptions revealing the world harmony. In social matters a humorous attitude towards evil mitigated bitter impressions; it never implied reconciliation with them, and frequently his humour developed into far from harmless irony.

Some people regarded as cynical such jokes of Einstein's as the one about God being a "gaseous vertebrate". But then, Mozart's music had also been labelled as cynical. This "playfulness" scandalised the legion of *bestia seriosa*–the Salieris, Italian and non-Italian, the prudes, German and non-German, the scholastic milieu of universities and academies, the intellectual philistines. They realised the power of clarity combined with irony as a weapon against dogmatism of all creeds.

And yet it was not the irony nor the ability to accept bitter impressions with a sardonic grin that appealed to Einstein in Mozart's music. Its appeal lay in its melodiousness, in the rational, luminating joining of separate sounds into a unique and at the same time unexpected musical pattern. One gains a similar impression in reading Einstein: unique and at the same time unexpected conclusions develop into a remarkable music of scientific thinking tempered with grains of irony, like Mozart's playful passages.

Chapter 8

MATHEMATICS AND REALITY

*All knowledge of reality starts from experience
and ends in it.*

Einstein

*Geometry remains a mathematical science
because the deduction of theorems from axioms
remains a purely logical problem; at the same
time it is a physical science insofar as its
axioms contain assertions relating to natural
objects the validity of which can be proved
only by experience.*

Einstein

One of the main epistemological premises on the road which
eventually led Einstein to relativity theory was his conception of the relationship between mathematics and reality.
Though formulated after the enunciation of the theory, this
conception had emerged prior to it and was a prerequisite for
the special, and particularly the general, theory of relativity.

At the Zurich Polytechnic Einstein spent much time in the
physical laboratory. He was a keen experimenter, and his
youthful interest contributed to some extent to the crystal-
lisation of relativity theory. Not that any of those experiments
ever became a departing point for it. But the nature of his
interest in experiments offers an insight into an interesting
aspect of his physical and mathematical thinking. This is
physical intuition, which precedes logical and mathematical
construction. It is worth elaborating on the rather vague
concept of intuition, which otherwise may be associated with
ideas lying in an entirely different domain.

We can judge of the mechanism of Einstein's scientific
thinking from, among other things, a document of considerable value for the history and psychology of scientific
creativity in general and the psychology of Einstein's
creativity in particular. In 1945, Jacques Hadamard, a French
mathematician, asked a number of his colleagues to define the

internal or mental images they make use of in their work. Here is what Einstein had to say:

"The words of the language, as they are written or spoken, do not seem to play any role in my mechanism of thought. The physical entities which seem to serve as elements in thought are certain signs and more or less clear images which can be 'voluntarily' reproduced and combined.

"There is, of course, a certain connection between those elements and relevant logical concepts. It is also clear that the desire to arrive finally at logically connected concepts, is the emotional basis of this rather vague play with the above-mentioned elements. But taken from a psychological viewpoint, this combinatory play seems to be the essential feature in productive thought—before there is any connection with logical construction in words or other kinds of signs which can be communicated to others."[1]

Logical constructions which can be expressed in words or mathematical symbols represent a secondary stage. At first there appear images of physical entities of a visual or motor nature which combine and associate among themselves.

"The above-mentioned elements are, in my case, of visual and some muscular type. Conventional words or other signs have to be sought for laboriously only in a second stage when the mentioned associative play is sufficiently established and can be reproduced at will.

"According to what has been said, the play with the mentioned elements is aimed to be analogous to certain logical connections one is searching for."[2]

The visual and muscular elements entering the associative play were probably of a kinetic and dynamic quality. We may surmise that the initial elements which the thinker projects in his mind to establish the associative play represent vague images of moving or changing bodies or vague muscular sensations of acting forces. In this associative play, images, some of them resembling physical entities, others merely symbols corresponding to more complex mechanical and non-mechanical entities, come together, combine or clash. These may be images of tossing seas symbolising and partly describing electromagnetic oscillations inaccessible to

[1] *Ideas and Opinions*, p. 25.
[2] Ibid., p. 26.

direct visual perception, or moving graduated rods representing reference systems, etc.

In the second stage, in which intuitive thinking is replaced by logical construction, the thinker as it were hears the words expressing concepts or sees them as mathematical symbols written down. In Einstein's case the visual and motor images of the initial associative stage were followed by an auditive representation of words expressing logical constructions. To Hadamard's question concerning the kind of "internal words" mathematicians make use of, Einstein replied: "Visual and motor. In a stage when words intervene at all, they are, in any case, purely auditive, but they interfere only in a secondary stage, as already mentioned."[1]

The described mechanism of thought was evidently best adapted for the construction of logical sequences permitting experimental verification.

According to Einstein concepts are not connected *directly* with sense-impressions and they need not possess direct physical meaning, which is frequently acquired in the complex, multi-stage process of constructing other concepts. Ultimately the logical conclusions become comparable with observations, which give physical meaning to the whole chain of thought. As mentioned before, in such construction logic and intuition go together. At each successive stage the latter anticipates, as it were, the physical conclusions of the constructed theory. Whenever logical analysis finds itself at crossroads, physical intuition prompts it towards the shortest cut to experimental verification. Like light, which always takes the shortest path through a system of mirrors, no matter how complex, so Einstein's thoughts took the shortest road that led from one concept to another—right up to the experimental verification of the whole chain of reasoning and the conceptions which allow for such verification. He was guided by physical intuition, or rather an "experimental intuition" which shows the nearest way to the experiment needed for the theory to acquire physical meaning. Einstein's intuition, it must be said, rested on the firm basis of the concepts and images of experimental physics with which he was so familiar. Light-reflecting mirrors, current-carrying circuits, rigid rods joining the moving parts of instruments,

_____
[1] *Ideas and Opinions*, pp. 25-26.

were images which projected themselves into Einstein's mind in a diversity of visual and motor associations, always ready for new sense-impressions and recombination.

Einstein's genius is seen in his ability to associate, combine and identify seemingly remote concepts. In the thinker's brain every concept (or, in the preceding stage, image) is surrounded by a cloud of virtual constraints or a field of forces which captures new concepts, often rearranges them, links them with a given concept, breeds new ideas and annihilates old ones. The mark of genius lies in the great power carried by such a cloud, the intensity of such a field, the radius of action of such forces.

Ultimately Einstein's experimental intuition became mathematical intuition. In his works we find methods of remarkable power and beauty which lead to a great number of conclusions without the need of supplementary surmises. The selection of such mathematical methods, was, as we shall see later, based on the elucidation of laws allowing for experimental verification. But this emerged later on, after physical intuition had led Einstein to a new idea, as compared with classical physics, division of concepts into formal and physically meaningful ones in principle capable of verification by observation. Before that, in Zurich, Einstein had no criteria for choosing between mathematical disciplines or problems.

"I saw," he writes, "that mathematics was split up into numerous specialities, each of which could easily absorb the short lifetime granted to us. Consequently I saw myself in the position of Buridan's ass, which was unable to decide upon any specific bundle of hay. This was obviously due to the fact that my intuition was not strong enough in the field of mathematics in order to differentiate clearly the fundamentally important, that which is really basic, from the rest of the more or less dispensable erudition. Beyond this, however, my interest in the knowledge of nature was also unqualifiedly stronger; and it was not clear to me as a student that the approach to a more profound knowledge of the basic principles of physics is tied up with the most intricate mathematical methods. This dawned upon me only gradually after years of independent scientific work. True enough, physics also was divided into separate fields, each of which was capable of devouring a short lifetime of work without having satisfied the hunger for deeper knowledge. The mass of insufficiently connected experimental data was overwhelming here also. In this field, however, I learned to scent out that which was able to lead to fundamentals and to turn aside from everything else, from the multitude of things which clutter up the mind and divert it from the essential."[1]

To Einstein the essential was that which could serve as the raw material or tool for evolving a trustworthy picture of the real world. He still lacked such a criterion in mathematics, but somewhere deep inside there already stirred the vague notion that the well-ordered system of geometrical theorems is an expression of the world harmony. The initial notion was simplicity itself: geometrical objects are pseudonyms of real bodies and by nature differ in no way from the latter.

"If thus it appeared that it was possible to get certain knowledge of the objects of experience by means of pure thinking, this 'wonder' rested upon an error. Nevertheless, for anyone who experiences it for the first time, it is marvellous enough that man is capable at all to reach such a degree of certainty and purity in pure thinking as the Greeks showed us for the first time to be possible in geometry."[2]

The error was that some geometrical theorems seemed not to be in need of any proof at all, as being based on self-evident premises. From these other, no longer self-evident, propositions could be deduced, thereby obtaining reliable information about real bodies by pure thinking, without the trouble of sensory observation. But the theorems' "self-evidence" had been based on the fact that the concepts figuring in them were ascribed the same kinds of relationships that are observed in nature between real bodies.

If the length of a segment is represented by a rigid rod, then all geometrical definitions involving length are self-evident—as long as the physical properties of the rod are what we take them to be. We say that the length of a segment is not affected by its motion, and regard this statement as self-evident because subconsciously we correlate geometrical concepts with their physical prototypes. But a geometrical

---

[1] *Philosopher-Scientist*, p. 15.
[2] Ibid., p. 11.

concept may acquire a new physical prototype. This is what in fact happened when Einstein arrived at relativity theory.

As Einstein says, the advance of science represents a flight from both "wonder" and "self-evidence". Science strips geometrical construction of "self-evidence" when experiments find fault in the observations which had given those constructions an apparently sound physical meaning. This is the flight from "self-evidence". But then science correlates new observations to pure logical constructions. The former cease to arouse wonder, the latter acquire physical meaning which could not have been gained by pure thinking alone.

The relationship between geometry and reality is one aspect of the relation of the logical to the empirical in science. Einstein expressed his epistemological views with regard to this relation on many occasions. They are closely linked with his work in physics. Some constructions referring to science as a whole, seem like generalised expositions of relativity theory. Some physical works seem like examples of epistemological schemes. A thoughtful approach to Einstein's scientific heritage refutes with equal force the idea that his creative thinking was "spontaneous" and lacked a consciously well-defined epistemological foundation, as well as the idea that his general conceptions were of an *a priori* nature.

In this context it is worth analysing a lecture by Einstein, "On the Method of Theoretical Physics", delivered at Oxford in 1933.[1]

It starts out with a piece of advice: if one wants to find out anything from the physicists about the methods they use, one should not listen to their words but fix one's attention on their deeds. "To him who is a discoverer in this field the products of his imagination appear so necessary and natural that he regards them, and would like to have them regarded by others, not as creations of thought but as given realities."

Notwithstanding, Einstein sets forth not the results of research but the methods used more or less consciously or subconsciously by the makers of physical theories. The task is to correlate the theoretical fundamentals of science with the results of experience. "We are concerned with the eternal antithesis between the two inseparable components of our knowledge, the empirical and the rational, in our department."

[1] *Ideas and Opinions*, p. 270.

Ancient philosophy remains a classical example of purely rational science that has grasped real relationships. It was a great triumph of reason which will never be shorn of its halo.

"We reverence ancient Greece as the cradle of western science. Here for the first time the world witnessed the miracle of a logical system which proceeded from step to step with such precision that every single one of its propositions was absolutely indubitable—I refer to Euclid's geometry. This admirable triumph of reasoning gave the human intellect the necessary confidence in itself for its subsequent achievements. If Euclid failed to kindle your youthful enthusiasm, then you were not born to be a scientific thinker."

This tribute to the rational component of knowledge is followed by a tribute to the empirical component: "All knowledge of reality starts from experience and ends in it." This formula, which we have taken as an epigraph to the present chapter, is in no way restricted to Einstein's remarks about "free creations of the human mind". But how does the kingdom of empirical knowledge coexist with the kingdom of creative thinking? "If, then, experience is the alpha and the omega of all our knowledge, what is the function of pure reason in science?" Einstein asks.

A complete system of theoretical physics, he says, is made up of initial concepts, of laws which are supposed to be valid for those concepts, and finally, conclusions to be reached by logical deduction. It is these conclusions which must correspond to experience.

"This is exactly what happens in Euclid's geometry, except that there the fundamental laws are called axioms and there is no question of the conclusions having to correspond to any sort of experience. If, however, one regards Euclidean geometry as the science of the possible mutual relations of practically rigid bodies in space, that is to say treats it as a physical science, without abstracting from its original empirical content, the logical homogeneity of geometry and theoretical physics becomes complete."

From this point of view, which has been consistently upheld in physics and geometry ever since the enunciation of relativity theory, geometry is free to create complex systems of logically sound conclusions without any reference to experience. But it is left to experience, and experience alone, to give these constructs physical meaning. This is the true meaning of Einstein's words about the creative, constructive function of mathematical concepts and methods in physics and their ability to approach reality.

"Experience remains, of course, the sole criterion of the physical utility of a mathematical construction. But the creative principle resides in mathematics. In a certain sense, therefore, I hold it true that pure thought can grasp reality, as the ancients dreamed."

Einstein expressed the same ideas, though from a somewhat different aspect, in his article, "The Problem of Space, Ether, and the Field of Physics".[1]

This article gives an even clearer insight into Einstein's views on the relationship between the mathematical and experimental fundaments of a physical theory. On the one hand, he writes, there is logical analysis with its high certainty but complete emptiness of content, and on the other hand, there is sensible experience. He illustrates the relation of these components of science on the following example:

"Suppose an archeologist belonging to a later culture finds a textbook of Euclidean geometry without diagrams. He will discover how the words 'point', 'straight line', 'plane' are used in the propositions. He will also recognise how the latter are deduced from each other. He will even be able to frame new propositions according to the rules he recognised. But the framing of these propositions will remain an empty play with words for him, as long as 'point', 'straight line', 'plane', etc., convey nothing to him."

What is meant by "point", "straight line", "plane", etc., conveying something? It means, Einstein says, that one can indicate the sensible experiences to which those words refer. The archeologist must carry out some experiments in the hope of making observations which will agree with the still meaningless words in the book he has found.

In 1926, Einstein outlined his general conception of the connection between geometry and physics in an appropriately entitled article,[2] in which he generalises the genesis of the

[1] *Ideas and Opinions*, pp. 276-85.
[2] "Geometría no euclídea y física", *Revista matemática hispano-americana*, Ser. 2, Vol. I, pp. 72-76.

new geometry and relativity theory in the historical aspect. The phylogenetic development of science went through the same stages as Einstein did as a scientist. Obviously, it was only retrospectively, after the enunciation of relativity theory, that Einstein could clearly formulate his understanding of the bond between logical constructions and observable phenomena. In retrospect he could also view the evolution from the initial identification of geometrical and physical concepts to their differentiation and, finally, synthesis. This was not a case of simply projecting the road which led him to relativity theory into the past. He did not seek retrospectively to impose upon the history of science the pattern which he had observed in the cognitive process. This pattern derives straight from the historical picture of mathematics and physics. Acquaintance with mathematical and physical ideas in their development prepared Einstein's mind for the idea of "flight from wonder" and "self-evidence" which found expression in relativity theory.

Einstein says that in ancient times geometry was a semi-empirical science which treated, say, a point as a real body the dimensions of which could be ignored. "A straight line was determined either by means of points optically aligned in the direction of vision or with the help of a taut thread. We thus have concepts which, as is the case with concepts in general, do not spring directly from experience. In other words, they are not conditioned by logical experience, yet they are directly correlated with sensible objects. As knowledge stood, judgements about points, straight lines or the equality of segments or angles, were at the same time judgements about known sensations associated with natural things."

This characteristic of the ancient conception of geometry and reality repeats Einstein's general epistemological position: concepts are not deduced logically from experience, nevertheless they are always connected with experience. Later on he reiterated this position in a general review of the road leading to geometrical concepts from their physical proto-types.

In its subsequent evolution ancient geometry—physical or semi-physical—gradually detached from its empirical roots. It was found with time that a great number of geometrical propositions could be deduced from a few axioms. Thus geometry became a proper mathematical science. "The desire to extricate the whole of geometry from the confused realm of semi-empiricism," Einstein writes, "led imperceptibly to erroneous conclusions comparable with the gradual conversion of revered ancient heroes into gods." Now the concept of "self-evident" came to denote something inherent in the human mind which could not be rejected without giving rise to logical contradictions. How then could those logically non-contradictory axioms, which are inherent in the human intellect and therefore "self-evident", in particular the axioms of geometry, be used to gain a knowledge of physical reality? It was at this juncture, Einstein writes, that Kant's conception of space as an *a priori* form of knowledge came to the fore.

Einstein did more than just reject Kant's ideas of *a priori* knowledge. He pointed out the real problems of science and the actual contradictions from which metaphysical delusions—in this case concerning the *a priori* nature of space—developed when certain aspects of knowledge were elevated to the status of absolute truths. The illusion of apriority was created by the axiomatic nature of geometry. The other source which tended to divorce geometrical concepts from their physical prototypes lay in physics itself.

"According to the much subtler view of physics on the nature of solid bodies and light, there are no objects in nature whose properties would correspond exactly to the basic concepts of Euclidean geometry. No solid body can be regarded as absolutely rigid, a beam of light is not an exact representation of a straight line nor of any one-dimensional image. According to modern scientific views, geometry taken alone does not strictly agree with any experiment; it must be used to explain experiments conjointly with mechanics, optics, etc. Moreover, geometry must precede physics, insofar as the latter's laws cannot be expressed without geometry. Hence geometry must appear as a science which logically precedes all experience and any experimental science."

In explaining this aberration of scientific thinking, Einstein once again refers to his initial thesis, which appears in many writings of his, on the method of science: considered logically, concepts are not identical with the totality of sense-impressions,

Einstein expresses the same idea most emphatically and going much further than ever before, in a letter to Solovine.[1]

"Strictly speaking," he writes, "geometry cannot be reduced to 'rigid' bodies, which in fact do not exist. And also to be taken into account is that rigid bodies cannot be treated as infinitely divisible."

Einstein states that bodies consisting of atoms cannot be exact prototypes of geometrical figures: corners do not end in true points, sides are not true planes, etc., and from the standpoint of the wave theory of light, a ray is not a prototype of a straight line. This alone is sufficient to nurture the temptation to regard geometrical concepts as conventional or *a priori*, independent of the results of physical experiment, and therefore immutable. To this Einstein adds another consideration arising from the measurement of spatial dimensions and, in particular, the location of bodies. We use measuring rods and a procedure in which we match the material points whose distance we want to know with material points of a known distance. But if these are material points, then we cannot completely ignore the action of our measuring rod on the measured body. It was this that Einstein had in mind when he continued in his letter: "Similarly, the assumption that the bodies we use for measuring do not interact with the measured bodies is not justified."

We shall have occasion to recall this remark in connection with Einstein's attitude towards quantum mechanics. The conclusion he draws is:

"Concepts can never be regarded as logical derivatives of sense-impressions. But didactic and heuristic objectives make such a notion inevitable. Moral: it is impossible to get anywhere without sinning against reason; in other words, one cannot build a house or a bridge without the use of scaffolding which, of course, is not part of the structure."

A rather unexpected conclusion for a follower of the great rationalists of the 17th and 18th centuries. They were firmly convinced that to sin against reason meant to sin against truth. But then, Einstein was not so much a follower as a successor of Descartes and Spinoza. He knew them, but he also knew Goethe's "Theory, my friend, is grey, but eternally green is the tree of life". Direct "sense-impressions", as Einstein saw

[1] *Solovine*, p. 129.

it, develop into the abstract concepts of theory by an intricate process which includes the ignoring of certain aspects of reality. The supreme expression of "sinless" rationalism—Laplace's "omniscient" being knowing the locations and velocities of all the particles in the universe—was a thing of the future to 17th-century rationalists, and of the past to the rationalists of the 19th and 20th centuries.

In any case, in the 19th century, with its established atomistic conception of matter and wave conception of light, nature was no longer a kind of applied geometry. It followed then that geometry was not nature in the abstract, and from this it was but one step to geometry as being based on *a priori* notions or conventions.

Growing pains are cured by further growth. The illusion of geometric apriority and convention disappeared with the further elaboration of the axiomatic foundations of geometry and the further development of ideas on the physical proto-types of geometry.

The emergence of comprehensive, elaborate geometric systems based on different primary assumptions and postulates undermined the idea of *a priori* geometry and *a priori* space. What, men asked, is the geometry of the real world? And does this question mean anything at all? Einstein first analyses Helmholtz's answer: the concepts of geometry are based on real objects and, in the final analysis, geometrical statements are statements about real bodies.

Poincaré takes a different view: geometric concepts are pure conventions. Einstein associates himself with Helmholtz's analysis and says that otherwise he could never have come to relativity theory.

As we shall see later on, relativity theory seeks to define the geometry which corresponds to objective reality and describes it most accurately. Thus geometry loses its indifference to the physical nature of its objects and the physical truth of its judgements, a feature which is characteristic of logic and mathematics. As Bertrand Russell says, pure mathematics consists completely of assertions of the type: if a premise concerning a certain object is true, there must exist another premise about which that object is also true. The essential thing is, Russell goes on, firstly, that the question of the truth of the first premise is ignored, and secondly, the nature of the object is ignored. Mathematics, Russell says, can be defined as a science in which we never know whether we are speaking the truth or not.

To ignore the ontological aspect of the matter means it is no longer complete. There are various ways of deducing the second premise from the first, and their choice depends on the content of the first premise and the nature of the object to which it refers. Mathematics—geometry in the present case —acquires ontological, physical meaning. To Einstein this meant that mathematical judgements must, in particular, allow for experimental verification.

Einstein's conception, we see, opposes both apriority and pure conventionalism in mathematics and the primitive idea of the identity of geometrical relationships with "self-evident" and immutable physical relationships. In the study of nature, pure thinking does not yield *a priori* results; they must be correlated with experience. Only then do they acquire physical meaning. There is no such thing as *a priori* self-evidence, but empirical self-evidence is equally illusory. Geometrical concepts gain new physical content, and in the process they change, too.

The foregoing analysis characterises the road which Einstein travelled in elaborating and developing the theory of relativity. It also reveals the impact of Einstein's early training in mathematics and physics. Things fell into place later, after relativity theory had been enunciated, but the building materials had to be prepared in advance. Their value and the place they occupied in the newly-built edifice depended on the form in which they contributed to its erection, and this in turn depended on the store of mathematical knowledge which later proved useful to Einstein.

At this juncture it would be appropriate to review in more systematic form some of the mathematical concepts that have appeared in these pages.

The totality of theorems of the simplest, elementary geometry taught at school, is based on the premise that the length of a line segment does not change when the segment is moved about and measured in different positions. The premise is of major importance, and it lies at the source of concepts which are essential in setting forth the fundamentals of relativity theory.

The length of a line segment is the distance between its ends. The location of any point is defined in terms of its distance to other points; and distance is defined in terms of the positions of points. The location of a point is a relative concept; it is specified by reference to other points or to lines or planes. Even definitions of position which are not associated with quantitative measurement, such as "above", "below", "to the right", "in front", require reference to other points, lines or planes with respect to which a given point may be "below" or "in front". Descartes found a way of quantitatively describing the position of a point in space. If this space is a plane, two mutually perpendicular lines—the coordinate axes—should be drawn through a point in the plane —the point of origin—and perpendiculars to them should be lowered from the given point. The lengths of these perpendiculars—the coordinates of the point—describe its location in the plane. Space in which the position of a point is described by two coordinates is called two-dimensional. It need not necessarily be flat, it can be curved, like the surface of a sphere. Our earth is a good example of such a surface and the location of a point is given by its distance from one of the poles (or the equator) and from a meridian accepted as zero. In such a coordinate system (frame of reference) the axes are curved.

To describe the position of a point by means of Cartesian coordinates in three-dimensional space we need a system consisting of three mutually perpendicular planes. The location of the point is given by three coordinates representing the lengths of perpendiculars drawn from it to the three planes.

We can replace a given Cartesian system with any other Cartesian system by choosing a new point of origin and drawing three mutually perpendicular axes in any direction. Such a replacement is called a *transformation* of coordinates. It changes the values of the coordinates, but not the length of a segment. If we know the coordinates of both ends of a line we can calculate its length. If we take any other reference system, determine the new coordinates of our line's end and calculate its length, we will obtain the same value as in the old system. The length of a line segment belongs to the category of quantities which do not change in the transformation of coordinates and which are called *invariants* with respect to such transformations.

When one deals with such geometrical concepts the mind envisages their physical prototypes. One visualises a line segment as something of a barbell: the distance between the two weights never changes and they comprise a *rigid mechanical system*. One visualises coordinate axes in a plane as two perpendicular lines drawn on the table, floor or ground. The notion of a three-dimensional frame of reference takes on the concrete image of a floor and two mutually perpendicular walls extending infinitely in all directions attached to a ship, the earth, the sun, or Sirius, as the case may be. One expects that the length of the bar (or the length and shape of any more complex mechanical system) is the same whether the coordinates of its points are measured in the ship system, or earth system, etc.; that is to say, we can take any point of origin to describe the geometrical properties of real bodies. This equality of all points in the selection of the point of origin of a coordinate system is due to what we call the *homogeneity* of space. We can thus declare that when Copernicus deprived a coordinate system attached to the earth of its privileged position he thereby postulated the homogeneity of space. At the same time he in effect declares that in going over to another coordinate system (Copernicus attached his to the sun) neither the shape, dimensions or the behaviour of bodies changes.

Accordingly we arrive at the notion that every direction in space is as good as the other—a property known as space *isotropy*. When the scholars of ancient Greece abandoned the idea that the antipodes risked falling "down" off the earth—that is to say the idea of some privileged direction in space—they in effect discovered that the quantities characterising the shape, dimensions and behaviour of bodies are the same in a frame of reference with one axis pointing "up" as in a system in which the axis is pointing "down".

But to get back to geometrical invariants, as mentioned before, the geometry taught at school is based on the assumption that the length of a line does not change when the line is shifted. It can be calculated according to a known formula from the coordinates of the two end points of the line. The coordinates, we have said, may change depending on the choice of reference system, but the length remains unchanged: it is invariant with respect to coordinate transformations. We may imagine some other formula connecting the length of the line with the coordinates of its ends. We may alter other basic assumptions of geometry without falling into any contradictions. This latter possibility delivered a powerful blow at the idea of *a priori* space.

Kant regarded the relationships of Euclidean geometry as *a priori*, intrinsic to the mind, and independent of experience. When Euclid, in the 3rd century B.C., deduced the totality of the theorems of geometry from a few mutually independent axioms, he included among the latter the so-called parallel lines postulate which states, in effect, that one, and only one, line not intersecting a given one can be drawn through a point lying outside the given line. This postulate is the basis of the proof that the sum of the angles of a triangle equals two right angles, that two perpendiculars to the same line are parallel, and of several other theorems, including the formula for finding the length of a line segment if the coordinates of its ends are given.

In 1826, Nikolai Lobachevsky demonstrated that non-Euclidean geometry which does not accept the parallel-line postulate is quite feasible. In Lobachevsky's geometry, through a point not lying in a line there can be drawn an infinite number of lines not intersecting the given line, the angles of a triangle total less than 180°, perpendiculars to a line diverge, and the length of a line is determined from the coordinates of its ends; this is not so in Euclidean geometry.

Thirty years later, Bernhard Riemann replaced Euclid's parallel lines postulate with the assertion that through a point not lying in a line it is impossible to draw any non-intersecting line at all. In other words, in Riemann's geometry parallel lines do not exist; the angles of a triangle total more than 180°, perpendiculars to the same line converge, and the formula for determining the length of a line from its coordinates is again different.

These paradoxical assumptions of Lobachevsky's and Riemann's geometries acquire simple and graphic meaning if we draw geometrical figures not on a plane but on curved surfaces. Take a sphere for instance. In such a surface the part of straight lines in a plane is played by the shortest arcs, joining two points (they are called *geodesics*). Examples of geodesics on the surface of the earth are arcs of meridians, the equator or any other great circle. But two meridians inevitably intersect, hence it is impossible to have two parallel geodesics. Perpendiculars to the equator—the meridians—

converge at the poles. Drawing a triangle between the equator and two meridians, that is, with its apex at one of the poles, we find that its angles total more than 180°. The length of the shortest segment between two points on a spherical surface is determined by a formula unlike the one for determining the length of a similar segment in a plane.

We can find curved surfaces in which the replacement of straight lines by geodesics subjects all relationships to Lobachevsky's geometry: any number of non-intersecting geodesics can be drawn through a point not lying in a given geodesic, the angles of a triangle made by geodesics total less than 180°, perpendiculars diverge, etc.

The transition from Euclidean geometry in a plane to non-Euclidean geometry in a plane can be carried out by curving the plane.

But how can one visualise non-Euclidean geometry in *space*, a transition from *three-dimensional* Euclidean geometry to *three-dimensional* non-Euclidean geometry? We find no visual image of curved three-dimensional space. But we can regard any transition from Euclidean to non-Euclidean geometrical relationships as the curving of three-dimensional space.

When Einstein was attending his lectures in Euclidean and non-Euclidean geometry at the Zurich Polytechnic, he had no idea of the geometric concepts that would lead him to the development of a new physical theory. Only many years later did he see that the problem of relativity of motion, which had attracted his attention in boyhood, had a direct bearing on the transformation of coordinates and the curvature of space. For this, a much broader meaning had to be attached to the concept of "space".

Einstein approached three-dimensional space and the three-dimensional Euclidean geometry describing its properties with the criterion of physical content. Do physical processes fit into the relationships of three-dimensional Euclidean geometry? Classical physics says Yes. Einstein's theory of relativity says No. It gives physical content to a four-dimensional geometry.

Chapter 9

POINTS OF VIEW
IN THE SELECTION OF SCIENTIFIC THEORIES
AND THE FOUNDATIONS
OF CLASSICAL PHYSICS

> *Nature in its simple truth is greater and more*
> *beautiful than any creation of human hands,*
> *than all the illusions created by the spirit.*
>
> R o b e r t   M a y e r

In his 1949 *Autobiographical Notes,* Einstein speaks of two points of view in the selection and evaluation of scientific theories. The first is concerned with the "external confirmation" of the theory: it must not contradict empirical facts. This demand is an evident one, but its application is a delicate matter, for it is often possible to secure the adoption of theory by means of artificial additional assumptions. The second point of view is formulated more vaguely as the "inner perfection", "naturalness" or "logical simplicity" of the theory. For "inner perfection" the theory should not be the result of an arbitrary choice among theories that are of more or less equal value.

These assertions concerning the points of view in selecting physical theories are, in Einstein's words, of meagre precision, and he declares that he is not immediately, and perhaps not at all, capable of substituting these hints by more precise definitions. "In any case," he goes on, "it turns out that among the 'augurs' there usually is agreement in judging the 'inner perfection' of the theories and even more so concerning the 'degree' of 'external confirmation'."[1]

It should be stressed, in the first place, that the two points of view, in effect, express the same idea. They serve as criteria for determining the ontological value of the theory

---

[1] *Philosopher-Scientist,* p. 25.

and its agreement with reality. This does not mean that there cannot be some purely formal, aesthetic criterion of beauty, simplicity or generality. Einstein, however, does not ascribe independent value to such characteristics. They merely offer additional indication as to the theory's validity.

Here is an example from another field to support the idea. There is no doubt that if, from the architectural point of view, a hydroelectric station is graceful, natural and attractive, the aesthetic impression of beauty possesses value of its own. However, it is at the same time also an indication of the harmony between the structure and its natural environment.

Einstein, with his remarkable sense of harmony, "naturalness" and, as he called it, "musicality" of scientific thinking, attached great importance to aesthetic impression as being dependent on the "inner perfection" of the theory. For him the point of view of "inner perfection" develops into a criterion for the selection of an unambiguous theory in agreement with the empirical facts. The theory with the greatest "inner perfection" is the one that rests, to the smallest degree, on arbitrary assumptions. Such a theory is better suited than any other to describe the structure and development of the world picture on the basis of uniform, universal laws of physical reality. It comes closest to the objective *ratio* of the universe.

Formally the point of view of inner perfection comes very close to the criterion of mathematical elegance as defined by Poincaré: the more propositions that can be deduced from a minimum of premises, the greater the elegance of the mathematical construction, which he compared with an antique colonnade supporting a pediment with natural ease and grace. To be sure, architecture (especially ancient) presents some of the best examples of one-value solutions: out of a great number of possible architectural forms only one corresponds to a minimum number of supplementary supports, only one solves the static problem with a minimum addition to the basic concept of the structure; this is the most elegant solution.

Einstein's demand for inner perfection is broader than the demand for a minimum number of additional supports, which is but one of several criteria of inner perfection. With him mathematical elegance acquires *ontological* meaning, the elegance of the theory is a reflection of its agreement with the real world. Relativity theory, we shall see later on, offered the most elegant explanation of the known facts in electrodynamics and optics.

Einstein's theoretical costructions are distinguished by their elegance. True, following Boltzmann, Einstein suggests that "elegance should be left to the tailors and shoemakers". His advice, however, applies to the exposition of the physical theory. The selection of the theory from among a number of others, all of which are in agreement with the empirical facts (which by themselves, Einstein says, cannot uniquely determine a theory) is an active process in which the mind proceeds from the point of view of inner perfection, in particular from the maximum of elegance and the minimum of independent premises on which the theory is based.

The dividing line between the epistemological positions of Einstein and Poincaré becomes immediately apparent when the question is asked: of what value is elegance, the smallest possible number of independent premises, etc.? To Poincaré elegance means essentially nothing, it is not an indication or a manifestation of the theory's deeper qualities. To Einstein elegance is an indication of the theory's trustworthiness, of its objective certainty—considerations which are impossible in a philosophy which bases science on *a priori* knowledge or arbitrary conventions.

The theory deriving from the least number of premises comes closer to reality for the simple reason that the world represents a *unified* system of bodies the behaviour of which is mutually conditioned, because nowhere in the causal chain of the wide world are there any loose ends which could serve as the starting point of an investigation. Every link in this chain has its whys and wherefores, and none can be treated as primary or independent. It is the absence of such links, the unity of the world, the universal, all-embracing nature of the unified chain of cause and effect that says much for the ontological value of elegance in physical theories. When the theory is based on but a few independent postulates it comes closer to the real unity of the world and reflects it in the best possible way. The order, rationalism and determinacy of the world are objective qualities. They lurk beneath the surface of all phenomena, whatever the exponents of "pure description" may say to the contrary. They do not constitute an *a priori* framework of knowledge into which sense-impressions are fitted. They are objective laws, whatever the exponents of the apriority of scientific concepts and laws may say. When a theory deduces its propositions from a minimum of primary laws it comes closer to the real unity of the universe.

This unity finds expression in the conservation of certain relationships, in going over from one point of space to another and from one instant of time to another. It was this invariance of the laws of physical reality that, due to the fact of their action being independent of spatial and temporal displacements, represented the point of departure on the road that ultimately led to relativity theory. The "inner perfection" of a theory is measured by its affinity to the real world unity. When Einstein began his quest for the equations expressing the laws of physical reality that would remain covariant (i.e., preserve their validity) in various spatial and temporal displacements, he sought for the maximum "inner perfection" of his theory. In effect this meant maximum agreement of the theory with the objective unity and determinacy of the world, with the conservation of physical relationships and with the natural causality embracing the infinite universe.

Einstein applied the points of view of "external confirmation" and "inner perfection" to classical mechanics as the foundation of physics long before he had even named them or had a clear picture of them.

Characterising physics as it presented itself when he was a student, Einstein writes: "In spite of all the fruitfulness in particulars, dogmatic rigidity prevailed in matters of principles. In the beginning (if there was such a thing) God created Newton's laws of motion together with the necessary masses and forces. This is all; everything beyond this follows from the development of appropriate mathematical methods by means of deduction."[1]

The problem here is not simply one of the dogmatic conception according to which all the laws of nature can be reduced to the laws of Newtonian mechanics. The 19th century had done away with that idea. The theories of heat, electricity and light were found to possess characteristic laws of their own, and men no longer accepted the idea of a

---

[1] *Philosopher-Scientist*, p. 19.

Laplacian omniscient being knowing the position and velocity of every particle in the universe as the ultimate in the knowledge of nature. The dogmatic approach lay elsewhere.

Most natural scientists took it for granted that it was possible to deduce the totality of physical knowledge from Newton's laws without falling into any serious contradictions. This acceptance of Newtonian mechanics as the immutable bedrock of physics was not shaken by 19th-century theories. Men already knew that the simple scheme of moving particles was not adequate for a deep interpretation of the known physical facts. The behaviour of large populations of moving molecules required such concepts for its explanation as the probability of states, irreversible transition from less to more probable states, etc., which did not fit into the classical pattern of mechanics.

And yet the conviction held that the totality of motions, no matter how complex, boiled down, in the final analysis, to bodily displacements faithfully obeying the laws of Newton. The concepts of absolute space and absolute time seemed as unshakable as the laws which postulated them.

Thus, when Einstein speaks of mechanics as the bedrock of physics he is far from the mechanistic view which originated in the 17th, rose in the 18th and fell under the impact of the great discoveries of the 19th century. The scheme, according to which all the laws of nature were reducible to mechanics was already sufficiently outdated by the turn of the century, and Einstein's remarks refer to the broader and more general conception according to which the Newtonian laws of particle motion and interaction are ever present behind the scenes of the complex laws of nature, without, however, overshadowing or superceding them in the world picture.

The development of electrodynamics led men to question both the applicability of the mechanistic interpretation of nature to electromagnetic processes and the accuracy of the laws enunciated by Newton and confirmed by two centuries of scientific and technological progress. We shall deal with this a little later. Now let us examine two of Newton's ideas, criticism of which paved the way to the revision of Newtonian laws as the basis of physics.

First, *absolute time*. Newton spoke of the uniform flow of absolute time which is the same for the whole of the universe.

This means that it is possible to speak of events taking place simultaneously, at the very same split second, at any points in infinite space. This conception of the same instant for all of the physical universe and the succession of such instants common to it, of the absolute passage of time and the simultaneity of distant events, is one of the corner-stones of classical physics. It seems to us that a given instant involves the whole universe, we are quite sure of this, and this conviction of ours seems (or rather seemed) unchallengeable and immutable, and maybe even *a priori*.

Einstein began by approaching the concept of absolute time from the viewpoint of "external confirmation". Do observations agree with it?

Time is not an *a priori* or arbitrary concept, hence observations may one day call for a revision of some logically harmonious notions involving it. On the other hand, the concept of time is not just a record of observations; it extends into the sphere of the objective causality of phenomena; therefore it should be approached from the non-phenomenological point of view of "inner perfection".

A point of interest is the extent to which knowledge acquired by Einstein at the Zurich Polytechnic could contribute to the revision of the concept of absolute time.

If absolute time is not an *a priori* logical concept, then it must agree with sensible observations capable of confirming its reality. Absolute time acquires physical meaning if one envisages an action of one body on another propagated instantaneously, i.e., with infinite velocity. A body may act on another body at a distance in many ways: through gravitational attraction, impact carried along a rigid rod, or light signalisation (the action of a source of light on an illuminated target). One single instance of action on a distant body transmitted with infinite velocity would suffice to give physical meaning to the concept of absolute simultaneity. Imagine any kind of instantaneous signal: an impact transmitted instantaneously through a rigid rod; instantaneous propagation of gravity; a sound transmitted with infinite speed; a radio wave travelling with infinite velocity from transmitter to receiver; a ray of light striking a screen at precisely the same instant when the light source is turned on. In each case simultaneity is a physical concept which lends itself to observation and can be proved to agree with objective reality. If a signal propagates with infinite speed, if an interaction between bodies can be instantaneous, then the events "body A acts on body B at a distance" and "body B experiences the action of body A" are simultaneous.

But in nature there are no instantaneous signals, and bodies interact with finite speed. There is no such thing as an absolutely rigid rod capable of instantaneously transmitting an impact. Propagation of gravitation or acoustic or electromagnetic waves is not instantaneous either. One by one the finite velocity of signals was discovered and the image of instantaneous action at a distance gradually disappeared from the overall picture of the world. As a result the concept of absolute simultaneity lost its "external confirmation". When it finally achieved agreement with observations, it was only at the expense of substantial losses in "inner perfection". The concept of absolute simultaneity and absolute time ceased to be a corner-stone of the world picture and came to be regarded as inexact and approximate. The decline and fall of absolute time is linked with the advances in optics and electrodynamics at the close of the 19th century. We shall soon speak of them. Here a few words are appropriate concerning the connection between the idea of absolute time and the treatment of three-dimensional geometry.

The idea of the world as a four-dimensional multiformity dates back to the 18th century. Whatever happens in nature takes place in space and time. A snapshot records an event that took place at some instant: but nothing can happen in an instant of no duration. It is a platitude that a point of zero dimensions, a line of zero breadth or a plane of zero thickness are not real bodies. So does a cube with a zero lifetime exist as a real body?

Such reasoning concerning the four-dimensional nature of the real world is so simple and natural that it took time before another view could develop. This other view was based on the acceptance of simultaneity as a physical concept, i.e., on the idea of instantaneous action at a distance. If an instantaneous snapshot shows two bodies joined by an absolutely rigid rod capable of instantaneously transmitting an impact, or if it shows a beam of light hitting a screen at the precise instant when the projector is switched on, then such a snapshot depicts a real event.

Instantaneous action at a distance contradicted the apparently natural view that every event takes place a certain time after the event that caused it. Observations, however, led people to believe that one sees an event at the very same instant it takes place, and even hears, for example, a bell tolling the very moment the rope is pulled.

The latter illusion disappeared quite long ago. The notion of the instantaneous propagation of light persisted well into the 17th century. That all interactions (signals) propagate with finite speed was established only in the 19th century. The man who first realised that he heard the bell tolling only several seconds after the rope was pulled, may have been as excited by his discovery as Einstein was when he saw the behaviour of the compass needle. An even greater "wonder" is the thought that some of the stars twinkling in the sky may actually have been dead for ages. Up to the 20th century the "flight from wonder" consisted in the elaboration of a conception of the world in which the finite velocity of signals could coexist with the notion of absolute simultaneity.

This possibility, Einstein says, could be envisaged in the following way. Imagine two screens with a lamp exactly halfway between them. The light from the lamp, travelling at a finite speed, reaches both screens at the same instant. If the time at which both screens are illuminated is identified, then the words "at the same instant" have physical meaning, and we can speak of simultaneity, of the same instant at distant points in space, of the uniform flow of time. Accordingly, the idea of an "instantaneous snapshot" should acquire physical meaning as a three-dimensional, purely spatial multiformity. We shall see shortly that the theory in which absolute time remained along with the finite velocity of signals could not receive "external confirmation". It was overthrown by the advance of optics and electrodynamics.

It should be noted that there is one peculiarity of the concept of absolute time in classical physics. The word "relative" is counterposed to "absolute", and it means that some definitions (or, if a property has been measured, quantities) have physical meaning only in reference to another definition. For example, the concepts of right and left have meaning only if there is given a directed axis on a plane with respect to which they can be established. Equally relative is the statement "two feet away", which requires the additional statement, "away from what". As far as spatial definitions are concerned these are trivial truths. The spatial location of a body is relative because it is meaningless in the absence of some body of reference. And every such body is as good as the other, all internal properties of things being expressed in the same terms whatever the choice of reference system.

"Absolute" quantities, on the other hand, have meaning independently of any reference to something extraneous to them. Absolute definitions of properties need no reference to any property taken as a point of origin. The absolute position of a body in space was easily visualised in ancient cosmology, with its notions of the centre and the confines of the universe. We shall see how much more complex the concept of absolute space grew when space came to be regarded as infinite.

Absolute time, it would seem, is time not referred to any arbitrarily selected initial instant (the beginning of the day, year, or of all time), and relative time is the time-lapse from such an arbitrary point of origin: the duration of a process is, for instance, a year, irrespective of whether it is counted from A.D. 1 or any other point of time. In this sense absolute time is the time counted from some privileged point of origin, which is independent of any of the arbitrary and equally good initial dates used in different calendars—from the beginning of the world, in fact. Thus it corresponds to the boundaries of the universe which must necessarily appear in defining absolute space.

However, it is not this conception of absolute time that we spoke of before. By absolute time, should be understood not time independent of a *temporal* frame of reference (a calendar, etc.) but time independent of the *spatial* location of the point at which it is measured. This makes the content of "absolute time" substantially different from other "absolute" quantities, such as "absolute space". When Aristotle's finite universe was destroyed absolute *space* was salvaged from the ruins. But when the myth of the creation of the world collapsed it meant the end of the concept of an absolute beginning to all time. What remained was the idea of a universal time-flow, independent of all and any events. All through the 19th century classical physics persisted in regarding time-flow as being independent of the spatial positions of the points at which it is measured. This was

Einstein's understanding of the absolute time which he went out to criticise.

Now, *absolute space.* Newton proceeded from the notion of infinite space. Hence the absolute position of a body in the sense of its distance from the boundaries or the centre of the universe, could not enter the picture of the world drawn in the *Mathematical Principles of Natural Philosophy* (the *Principia,* as his great work is commonly called). A new criterion of absolute space appears—the change in internal processes in the displacement of a body from one spatial point to another. We know nothing of the boundaries of space or of any absolutely motionless bodies in it. The location of a body is referred not to such boundaries or bodies, but to space itself, to the void in which all bodies have their place. Position not referred to a body of reference; but position referred to the boundless, infinite void of outer space contradicts the testimony of our senses: no one can see or even visualise the position of a body without reference to some other body. The ancients had the absolutely fixed earth and the boundaries of the universe, although they were hard put when it came to the location of the universe and its centre, the earth. Now the difficulty was in defining what was meant by the absolute position of a given body. Newton got around this difficulty in the following manner.

The ancients proceeded from the absolute position of a body: its orientation with respect to the fixed earth and the confines of outer space. They accordingly defined absolute motion as a body's displacement from one absolute place to another. Newton reversed the argument and proceeded from absolute motion. Absolute motion displays itself in changes in the rhythm of internal processes in a moving body. Such a criterion does not require a reference frame. Absolute space is defined out of absolute motion: a displacement through absolute space takes place in the course of an absolute motion, i.e., one in which a body or system suffers internal changes.

What are these internal changes? What kind of motion gives rise to them?

The cause of internal changes are inertia forces, which disrupt the normal rhythm of mechanical processes in a system moving with acceleration and affect the behaviour of bodies within it. When a system moves from one part of space to another with an acceleration the bodies within it behave differently than when the system is at rest or in a rectilinear uniform motion. In a system moving without acceleration—an inertial system, that is—a motionless body remains motionless; a body in uniform motion left to itself continues to travel with the same velocity; a body subjected to a force moves with an acceleration proportional to that force. Acceleration changes the picture altogether: bodies left to themselves behave as if a force has been applied. Forces of this kind are called inertia forces, although in classical mechanics forces, generally speaking, exist due to the interaction of bodies. Inertia forces are not associated with any interaction, they are caused by acceleration and they are proof of the absolute nature of accelerated motion.

These forces appear as a criterion of absolute motion in daily experience. An example of relative motion is the smooth, uniform motion of a train when it is impossible to say whether it is moving relative to the train on the neighbouring track or, on the contrary, it is the other train that is moving in the opposite direction. If the train accelerates or slows down the jolt disturbs the equivalence of the two motions and the passengers can say for sure that it is their train that is moving. Even without a frame of reference inertia forces enable an observer to describe the motion of a system, register its absolute nature and give physical meaning to the concept of absolute motion not referred to bodies, motion referred to space itself.

Newton's famous example with the rotating bucket, which he presents in his *Principia* as proof of absolute motion and absolute space, is essentially in the same category of observations. Newton took a bucket of water tied to a rope and, by twisting the rope tight, made the bucket spin rapidly about its vertical axis. Centrifugal forces caused the water to rise along the walls of the bucket. From the point of view of relative motion, the rotation of the bucket with respect to the earth, the sky, etc., and the rotation of the universe around the bucket must yield the same physical effect, and the statements "the bucket rotates relative to the world" and "the world rotates relative to the bucket" describe the same process. But centrifugal forces, and inertia forces in general, violate the equivalence of these two statements. The surface of water is in no way affected by the world revolving about the bucket but it rises most obviously in the spinning bucket. Hence, the rotation of the bucket is absolute.

What do we mean when we say that the two statements made above are equivalent? We take a reference system (a set of coordinate axes) in which the earth is fixed and the bucket revolves. Then we take a coordinate system attached to the bucket, that is, a frame which turns with the bucket, or it would be better to say, in which the bucket is fixed and the world turns. The transition from one conception (the rotating bucket) to another (the rotating world) represents a change-over from one coordinate system to another. Does such a transformation from a rotating bucket to a resting one or from a resting bucket to a rotating one yield any internal effects? We have seen that the transformation involves a change in the behaviour of bodies (the particles of water) inside the system. This is an indication of *absolute* motion. Newtonian mechanics tells us that the statements, "system *A* moves with an acceleration relative to system *B*" and "system *B* moves with an acceleration relative to system *A*" describe different situations. The quantities describing the internal state of accelerated systems are not invariant with respect to coordinate transformations.

The appearance of inertia forces when system *A* starts moving with acceleration, and their absence when it is at rest or in uniform motion, reveals that accelerated motion is *absolute*, and not merely with respect to *B* (in which case we could have said that *B* was moving relative to *A*). Newton regarded this absolute acceleration as taking place relative to something absolutely stationary. Accordingly, one can say that system *B*, where inertia forces are absent, has no acceleration with respect to something *absolutely* at rest. This "absolutely stationary" something which causes inertia forces to develop in accelerated motion is, in Newton's view, space—empty, absolute space.

In drawing a picture of non-accelerated, coasting motion we encounter any manifestations of absolute space which can be observed. Galileo showed this in his *Dialogue on the Two Great World Systems* on the example of events observed in the cabin of a ship in uniform motion. Everything takes place as if the ship were at rest. Gnats fly about and water drips into a bottle placed directly underneath in exactly the same way when the ship is at rest and when it is moving without acceleration. These observations were summed up in the classical *principle of relativity* for inertial motion.

As Einstein pointed out, however, the inertia law is far from obvious. It owes its "obviousness" to tradition in the analysis of observations and concepts which had once seemed paradoxical. In fact, empirical evidence tells us that bodies whose motion is not sustained by a constant force tend to come to a halt. The logical convention ascending to Aristotle, which was still widespread in the 17th century, regarded circular motion as the most natural mode of motion.

"The idea that a body left to itself must move in a straight line does not follow from experience," Einstein says. "Quite the opposite! And the circle was declared the simplest path of motion by Aristotle and other great thinkers of the past."[1]

The concept of inertia was not a result of "pure description" of directly observable facts. On the contrary, it was an upshot of the clash between traditional observations and generalised ideas, an upshot of the quest for a consistent general world picture, of the investigation of new observations which did not fit into Aristotle's scheme of motion as always requiring an impressed force to sustain it.

In the 17th century the concept of inertia was in many respects the starting point of a new science. It embodied, first of all, the basic idea of 17th-century rationalism—the liberation of nature from anthropomorphic patterns. In fact, the very meaning of the concept of "nature" changed. Before, it was understood to denote some transcendental force standing above the material world and governing it. "Nature is God's minister," as La Boétie, the 16th-century French writer, put it. Now nature was identified with the material world, thereby freeing the universe from transcendental forces. The mechanical equivalent of this idea was the concept of motion which does not have to rely on forces extraneous to nature to sustain it. A body's motion at any given instant was explained by the fact that it had been moving the instant before; acceleration was explained by the action of other moving bodies or, in the final analysis, by the universal motion of all bodies, as Spinoza implies in the passage from

[1] Moszkowski, op. cit., S. 52.

his *Ethics* quoted in the epigraph to Chapter 5. Aristotle's "prime mover" was eliminated by the scheme of nature as a mechanism consisting of nothing but interacting parts. To Robert Boyle nature was a "cosmic mechanism", and there was no need to seek a metaphysical cause for its functioning, just as we do not have to seek a metaphysical cause for the working of a clock. The free motion of bodies and the absence of metaphysical causality in nature find expression in the conservation of the state or states which derive from the laws of nature: *Omnis natura est conservatrix sui.*

Spinoza's views on the conservation of bodies and their states are of special importance in analysing the ideological sources of Einstein's theories. To Einstein the classical principle of relativity, the homogeneity of space, and the uniform velocity of a body left to itself represented more than just a body of 17th-century physical ideas. They were an embodiment of the world harmony, of the objective world ratio subordinated to the universal causality and free from any non-causal effects. That is why Einstein concentrated the whole force of his intellect on this idea. His understanding of inertia and the relativity of inertial motion ascends to Spinoza.

In presenting Descartes's philosophy, Spinoza links inertia with the conservation of the state of things treated as entities. It follows therefore that a body once put into motion continues to move infinitely unless retarded by an external cause.

Spinoza links the concept of inertia (or, more precisely, the more general concept of conservation of state) with the concept of the preservation of the physical existence of a thing, the preservation of its identity to itself. "Every thing seeks, as far as this depends on itself, to remain in its existence (being). But being consists in the sustenance of internal qualities. If the "thing" is a system of bodies, its "being", its individual existence, is dependent on the behaviour of the component bodies as a function of their internal interactions.

Translated into the language of mechanics, this means that in coasting motion the relationships between the motions and the body interactions within a system that caused them, do not change. Hence, internal relationships within a coasting system can offer no clue to its motion. Motion is nothing more than a change in distances between bodies, and we can declare with equal confidence that a given system is moving relative to another body or that that body is moving relative to the system.

The concept of inertial motion, that is, motion under no forces which persists as a conserved state, was advanced by Galileo, and it was he who pointed out its relative nature. Mechanical events are the same in all coasting systems and we can judge of their motion only by the changing distances to reference bodies. We are quite justified in calling any given inertial system stationary, in which case other bodies formerly assumed motionless will be the moving ones. This is the classical principle of relativity, which represents a generalisation of observations similar to those in the ship's cabin in Galileo's example.

The Galileo-Newton relativity principle appears as a natural basis for the classical world picture which consists solely of bodies in relative motion and interaction. From this point of view the distinction accorded to accelerated systems seems arbitrary. The explanation of inertia forces in terms of absolute motion does not follow from the picture of moving and interacting bodies. For these inertia forces are explained not by the mutual relationships of bodies but by a body's relation to *space*. Inertia forces appear to be generated by acceleration with respect to empty space. This conception elevates empty space to the status of a causal agent of physical events.

It was from this aspect that Mach launched his criticism of Newton's concept of the absolute motion of accelerated systems. As opposed to the Newtonian notion of inertia forces as being proof of absolute acceleration, Mach advanced the principle that everything in nature is explained by the interactions of masses. Later Einstein ceased to regard Mach's principle as being universally applicable; he allowed for the existence of natural processes with respect to which Mach's principle had no meaning. Einstein proceeded from the concept of field as a real medium capable of influencing the behaviour of bodies moving in it. Furthermore, events in a field are not reduced to interactions between given bodies. In carrying out a reform of Newtonian mechanics it is no longer possible to introduce a scheme based entirely on bodies and their interactions. As Einstein writes, Mach's conjectures that inertia must depend upon the interaction of masses "presupposes implicitly, however, that the basic theory should be of the general type of Newton's mechanics: masses and their interaction as the original concepts".[1] In dealing with Newtonian mechanics or a mechanics of the same general type, however, the negative aspect of the critique of Newton's absolute acceleration retains its importance: to assume that the behaviour of bodies is affected, not by other bodies, but by the space in which they are moving, meant to introduce an arbitrary, alien assumption into the world picture. Such an assumption contradicted the universal harmony and unity.

Empty space, Einstein says, is incapable of affecting the behaviour of bodies in any way. Their behaviour depends only on interaction between masses. As we shall now see, this principle became a departing point for a concept utterly incompatible with Mach's general epistemological ideas.

Mach takes his critique of Newton's absolute acceleration as an occasion for a critique of objective reality. For Einstein criticism of absolute acceleration and absolute space serves to rehabilitate the rational scheme of the universe as a knowable reality undermined by the "absolute" concepts. As Einstein sees it, Newton's absolutes contradict the *basic* meaning of his system. Einstein fights with Newton for Newton, against Newtonian absolutes for the main purport of the Newtonian system.

Einstein regarded Newton as a symbol of the struggle for objective truth. The principal feature of the Newtonian system is the possibility, in principle, of deducing from the basic physical principles conclusions that can be confirmed by experiment. This possibility is a refutation of all the arguments of agnosticism. If logical conclusions agree with empirical facts then logical constructions are a reflection of reality.

In his article, "Isaac Newton", written in 1942, Einstein has the following to say about the creator of classical mechanics:

"Such a man can be understood only by thinking of him as a scene on which the struggle for eternal truth took place. Long before Newton there had been virile minds who con-

[1] *Philosopher-Scientist*, p. 29.

ceived that it ought to be possible, by purely logical deduction from simple physical hypotheses, to make cogent explanations of phenomena perceptible to the senses. But Newton was the first to succeed in finding a clearly formulated basis from which he could deduce a wide field of phenomena by means of mathematical thinking, logically, quantitatively and in harmony with experience. Indeed, he might well hope that the fundamental basis of his mechanics would come in time to furnish the key to the understanding of all phenomena. So thought his pupils—with more assurance than he himself—and so his successors, up till the end of the 18th century."[1]

Newton erected a system of basic principles on the basis of all the known facts. From the basic principles by "the free creation of the mind" he deduced corollaries. These take the form of precise quantitative relationships confirmed by observations. When an observed phenomenon is deduced in this manner from basic postulates it stops being a "miracle". "It is the goal of every activity of the intellect," Einstein continues, "to convert a 'miracle' into something which it has grasped."[2] With Newton some phenomena were not linked with the basic postulate of the dependence of natural processes on the interaction of masses. The theory of relativity reconciled the totality of phenomena with this postulate. Although relativity theory was later found to overstep its boundaries, the basic idea remains: the agreement of the conclusions of Newtonian mechanics with empirical facts proves the mind's ability to form a valid conception of the world. Such knowledge is never final, it advances infinitely, all the time coming closer to the objective truth. That is why Einstein begins his essay on Newton with a tribute to reason and, what is especially characteristic of Einstein's world outlook, with sociological and moral conclusions deriving from the power of reason.

"Reason, of course, is weak, when measured against its never-ending task. Weak, indeed, compared with the follies and passions of mankind, which, we must admit, almost entirely control our human destinies in great and small

---

[1] A. Einstein, *Out of My Later Years*, Thames and Hudson, London, 1950, p. 219. (Afterwards referred to as *Later Years*.)
[2] Ibid., p. 220.

things." This, it will be recalled, was the height of nazi aggression. "Yet the works of the understanding outlast the noisy bustling of generations and spread light and warmth across the centuries," he continues, and he calls upon people to turn to the memory of Newton as proof of the power of reason.

This tribute to reason, so characteristic of Einstein's philosophical, sociological and moral principles, is closely linked with his stand with regard to classical mechanics. Einstein did not seek to extinguish the light-giving sun of Newton's ideas. He only sought to remove from it the spots of metaphysical absolutes. Actually, as we shall see, relativity theory was much more than a mere revision of Newtonian mechanics undertaken to remove its absolute categories. It replaced the sun of Newtonian ideas with other suns, without, however, shaking the fundamental idea: the light of reason illumines the objective, harmonious, knowable world.

BROWNIAN MOVEMENT

> *Thermodynamics ... is the only physical theory
> of universal content concerning which I am
> convinced that, within the framework of the
> applicability of its basic concepts, it will never
> be overthrown.*
>
> *E i n s t e i n*

In 1905, shortly before the publication of his fundamental paper on the special theory of relativity, Einstein completed a series of articles on the classical theory of molecular motion. The final paper of this series, which appeared in the *Annalen der Physik*, offered an explanation of the apparent motion of small but microscopically visible particles suspended in a liquid known as *Brownian movement*.

Einstein's investigations in thermodynamics and particularly his theory of Brownian movement, are of independent interest. Still, in the scientific biography of the creator of relativity theory they should be treated in relation to the leit-motiv of his life.

We have just got acquainted with the opening bars of this leit-motiv. Relativity theory is still in the offing, yet we can already discern the tendency leading up to it. Einstein seeks the most general, the most natural ("internally perfect") theory describing the most fundamental processes of nature. These processes lie beyond the limits of "pure description", they constitute the inner causal basis of phenomena. To such processes belong the relative displacements of material bodies and material systems comprising them. This relative motion of bodies is regarded as the objective groundwork of natural phenomena, a conception which turns a chaos of individual facts into a harmonious picture of the world.

As we will see, it can be made to conform with any theory "of the general type of Newton's mechanics", i.e., with a world picture in which the elementary processes are the motions and interactions of bodies which remain identical to themselves. The roots of relativity theory lie in the classical scientific ideal in which relative motion is the primary concept. As a result of a generalisation and elaboration of this ideal it was rid of everything in the classical physical theories which contradicted it.

In thermodynamics the models of the kinetic theory of gas, which treat molecular motions and collisions as the objective basis of heat phenomena, approach the classical ideal. But these models could offer a correct explanation of the known phenomena only together with macroscopic laws governing processes in which individual molecules and their motions are not taken into account.

In his *Réflections sur la Puissance Motrice du Feu*, Sadi Carnot advanced the principle of irreversibility: heat flows only from warmer to cooler bodies. The reverse flow can be attained only by an input of energy. The irreversibility of heat flow is a typical example of the thermodynamic processes which forced 19th-century science to deviate substantially from the mechanistic notions of the preceding century. Can an exact knowledge of the positions, velocities and accelerations of molecules explain the irreversibility of heat flow? Only as much as an exact knowledge of the positions of air particles at every given moment, can offer an idea of the content of vocal speech which, after all, cannot be reduced solely to the acoustic effects due to the oscillational motion of the particles. One does not have to know the coordinates and velocities of the particles of a metal rod in order to explain why heat spreads from the hot end to the cold. In fact, the laws of mechanics (which govern collisions between molecules, their paths from collision to collision, and the microscopic picture as a whole) do not agree with the concept of irreversibility.

The kinetic theory treats heat as a result of random motions and collisions of molecules. Every collision can be thoroughly described in terms of mechanics. However, thermodynamic laws (which govern the behaviour of large molecular populations, i.e., macroscopic processes) are not concerned with the various fates of individual molecules. The macroscopic laws of thermodynamics are statistical probability laws: they derive from the *probability* of a molecule's fate, and when the number of individual fates is very large reality follows probability. If we take a classical example of probability theory—the frequency of the occurrence of heads or tails in tossing a coin—we find that the chances of the coin falling one way or the other are the same for a hundred as for a thousand toss-ups (which corresponds to the equal probability of heads or tails in each toss-up). Ten tosses, however, may not reveal the equality of probabilities, as the coin may well fall heads up all ten times, and no law can be deduced. Similarly, the behaviour of a dozen molecules is not governed by any thermodynamic law. They may have the most diverse velocities which may change instantaneously without following any apparent pattern. When we have a very large population of randomly moving molecules, however, we can be quite confident that in time their velocity distribution will agree more and more with probability data. In a metal rod that is not being heated the most probable is a uniform mean velocity of the molecules, that is to say, the same temperature along its entire length. If one end is hotter the mean velocity of the molecules at that end is greater than at other parts, but in time the temperature evens out. This is a macroscopic law which governs only large populations of molecules.

The existence of macroscopic thermodynamic laws, which differ from the purely mechanical laws governing the behaviour of individual molecules, confronted science with a number of questions of principle. What is the relation of macroscopic thermodynamics to molecular mechanics? A similar question could be asked concerning the macroscopic statistical laws of biology: what is the relation between the laws governing the evolution of species and the laws determining the fate of an individual creature?

The complex macroscopic laws cannot, evidently, be reduced to microscopic laws. We can never hope to understand the irreversibility of heat flow between bodies or within a given body, nor thermodynamic processes in general, if we restrict ourselves to the laws of mechanics and attempt to reduce phenomena more complex than a simple displacement to these laws. In this sense thermodynamics points to certain limits in the explication of nature from the standpoint of Newtonian mechanics. These limits can be overcome by introducing new concepts to explain complex processes not to be found in Newtonian mechanics. To these concepts belongs, among others, the concept of irreversibility. Such concepts are specific to each concrete series of phenomena and they provide a natural basis for classifying sciences, for drawing certain boundaries between different disciplines which delineate the direct applications of Newtonian laws and concepts to other divisions of natural science besides mechanics.

The great discoveries of the 19th century revealed that physics, with its statistical laws and irreversibility, was not reducible to mechanics, nor chemistry to physics, nor biology to a totality of mechanical, physical 'and chemical phenomena, as organic life cannot be reduced to mechanical, molecular, chemical and other like processes, without which, however, it is impossible. The idea that higher forms of motion cannot in principle be reduced to simpler and more general forms was expressed in general form by Engels in his *Dialectics of Nature*. He stresses the relative nature of this irreducibility, insofar as the higher forms of motion are *inseparable* from the lower ones. Although higher forms of motion cannot be reduced to lower ones, Engels writes, nevertheless, every higher form of motion is always necessarily associated with a real (external or molecular) motion.[1] The idea that physical—and specifically thermodynamic—laws are neither reducible to nor inseparable from mechanics and the motions of material particles offers an insight into the true sources of some of the scientific and philosophical controversies of the late 19th century.

Failure to take into account the facts of "non-reducibility" led to a resurrection of mechanistic views; failure to take into account the fact that thermodynamic processes are inseparable from the motions of individual molecules led to attempts to divorce the concept of motion from its material basis. Wilhelm Ostwald, the German physical chemist, suggested that the energy figuring in thermodynamics had nothing to do with molecular motion; ultimately he demanded that the concept of energy replace that of matter. Mach arrived at similar conclusions, and he branded adherence to the atomistic structure of matter as pure "belief".

With these preliminary remarks we may proceed to analyse Einstein's work on Brownian movement and its value.

---

[1] F. Engels, *Dialectics of Nature*, Moscow, 1964, p. 246.

In 1827, the Scottish botanist Robert Brown observed in a microscope that pollen dust suspended in water displayed a constant random motion. In the course of an almost infinitesimal time interval each particle suffers a minute, hardly observable displacement. When photographed with a long exposure such a particle presents a blurred blob on the photographic plate. Pictures taken, say, every thirty seconds give a succession of positions making a broken line when joined.

Einstein explained the phenomenon in terms of the kinetic theory of heat and the picture of randomly moving and colliding molecules, taking into account the inevitable fluctuations in the random impacts suffered by the pollen particle from the molecules of the surrounding liquid.

By fluctuation we mean a violation of the most probable temporal or spatial distribution of events. When we increase the number of events, for instance, when we toss a coin ten, a hundred, a thousand times, etc., the actual distribution of the events "heads" or "tails" tends to the most probable, "fifty-fifty", distribution. When we reduce the number of events (the number of toss-ups of the coin) we have increasing grounds to expect some violation of the probability, such as the "unlikely" occurrence of several heads in succession, followed by several tails. Theoretically, of course, there is nothing to prevent us from achieving twenty heads in as many toss-ups, though this would be a very rare case indeed. With five toss-ups, however, such a fluctuation is much more likely. In the random motions of molecules the number of impacts suffered by a suspended particle may be unbalanced to one side. The larger the particle the less the probability of such a fluctuation, since the greater the number of molecules hitting it, the higher the chance of the impacts corresponding to the probability pattern and balancing each other. When the particle is very tiny the possibility of fluctuations and imbalance in any direction is much greater. This imbalance over a small time interval results in a displacement which can be observed in a microscope.

Imagine a large vessel filled with a liquid in which the most probable uniform temperature distribution has been achieved; that is to say, the velocities of the particles are on the average the same in all parts of the vessel. There are no currents or eddies, no macroscopic movement, no prolonged violations of the absolutely random, averagely uniform movement of the molecules. Nevertheless, small, microscopic violations of the uniformity do constantly take place. These fluctuations become apparent when we go over to very small physical scales. They cause the literally microscopic (in the sense that they can be observed in a microscope) displacements of the pollen particles in our vessel.

Now suppose that macroscopic laws are superimposed on these microscopic laws (which are purely mechanical laws of molecular motion). The liquid is warmed at one end of the vessel. When we now observe the Brownian movement, we will notice a lack of symmetry in the particle displacements. The displacements corresponding to the direction of the currents caused by the heating will predominate over displacements in the opposite direction. A photograph will reveal that after a large number of Brownian displacements a particle will have moved a long way from its initial position in the direction of the current.

In order to demonstrate more clearly the relation between the microscopic laws of kinetic theory describing molecular motion and the thermodynamic laws governing the behaviour of big, macroscopic masses, let us depart for a moment from physical theory to Darwin's theory of evolution. Essentially it is based on the individual fates of separate organisms which, from the point of view of the entire species, are in each case determined by purely random causes. Let the environment be unchanging, enabling the species to achieve maximum adaptability to it. In such conditions individual changes and fluctuations appear as sporadic, balanced changes in individual members of the species which do not affect the species as a whole, just as the fluctuations causing Brownian movement do not violate the uniformity of the liquid or cause it to circulate. The less the number of individuals under observation, the greater will be the relative number of such fluctuations. When the habitat calls for a change in the characteristics of the species, the symmetry of individual variations and fluctuations is disturbed. They accumulate in one direction, are inherited and lead to greater changes in the species than can be balanced by oppositely directed variations. The laws of natural selection operate statistically. They are superimposed, as it were, on the laws governing the individual destinies of an organism, they determine only the probability of this or that fate for any individual taken by itself. In going over to a large number of organisms, to the fate of the species as a whole, these probabilities reflect the actual course of events. The idea of such statistical macroscopic laws (which in isolated cases determine the probability of a certain course of events, which becomes a certainty only when very many cases are involved) is one of the basic principles of 19th-century natural science. It did not encroach on the basic image of classical science—motion (not the probability of this or that motion, but the motion itself) which for every atom, instant, and point is precisely determined by a primary impulse and the interactions with other bodies at a given instant. Behind all statistical laws is particle motion, which is subject to the *dynamical* laws presented in Newton's *Principia*.

In his theory of Brownian movement Einstein focused his attention on these dynamical, non-statistical laws ("trans-statistical" or "substatistical", we might call them, as they lurk on the fringes of the statistical laws of thermodynamics). With the tools and concepts of statistics Einstein demonstrated the existence of "trans-statistical" dynamical laws of motion of individual molecules.

Relativity theory has shown the primary dynamical laws of the world to be different from those described by Newton in his *Principia*. This, however, has not changed the dynamical nature of mechanical laws (unlike the statistical laws of thermodynamics).

This dynamical nature of mechanical laws, which contradicted the conceptions of probability, was overthrown twenty years later by a new revolution in science. The sources of this revolution can be found in the same volume of the *Annalen der Physik*, in Einstein's paper on light quanta. However, Einstein's attitude towards the idea of statistical laws as the basic laws of the world was very complicated, and it must be understood in order to realise the harmony of Einstein's work as a whole. We have dwelt here in such detail on the statistical nature of thermodynamic laws in order to make it easier to set forth and explain Einstein's attitude towards quantum-statistical laws. This is a question of interest not only to physicists. The approach of the greatest physicist of our time to the fundamental, primary laws of the world is not just a point of interest in the history of physics, it is one which has a bearing on the whole cultural history of the 20th century.

As a youth, Einstein was greatly impressed by the inseparability of the laws of thermodynamics from molecular mechanics. Thermodynamics in his eyes is not a negation of particle motion, i.e., of mechanics as the basis of the world picture (as Mach and Ostwald believed), nor is it governed *directly* by mechanical laws (as the disciples of the mechanistic philosophy believed). Einstein regarded thermodynamics as an extensive domain of the mediated application and confirmation of the laws of motion of discrete parts of matter. To 18th-century mechanistic philosophy and its disciples physical problems solvable with the help of mechanics were essentially of one type. In the 19th century these problems differed widely among themselves in complexity and variegation and in many cases they could not be reduced to one another. For Einstein such a diversity of problems and things was proof of the strength and validity of a theory which, in the final analysis, while not negating the specific nature of different problems, provides the key for their solution. "A theory," he writes, "is the more impressive the greater the simplicity of its premises is, the more different kinds of things it relates, and the more extended is its area of applicability. Therefore the deep impression which classical thermodynamics made upon me. It is the only physical theory of universal content concerning which I am convinced that, within the framework of applicability of its basic concepts, it will never be overthrown (for the special attention of those who are sceptics on principle)."[1]

What is it that gives classical thermodynamics such exceptional stability?

The classical laws defining the accelerations, velocities and positions of molecules at every instant—the Newtonian laws of mechanics—have given way to other, more accurate laws. Unshaken remains the proposition that in spatial and temporal domains of sufficient magnitude, thermodynamic systems move from less probable to more probable states, with the derivation of this law from a large number of random motions of individual molecules. The laws governing

[1] *Philosopher-Scientist*, p. 33.

these motions may change, but the bond of complex, irreversible statistical processes governed by probability with particle motion remains unshaken.

The theory of Brownian movement shattered the illusion that macroscopic laws were independent of kinetic models in which molecules feature. In commenting on how the laws of Brownian movement and other discoveries in the science of heat and molecular motion convinced the sceptics of the reality of atoms, Einstein notes that Mach's and Ostwald's scepticism derived from their preconceived positivistic notions.

"The antipathy of these scholars towards atomic theory can indubitably be traced back to their positivistic philosophical attitude. This is an interesting example of the fact that even scholars of audacious spirit and fine instinct can be obstructed in the interpretation of facts by philosophical prejudices."[1]

Facts by themselves, Einstein says, cannot yield scientific knowledge without free conceptual construction. Einstein attacks Mach's conception of facts as constituting observations not supported by the objective causes of observable phenomena. To conceptual constructions belong the various hypotheses about atoms, molecules and their motions, which are not directly observable. Mach regards such an invasion of a domain that is not directly observable as "metaphysics". Ostwald restricts the problem to a description of macroscopically observable energy transformations without penetrating into the underlying world of moving material particles. To Einstein the cognition of physical processes consists in just such penetration. A description of directly observable facts (macroscopic processes, in the present case) does not by itself yield an unambiguous theory. Concepts based directly on empirical data do not derive uniquely from objective reality. Their "self-evidence" is an illusion due to long usage. We have already spoken of this point of view, which Einstein opposed to the views of Mach and Ostwald. We shall see later on that a critical revision of the most "self-evident" concepts of mechanics, which derived straight from observations, led to the enunciation of relativity theory. The question here is of the connection between Einstein's anti-positivistic viewpoint and the atomistic undercurrent of thermodynamics.

[1] Ibid., p. 49.

Chapter 11

PHOTONS

Are rays of light not very small corpuscules emitted by luminescent bodies?

N e w t o n

In the last chapter we spoke of the "classical ideal" of science as a world picture in which the laws and motions of bodies may differ from Newton's conception, but which is of the same type: its primary concepts are the relativity of motion and the interaction of particles and the bodies they constitute. The clash between Newtonian mechanics and thermodynamics ended happily for the former and for the "classical ideal" in general. Newtonian mechanics retained its positions in the background of the statistical laws of thermodynamics. This, however, could not in itself guarantee the absolute accuracy of Newton's variant of the "classical ideal". Subsequent clashes (e.g., with electrodynamics) led to the elaboration of new variants.

Relativity theory meant the liberation of the "classical ideal" from contradictions and arbitrary assumptions: at the price of Newton's variant, it provided the ideal with "external confirmation" and "inner perfection". How this was achieved will be shown when we get to Einstein's work on the special theory of relativity (1905) and the general theory of relativity (1916). Subsequent advances went still further. They challenged not only Newton's variant of the "classical ideal" but the ideal itself, the world picture of displacements and interactions of immutable bodies as the elementary concepts. We shall deal with this result of relativity theory in connection with Einstein's work in the 1930s-1950s.

This subsequent revision of the "classical ideal" was due not so much to relativity as to another theory of Einstein's, also expounded in 1905: the theory of light quanta, or photons. To be sure, it began with a victory for the "classical ideal", but the subsequent development of the ideas advanced by Einstein in his photon theory soon began to jeopardise the "classical ideal" as a whole. And when the principles of relativity merged with quantum theory the mutual displacements of immutable bodies ceased to enter the world picture as a primary, most fundamental conception.

In 1900, Max Planck resolved some of the contradictions of radiation theory by assuming that the energy of electromagnetic waves (light) is emitted and absorbed in discontinuous, further indivisible portions called *quanta*.

Einstein, in 1905, enunciated his theory according to which light is not merely emitted or absorbed discontinuously but actually consists of discrete, indivisible portions, *light quanta*, which later came to be known as *photons*. They are particles which travel in vacuum at a speed of 300,000 kilometres per second. Later, in the twenties, they were named *photons*.

The existence of photons or light quanta does not in itself follow from the fact that light is emitted and absorbed in indivisible portions. The relation between the photon hypothesis and Planck's theory was expressed by Einstein in the following way: "Even though beer is always sold in pint bottles, it does not follow that beer consists of indivisible pint portions."

Philipp Frank in his biography of Einstein extends the analogy.[1] If we wish to investigate, he says, whether the beer in a barrel actually consists of definite portions or not we can take a number of containers, say ten, and pour the beer randomly into them. We measure the amount in each container and then pour the beer back into the barrel. We repeat this process a number of times. If the beer does not come in portions, the *average* value of the beer poured into each container will be the same. If it consists of indivisible portions there will be variations in the average values. In the extreme case of the whole content of the barrel being one portion it will pour out each time into one container, and the difference between the contents of the ten containers will be the greatest, the one containing all the beer and the rest empty. If the beer consists of two, three, etc., indivisible portions, the variations in the average values will be successively smaller and smaller. According to these variations, i.e.,

[1] Ph. Frank, op. cit., p. 91.

according to the fluctuations, we can judge of the size of the indivisible portions of beer.

Now consider electromagnetic radiation. Like the beer in the barrel, let it fill a closed box, which we can imagine to be divided into a number of cells. Can we divide the energy of radiation into an infinite number of parts or will we come down to some further indivisible "portions"? And if electromagnetic radiation is discrete, what is the value of its smallest "portion"?

These questions can be answered by measuring the variations of energy among the cells from the average value. If the portions of radiation are large, the variations of energy among the cells will be large, and if they are small the variations will be small.

Measurements show that in violet light (high electromagnetic frequencies) the variations of energy are comparatively large. In red light (lower frequencies) they are smaller. The conclusion is that violet light consists of larger portions of energy than red light.

We can therefore say that "the beer" is not only "sold in pint bottles" but actually comprises indivisible "pint portions", which is to say that light consists of indivisible particles. It is not just emitted and absorbed in indivisible particles: in the interim between emission and absorption it also consists of indivisible particles whose energy is the greater the higher the electromagnetic wave frequency. The energy of light quanta (photons) is proportional to the frequency and has a specific value for a specific (monochromatic) light. The corpuscular structure of light and the existence of photons is unambiguously proved by a number of experiments. Especially convincing in this respect is the so-called photoelectric effect, which consists in the generation of electric current by incident light. Light falling on a metal plate knocks electrons out of it; the motion of these electrons generates electric current.

A certain energy is required to knock out an electron. This energy, it was found, does not depend on the distance travelled by a ray of light. Imagine a light source, that is, an emitter of electromagnetic radiation. As the radiation propagates in all directions the energy density at the wave front decreases. The energy of the knocked-out electrons, however, does not decrease, though of course fewer are knocked out. If the radiation energy is just sufficient to strike an electron out of a metal plate the ejection will take place (that is, we will have a photoelectric effect) even if the light source is very far away. As H. A. Kramers remarked, the effect is the same as if a sailor has dived into the sea and the energy of the wave from the splash reaches the other end of the sea and washes another swimming sailor on to the deck of *his* ship.

It follows thus from the theory of the photoelectric effect that the energy needed to eject an electron does not depend on the distance between the light source and the metal plate. It does depend, however, on the electromagnetic radiation frequency. In each case an electron receives just the right amount of energy needed to eject it, only the greater the distance the fewer electrons are ejected. This pattern, Einstein concluded, corresponds to the picture of discrete particles speeding away from a light source in all directions. The farther the distance from the source the less the average number of particles in a unit volume of space and the less the probability of encountering a light quantum at a given point. Once it has been encountered, however, its energy is the same at any distance from the source and is dependent only on the oscillation frequency.

But, the observant reader may ask, how can we speak of oscillation frequency if light consists of particles? This indeed was just about the worst predicament in which 20th-century physics found itself, and it originated in Einstein's theory of light quanta.

There is no denying the existence of electromagnetic waves and the wave nature of light. But neither is there any denying the corpuscular nature of light, the fact that light is made up of photons. The contradiction is a baffling one, and it was two decades before the physicists could resolve it.

This contradiction, this paradoxical combination of wave and corpuscular properties is characteristic of Einstein's scientific ideas. Not for one moment did he doubt that light actually possesses both wave and corpuscular properties. He was not the man to shy away from a paradox, even though it undermined two fundamental classical notions, viz., that particles are particles and cannot possess wave properties, and waves are waves and cannot possess corpuscular properties.

As mentioned before, the paper on light quanta appeared in the same volume of *Annalen der Physik* as the original paper on special relativity, which postulated an equally, if not more, paradoxical premise: light propagates with the same velocity relative to all bodies moving relative each other.

In both theories Einstein's presentation of paradoxical situations is not just a superficial phenomenological upshot of non-paradoxical processes. We shall see further on that Hendrik Lorentz explained the constancy of the velocity of light on the basis of non-paradoxical processes. And Planck believed that light was a purely undulatory process and there was nothing corpuscular about it at all. He considered the observed discontinuity in the energy spectrum of light to be due solely to some as yet inexplicable peculiarities in the mechanism of light radiation and absorption. One finds a distinct analogy in the difference between Einstein's approach to both problems and Lorentz's and Planck's, respectively. In both cases Einstein's superiority is seen not only in the content of his physical ideas but also in his remarkable sense of the paradoxical in physical reality, or what amounts to the same thing, a sense of the trustworthiness and objectivity of seemingly paradoxical conclusions, even though they contradicted both "self-evident" empirical facts and "self-evident" logical constructions. The photon theory, with its paradoxical merger of mutually exclusive wave and corpuscular properties of light, remained unrecognised for several years. In fact, when several leading German physicists, among them Planck, wrote a letter to the Prussian Academy of Science, in 1912, in which they recommended Einstein for membership, they actually inserted an apology for his light-quantum hypothesis.

"He should not be judged too severely," they wrote, "for occasionally losing sight of his objective in his logical reasoning, such as is the case in his theory of light quanta. For in even the most exact of the natural sciences one must take risks to achieve anything really new."

Chapter 12

THE CONSTANCY
OF THE VELOCITY OF LIGHT

> *Imagine two physicists. Each one has a laboratory equipped with all conceivable physical instruments at his disposal. Suppose that one laboratory is located somewhere in an open field, and the other is in a railway carriage travelling with uniform speed in some direction. The principle of relativity states: if the two physicists use all their instruments to study the laws of nature—the one in the stationary laboratory and the other in the mobile laboratory—they will both discover the same laws of nature, provided that the train is moving uniformly and without jolts. In more general terms we can say: according to the principle of relativity, the laws of nature do not depend on the translational motion of reference systems.*
>
> *Einstein*

Einstein began to puzzle over the question of the speed of light in different frames of reference moving relative to one another from the time he was sixteen years old, while a student in Aarau, and later in Zurich, ten years before he enunciated the theory of relativity. In his mind's eye he pictured moving reference systems as bodies with measuring rods and clocks attached to them, thus making it possible to ascertain their positions and velocities at any instant. A frame of reference thus took the shape of a real body, with a point of origin and infinite coordinate axes attached to it together with a great number of rods of indefinite length, and at any given instant any body, no matter where it was, coincided with certain intercepts on the measuring rods; that is to say, it had specific coordinates. The "given instant" was of course the same at every orientated point of space, and clocks located at all such points could be compared. To eliminate the possibility of confusion, a man moving with the given reference system would have to be oblivious of any other systems, his sole duty being to measure the position of bodies with the measuring rods confined to his particular frame of reference.

This "observer" figures in practically all expositions of relativity theory, although he is just as imaginary as the co-ordinate axes and measuring rods nailed to the moving body, which constitute the frame of reference in which that body is at rest. The introduction of "observers" in no way detracts from the objective nature of the relativity theory, just as saying an "Imaginary string stretched from the earth to the sun..." does not make the objective reality of a definite distance between two celestial bodies dependent on real or imaginary measurements. This nebulous "observer" can be pictured as a passenger travelling in a railway carriage or in a ship's cabin (as in Galileo's example which he used to demonstrate the classical principle of relativity) with curtains drawn across the window or porthole.

Imagine a ship sailing along with the same velocity as the waves on the surface of the sea. To an observer on deck, i.e., to a man in a position to measure velocity only relative to the ship, the waves seem motionless. With nothing but the sky above to help him in his observations he will see only a motionless expanse of water. Wave motion will mean nothing to him since the waves are not moving in respect to the ship. These subjective impressions, however, are an expression of the objective fact that the waves are really stationary, in respect to the frame of reference in which the ship moving together with the waves is at rest (the frame is attached to the ship).

The problem which intrigued Einstein was whether observations would be similar in the case of electromagnetic waves, specifically, light. Light travels along the surface of the earth at a velocity of approximately 300,000 kilometres per second. If the ship is sailing with the same speed, then to the observer on deck, the light will have zero velocity. In such a case, the optical phenomena on board the ship would suffer a drastic change, for example, a flash appearing on the stern would not light up a screen on the bow. The electromagnetic field would be like the motionless seas surrounding the ship: it would vary in space, with ridge following trough, but without changing with time. Such a modification of the optical phenomena would enable the observer to register absolutely the motion of the system: with the requisite optical instruments he would be able to distinguish between a moving and a stationary ship. This, however, contradicts Maxwell's theory, according to which light is the result of the motion of electromagnetic waves. It also contradicts the intuitive conviction concerning the impossibility of registering uniform rectilinear motion by means of internal effects restricted to the moving system.

Einstein writes of the paradox which he had already hit on at the age of sixteen: "If I pursue a beam of light with the velocity c (velocity of light in a vacuum), I should observe such a beam of light as a spatially oscillatory electromagnetic field at rest. However, there seems to be no such thing, whether on the basis of experience or according to Maxwell's equations. From the very beginning it appeared to me intuitively clear that, judged from the standpoint of such an observer, everything would have to happen according to the same laws as for an observer who, relative to the earth, was at rest. For how, otherwise, should the first observer know, i.e., be able to determine, that he is in a state of fast uniform motion?"[1]

Essentially the paradox is a manifestation of a conflict between two classical principles of mechanics projected into the new domain of electrodynamic phenomena. One is the *classical rule for the addition of velocities.* A man walking down the corridor of a railway carriage at 5 kilometres an hour relative to the carriage in the direction of the train travelling at 50 kilometres an hour relative to the earth, is moving, relative to the earth, at the velocity of $50 + 5 = 55$ km per hour; if the man is walking in the opposite direction of the train's motion, then his speed relative to the earth is $50 - 5 = 45$ km per hour. If the man is travelling at a velocity of 55 km per hour relative to the earth in a train speeding at 50 km per hour, then we know that he is walking along the corridor at $55 - 50 = 5$ km per hour relative to the carriage. If waves at sea are propagating with a velocity of 30 km per hour relative to the shore, and a ship also moves at 30 km per hour in the same direction,

[1] *Philosopher-Scientist,* p. 53.

the velocity of the waves relative to the ship is $30 - 30 = 0$, and relative to the ship they are motionless. But what happens in the case of electromagnetic waves? Is this self-evident rule for velocity composition valid?

The classical rule of adding velocities corresponds to a coordinate transformation from one system to another, one moving relative to the former without acceleration. When, in such a transformation, we stick to the concept of simultaneity, in which two events can be simultaneous regardless of whether they are registered in one coordinate system or in any other inertial system, the transformation is called a *Galilean transformation*. In a Galilean transformation the spatial distance between two points—the difference between their coordinates in one inertial reference system—is always the same as in any other inertial system.

The second principle is the principle of relativity. On board a ship moving uniformly in a straight line its motion cannot be detected by any internal mechanical effects. Does this principle extend to optical phenomena? Is it not possible to detect the absolute motion of a system from the optical or, what is the same thing, electrodynamic phenomena caused by it? Intuition (most obviously in accord with the classical principle of relativity) tells us that there is no way of observing absolute motion. But if light propagates with a certain velocity in respect to all moving inertial systems, then this velocity must change in passing from one system to another, as follows from the classical rule of velocity composition. Mathematically speaking, this means that the velocity of light is not invariant with respect to the Galilean transformation. But this violates the relativity principle, or rather, it does not allow the principle to be extended to optical phenomena. Thus electrodynamics destroyed the link between two seemingly self-evident conceptions of classical physics: the rule of velocity addition and the principle of relativity. Moreover, with respect to electrodynamics they prove to be incompatible. A consistent picture of the world thus had to be paradoxical, "mad", and contrary to customary, and therefore "self-evident", propositions. Which of the two should be rejected, had to be decided by experiment.

The decisive test was carried out in 1882 by the American physicist Albert Michelson. He constructed an instrument, called an *interferometer*, capable of detecting very small differences in the velocity of light. It consisted of two tubes of equal length along which light rays were directed. Michelson pointed one tube in the direction of the earth's motion, and the other at right angles. The earth's motion through the world ether was to display itself in the faster speed of light relative to the earth when it is travelling opposite the earth's motion as compared with its speed travelling in the direction of the earth's motion, when catching up with the earth. It is impossible to measure the speed with which light propagates from one end of the tube to another. What can be detected is the difference in the time needed for a beam of light to travel in the different directions along it. A beam propagating in the direction of the earth's motion will arrive at the other end of the tube slightly later than it would in a motionless tube; the return path takes slightly less time, but not enough to make up for the original retardation. As a result the beam travelling back and forth in the longitudinal tube takes slightly longer to reach the eyepiece of the instrument than a beam in the lateral tube. This lag can be detected, *provided that the earth's motion affects the velocity of light with respect to the earth.*

The earth travels through space at a speed of about 30 kilometres per second, fast enough for Michelson's interferometer to detect its effect on the velocity of light. The experiment, however, yielded a negative result, meaning that the velocity of light was independent of the earth's motion through the ether. It could be assumed, of course, that the interferometer carried the ether along with it, thus remaining at rest relative to the ether. This conjecture, however, was overthrown by other optical experiments.

At the close of the 19th century, Lord Kelvin remarked that science had finally reached a haven and solved all basic problems; all that was left was to work out the details. Still, he mentioned two unsolved problems. One referred to difficulties encountered by radiation theory, which led Max Planck to his idea of quanta, enunciated in 1900. The second was the result of Michelson's experiment. With these two exceptions, Kelvin believed, science had nothing to fear and could consider itself safe from any radical revision of its theoretical foundations. As is often the case, the weatherman had hardly announced a spell of fine weather when lightning struck. And it struck from the two small clouds which Kelvin had spoken of. The results of Michelson's and other similar experiments overthrew what had once seemed the most self-evident conceptions of the world. And then in 1905, an official at the Bern Patent Office declared that light actually propagates with the same velocity in all directions in respect to all bodies in uniform relative motion: whether travelling head on, or sideways or trailing one another.

The paradoxical nature of this statement is illustrated by the following example. Two swimmers dive from the deck of a fast ship and swim with the same speed, one towards the bow, the other towards the stern. Quite obviously, the one swimming towards the stern will reach it much sooner than the swimmer forced to catch up with the ship. Yet according to the new principle and contrary to the obvious the swimmers take the same time to cover the distance, that is, their speed relative to the ship is the same. A difference in speeds would have been an indication of the ship's motion. In the absence of such a difference the ship's motion can be judged only according to the changing distance to the shore or to some other ship moving relative to it; in which case we could say with equal justification that it is the shore that is moving with respect to the ship. This is how light behaves. Optical processes in a body provide no internal criteria of motion, they offer no grounds to speak of absolute motion. Light propagates with the same speed with respect to different bodies in relative motion. A short while ago we spoke of reference systems made up of imaginary measuring rods used for measuring velocity, including the velocity of light. The fundamental postulate of Einstein's theory of relativity is expressed in the following terms: "The velocity of light is the same in all reference systems moving relative to each other without acceleration."

We can attach a reference system to our ship and consider objects on the deck to be at rest; we can attach it to the shore and record the motion of the objects being carried away by the ship; we can also attach it to the earth, to the sun or to Sirius, and each time we will have a different picture of the bodies moving in the universe. However, going over from one reference system to another changes nothing in the course of internal phenomena in the bodies. A body is fixed in one system and moving in another, but the definitions of "fixed" and "moving" are relative: they have meaning only when referred to a frame of reference; a body's motion is expressed by and only by the changes in its distances to other bodies; rest is expressed by and only by the constancy of these distances. There are no internal differences, no differences in the course of internal processes, and *no differences in the velocity of light.*

This meant the death of the notion of a privileged absolute frame of reference, of the conviction that there existed an absolute system in which one could obtain the "true" values of motions and velocities, in contrast to other reference systems in which motion and rest represented merely apparent states. This achievement marked the conclusion of the Copernican revolution, which deprived the earth of its absolute "fixedness" and the reference systems in which the earth was motionless of their privileged nature. After Copernicus and Galileo had demonstrated that the motion of bodies as observed from the earth and measured in reference systems attached to the earth was not of an absolute nature, further advances of the concepts of relativity could no longer cause men to wonder. But the overthrow of the last line of defence of the idea of absolute motion required acceptance of the most paradoxical picture one could imagine: a picture in which light propagates with the same speed in systems moving relative to one another.

Acceptance of the paradoxical nature of the new world picture is the departing point for an analysis of its impact on scientific thinking. Einstein's paradoxical statements, however, would not have caused such widespread repercussions if they had not been so closely linked, logically and historically, with both the "classical ideal" and previous upheavals in science which served to rid it of anthropocentric absolutes.

Chapter 13

THE PRINCIPLE OF THE CONSTANCY OF THE VELOCITY OF LIGHT AND CLASSICAL PHYSICS

We have here no revolutionary act but the natural continuation of a line that can be traced through centuries.

E i n s t e i n

There can be no doubt that a person strolling up and down a ship's deck moves with different velocity relative to the deck, a passing ship or the shore. Similarly, it was taken for granted that light too propagates with different velocities in systems moving relative to one another. This conviction had to be shattered before the liberation of science from anthropocentrism, begun by Copernicus and Galileo, could be finally achieved. The new attack on absolute motion gave rise to even more paradoxical concepts than had the heliocentric philosophy. When, in the 16th-17th centuries, the "fixed" earth was postulated to be in motion, the state of motion was understood in the same sense as before. In comparison, however, a non-Euclidean geometry, with the angles of a triangle summing up to more or less than two right angles and diverging or intersecting perpendiculars to the same line, presented a much more paradoxical case. But then, geometrical theorems can be, and often are, treated as free creations of the intellect, which deduces them logically and consistently from arbitrary assumptions—which can be paradoxical if only by virtue of their arbitrariness. The "madness" of Einstein's theory is in one respect of the same order of "madness" as a non-Euclidean geometry. Even today it is hard to visualise something having the same speed with respect to systems in relative motion. It was once equally difficult to visualise non-Euclidean geometrical relationships. But there is one important distinction. A mere declaration, however mad, need not cause any surprise or consternation.

It is "mad" reality, a departure from the customary in real phenomena and in theories explaining them, that causes one to wonder. There is nothing arbitrary in the propositions on which the theory of relativity is based. On the contrary, they rest on the solid groundwork of experience. It is motion itself which contradicts both the evidence of our senses in observing the behaviour of physical bodies and the seemingly *a priori*, logical, inherent self-evidence of geometrical axioms. Einstein threw both types of "self-evidence" out of the window: the empirical self-evidence of observable phenomena and the *a priori* self-evidence of geometrical axioms.

In spite of its paradoxical appearances relativity theory creates an impression of something truly constructive, something *crowning* the edifice whose foundations were laid by modern science.

The classical world picture developed in the 17th century is based not only on the "self-evident" rule: a body moving with one velocity in respect to one system must necessarily be moving with another velocity in respect to a system moving relative to the original one. It treats the world as a totality of bodies in relative motion. The concept of an ether pervading the whole of space, meant a breaking down of the frame of the initial classical world picture. Relativity theory restored this frame—though, at the expense of the "self-evident" law of velocity addition. In this sense the very structure of relativity theory is paradoxical: on the one hand, there is the "mad" idea of a velocity that remains constant irrespective of the relative motions of different frames of reference, whilst on the other hand, there is the age-old picture (extending back to Demo-critus) of a universe comprising only bodies in relative motion.

By comparison, classical physics created an impression of an unfinished building. Bodies moved not only relative to one another, but also absolutely, in the stationary ether, which provided a frame of reference for determining their absolute velocities. Motion through the ether should affect the velocity of light. This made optics a basis for establishing absolute motion—although in the case of uniform motion in a straight line, there would seem to be no such thing. By rejecting the classical principle of the addition of velocities, Einstein's theory extended the principle of relativity to all processes taking place within uniformly and rectilinearly moving systems. No processes, whether mechanical or optical, are affected by the motion of such systems. Uniform motion has no internal effects and its sole manifestations are changes in the mutual positions of physical bodies.

This consideration came very close to the classical principle of relativity, which in turn facilitated acceptance of Einstein's theory and lent it credibility in spite of its "mad" postulate of the constancy of the velocity of light. The new theory was so obviously a consummation of the classical world picture that it came within the latter's halo of trustworthiness—which embraced both the rule of velocity addition and the classical principle of relativity. The problem was whether both mechanical and optical phenomena were subject to, first, the principle of relativity and, secondly, the classical law of velocity addition.

Optical phenomena, it was found, obeyed the relativity principle but not the velocity addition rule. Thus, amplification of the relativity principle called for a revision of classical kinematics, with its accepted notions of bodily motions in space. Soon it was found that such an amplification also required a revision of classical dynamics, i.e., the science of forces and the accelerations associated with them. The connection of relativity with classical physics lies not only in its amplification of the latter. When bodies are moving slowly as compared with the velocity of light we can treat that velocity as infinite, and we arrive at the relationships of the old, classical, mechanics which turn out to be an approximate description of reality. Relativity theory turns into the approximate theory, when the ratio of the velocity of a moving body to the velocity of light tends to zero or, what amounts to the same thing, when the ratio of the velocity of light to that of the body tends to infinity. Such a relationship between two theories, in which one turns into the other when some parameter tends to zero or infinity, exists in mathematics. On a spherical surface the sum of the angles of a triangle is more than two right angles: the relationships are those of a non-Euclidean geometry. With the radius of the sphere increasing indefinitely these relationships tend asymptotically to Euclidean relationships, and we can say that on the surface of a sphere of infinite radius non-Euclidean geometry turns into Euclidean geometry.

This, of course, does not mean that every physical theory necessarily turns into another when some parameter increases indefinitely. In 19th-century physics there existed a somewhat similar relationship between two theories. In the science of molecular motions irreversible processes appear when the number of molecules is sufficiently large, and the laws of irreversible processes become more and more exact with their number increasing. But the fundamental problem in the science of heat is precisely that of the connection between reversible processes in systems comprising small numbers of molecules and irreversible processes in large statistical populations. This conception of different theories which are valid (that is, they provide a sufficiently accurate description of reality) for phenomena of different scales in itself shatters the schemes of Mach and Poincaré. If the macroscopic laws of thermodynamics encounter unexpected, "wonderful" phenomena in going over to the molecular scale, what is then left of the *a priori* or arbitrary interpretation of thermodynamics? And what is left of the idea of "pure description" if the theory which served as the standard for such a description—thermodynamics—turns into a theory in which directly unobservable molecules and their motions figure?

In the science of heat the difference between macroscopic thermodynamics and molecular mechanics is not of a paradoxical nature. Thermodynamic laws are a superstructure to the laws of particle mechanics and do not undermine them. The fact that in large ensembles statistical laws come into play does not contradict the fact that in the world of individual molecules the laws of Newtonian mechanics hold with the utmost consistency and precision.

The position of classical mechanics in relativity theory is of a different nature. Not that the phenomena of nature cannot be reduced to simple mechanical problems. The fact of the matter is that the old laws of mechanics are found to be inaccurate or, strictly speaking, wrong. Hence one can no longer speak of two equally valid approaches to physical phenomena. One must choose a new basic image for describing the world. It is not a question of complex laws being reducible or otherwise to some basic, elementary law. It is a question of the law itself. If it differs from the known "self-evident" law, then the paradox cannot be resolved by a carving out of spheres of influence. Equality is replaced by hierarchy.

Taking into consideration the finality of the velocity of light and its constancy in all inertial systems means a deeper, more general and more accurate approach to physical reality. Relativity theory, it should be stressed once again, postulates the paradoxical nature of the deepest, most precise, and most trustworthy laws of physical reality. The mind must digest not its own aporias, but the authentic "wonder" underlying the "extra-personal" world. This relationship between relativity and Newtonian mechanics makes possible an explanation of the latter, an explanation of the reasons why at certain velocities observations do not contradict Newtonian mechanics. Thereby the experiments and the testimony of experience which confirm the validity of Newtonian classical mechanics also support the new mechanics of Einstein.

Trustworthiness is what has made relativity the most remarkable theory in the history of physics. Its impact on the public at large is due as much to its complete trustworthiness as to its paradoxical qualities. These also explain the heightened—though not always kind—interest which the theory has aroused.

The situation was without precedence. The paradoxes of Zeno, regardless of logical analysis, are after all challenges to the intellect, not paradoxes of nature: no one really doubts that Achilles can overtake the tortoise. The paradoxes of non-Euclidean geometry became paradoxes of physical reality only after the enunciation of relativity theory. The trustworthy, objective paradoxical nature of reality was something new. Einstein was prepared to accept the idea of paradoxical reality by virtue of his philosophical conceptions, which developed from a "merely personal" outlook into the ideological basis of the theory of relativity.

To Einstein the paradoxes of physical reality were proof of the objective nature of the world and arguments against the idea of the *a priori* nature of our knowledge of the world. All our sense-impressions are based on the objective reality of things. Knowledge of reality comes in the confrontation of logical constructions with observable phenomena, which gives rise to new and better constructions. The trustworthy world picture was confronted with the "wonder" of the constancy of the velocity of light in all inertial systems, which did not fit into the accepted logical constructs with their notions of the uniform flow of time all over the infinite universe and other fundaments of the classical world picture. Step by step Einstein built up a new image of the world. His task was essentially a constructive one. The negative aspect of the matter—the destruction of the old picture—consisted only in presenting it as being a less exact approximation to physical reality than the new one. Every such picture is restricted by certain conditions and in time is bound to be confronted with a new "wonder". In its "flight from wonder" it will develop into a more general and more accurate picture.

Chapter 14

THE LORENTZ CONTRACTION

Einstein's achievement is that he was the first to formulate the principle of relativity as a universal strict and exact law.

Lorentz

When Michelson's experiment threatened the very existence of the world ether, Hendrik Lorentz, the great Dutch physicist, came to the rescue. To account for the failure to observe the dependence of the velocity of light on the motion of the earth in the interferometer, Lorentz postulated that all bodies moving relative to the ether tend to contract in the direction of motion. He deduced this contraction from electrodynamics by assuming that all bodies are made up of elementary electrical charges. Motion relative to the ether develops forces which crowd the charges in the direction of the motion. No electrodynamic phenomena were required to explain the hypothesis, and it was introduced *ad hoc* for the sole purpose of explaining the negative result of Michelson's experiment. There was no way to prove the contraction of moving bodies by direct observation, but this did not worry Lorentz: for the measuring rod with which one would undertake to measure such a body would also contract in the same direction and by the same ratio.

The contraction hypothesis explains the results of Michelson's experiment without affecting the fundamentals of classical mechanics. Light propagates in the longitudinal tube of the interferometer slower than in the lateral one. Much as the former has contracted, it takes the beam the same time to traverse it as the lateral tube. Thus there is nothing paradoxical in the constancy of the velocity of light. It is simply a phenomenological result of the mutual cancelling out of two purely classical effects: the retardation of light due to the interferometer's motion through the ether and the contraction of the interferometer tube by precisely the amount needed to make the beam pass along it in the same time. The Lorentz contraction is of the same classical order as the contraction of a wet string. The only difference is that the latter can be observed by applying a dry string to the wet one, whereas the Lorentz contraction cannot be detected in view of the absence of a "dry string", that is to say, a non-contracting measuring rod. It will be readily observed that Lorentz's hypothesis hardly satisfies Einstein's requirements for a scientific theory. Although it is in accord with the observable facts, it lacks "naturalness" and the other characteristics of "inner perfection". This was its weakest point: being invented *ad hoc* it had no foundation of observable effects to support it.

Nevertheless, Lorentz's theory gave scope for the development of the idea of the relativity of motion, though this relativity was of a phenomenological type. The apparent relativity of motion deriving from the apparent constancy of the velocity of light actually camouflages an absolute motion manifest in the different speeds of light in stationary and moving systems. For if one could observe the Lorentz contraction in moving bodies by direct measurement, one would have proof of absolute motion. It cannot be detected, however, and in Lorentz's theory absolute motion reigns, though it doesn't rule; it simply reigns behind the observable scene without affecting phenomena lending themselves to observation. Therefore Lorentz's theory, although essentially classical in its basic premises, insofar as it embraced the idea of absolute motion, did not prevent the elaboration of the mathematical formalism of relativity theory, the development of the transformation formulas in which the velocity of light was constant.

These formulas were developed in the works of Lorentz and Poincaré published almost simultaneously with Einstein's original paper on special relativity. However, they contained nothing like a physical theory which could become the bedrock of a new world picture.

The relativity theory states that all motion is relative and the speed of light is the same in all moving systems. The important point is that this is not a phenomenological conclusion like the Lorentz contraction.

One can no longer speak of a "proper" length of a body absolutely stationary with respect to the ether which grows smaller when the body starts to move. Actually the contraction is reciprocal. Suppose we have two systems, XYZ and X'Y'Z', moving relative to each other. If a rod is stationary in the unprimed system and moving in the primed one it will be shorter when measured in the latter than in the former. Alternatively, if it is at rest in the primed system it will turn out to be shorter when measured in the unprimed system. Is the contraction real? The answer is, Yes. The dimensions really contract, and the real cause of the (reciprocal!) contraction is the *reciprocal* motion of the systems. Of course, the idea of reciprocally contracting rods is paradoxical indeed, but it represents a real relationship in the bodies' dimensions, a relationship which is not dependent on observation. It is dependent on the real reciprocal displacements of the bodies, which is easier to visualise than the absolute motion not referred to other bodies which figures in classical mechanics.

Einstein's theory deduces the Lorentz contraction from the most basic and most general concepts of science, from a stricter and more precise analysis of the concepts of time and space. From this analysis Einstein develops an explanation of the new experimental fact yielded by Michelson's experiment. In this sense Einstein's theory fits into the scheme of "external confirmation" and "inner perfection".

When a new, extremely paradoxical fact—the constancy of the velocity of light in Michelson's interferometer—called for some kind of explanation, Lorentz advanced an idea which, while agreeing with the new facts as well as with the earlier known ones, did not derive naturally and unambiguously from them. Einstein's explanation of the new and paradoxical fact is based on a revision of the whole world picture, on an entirely new interpretation of space and time, in short, on a more profound, more general and more concrete interpretation of the totality of known facts. The "flight from wonder" thus culminates in a theory combining "external confirmation" with "inner perfection".

The difference between the theory of relativity and the ideas of Lorentz and Poincaré, advanced at about the same time, lies in these epistemological features of relativity. In February 1955, in reply to a question from Seelig concerning the relation between his work and that of Lorentz and Poincaré, Einstein wrote:

"Looking back at the evolution of the special theory of relativity, it seems obvious that by 1905 it was ripe for discovery. Lorentz already knew the value of the transformations, which were later named after him, for his analysis of Maxwell's equations, and Poincaré further elaborated this idea. As for myself, I was familiar only with Lorentz's fundamental work, written in 1895, but not with his later work, nor with Poincaré's related investigations. In this sense my work was independent. The new idea in it was that the Lorentz transformations go beyond Maxwell's equations and apply to the fundaments of space and time."[1]

These comments, of course, make all the difference in the world. Einstein stresses that the ground had been prepared for the relativity theory and that papers written at the same time as his *On the Electrodynamics of Moving Bodies* contained important ideas paving the way for the concept that the velocity of light is independent of the motion of inertial systems. But in Einstein's theory the Lorentz transformations (which provide for length contraction, time dilation and the constancy of the velocity of light) figure as a universal law transcending the boundaries of electrodynamics and embracing the general relationships of space and time. This is what Lorentz meant when he added the note to his original 1904 paper, quoted in the epigraph to this chapter.

Einstein's basic idea is the necessity of experimental verification of a logical construction. A concept cannot be in *a priori* agreement with reality. It must lead to conclusions capable of experimental verification. Absolute motion does not stand up to such verification. The conclusions of relativity theory are not derived from clever propositions: they follow naturally from general principles.

"The theory of relativity is characterised, among other things, by the epistemological point of view," Einstein writes. "There are no concepts in physics whose usage is necessary or can be justified by *a priori* considerations. A concept acquires right of existence only by virtue of its clear and unambiguous connection with phenomena, and accordingly, with physical reality. In the relativity theory such concepts as absolute simultaneity, absolute velocity, absolute acceleration, etc., are rejected as they have no unambiguous con-

[1] C. Seelig, op. cit., S. 116.

nections with experience. . . . It was necessary to define every physical concept in such a way so as to be able (in every specific case) to decide in principle whether it corresponds to reality or not."[1]

The ability to proceed, in the development of concrete physical theories from the most general and apparently solved problems of reality is characteristic of Einstein. In a conversation with James Franck he once said: "I sometimes ask myself: how did it come that I was the one to develop the theory of relativity? The reason, I think, is that a normal adult never stops to think about problems of space and time. These are things which he has thought of as a child. But my intellectual development was retarded, as a result of which I began to wonder about space and time only when I had already grown up. Naturally, I could go deeper into the problem than a child with normal abilities."[2]

This rather surprising statement (which seems to imply that the theory which revises the basic concepts of space and time owes its existence to the mental retardation of its creator) contains an important germ of truth. It can be said that the mental ontogeny of many children and adolescents, in a sense, repeats the development of human thinking as a whole: general thoughts about physical reality are followed by more mature and more specific interests. Einstein retained this feeling of the first look at the world—the secret of the success of many a great thinker and artist—without the "grown-up" conviction that the basic problems of the world have all been solved. This feeling was not quenched by the acquisition of deeper knowledge or the development of new interests. Einstein pondered on problems of motion and came to an idea which belonged to the childhood of mankind: the ancient idea of relativity, which subsequently retreated in the face of mechanics and the ether concept as a universal absolute body of reference. When attempts to detect the ether wind failed, relativity regained its place as the bedrock of physics. Einstein was quick to assume that the failure to detect motion through the ether could only mean that there was no ether to move through, hence the meaninglessness of the concept of motion referred to it. What remained then was

[1] *Solovine*, p. 21.
[2] C. Seelig, op. cit., S. 119.

to draw the necessary conclusions from the fact that, in principle, there is no such thing as absolute motion referred to some privileged frame of reference.

The creators of thermodynamics had followed a similar course. When all attempts to construct a *perpetuum mobile* failed, they made a universal principle of this failure by postulating that energy can neither disappear nor appear out of nothing. After that thermodynamics could rid itself of artificial hypotheses and elaborate the corollaries of energy conservation.

Einstein appended to one of his letters to Maurice Solovine the following brief exposition of the basic ideas of relativity:

"In spite of the diversity of the physical experiments which constitute the basis of the relativity theory, its method and content can be summed up in a few words. Contrary to the fact, known already to the ancients, that motion can be perceived only *relatively*, physics based itself on the concept of *absolute* motion. In optics it was assumed that there existed a kind of motion different from all others, namely, motion through the luminiferous ether, to which the motion of all corporeal bodies could be referred. The luminiferous ether thus represented an embodiment of the concept of absolute rest. If the stationary luminiferous ether pervading the whole of space really existed, motion could be referred to it, thereby acquiring absolute meaning. This concept could serve as the basis of mechanics. However, when all attempts to detect such a privileged motion through the hypothetical luminiferous ether failed, the problem had to be reconsidered. This was undertaken systematically in the relativity theory. It assumes the absence of privileged states of motion in nature and analyses the conclusions deriving from such an assumption. Its method is analogous to the method of thermodynamics. The latter represents no more than a systematised answer to the question: What are the laws of nature that make the construction of a *perpetuum mobile* impossible?"[1]

[1] *Solovine*, p. 19.

Chapter 15

SPACE, TIME, ENERGY, AND MASS

> *Applied to Maxwell's equations, the principle of relativity requires, in particular, that mass be a direct measure of a body's energy. Light carries mass. A fascinating and intriguing idea. I only wonder if God might not just be jesting and making a fool of me.*
>
> *Einstein*

We have already spoken of the classical concept of absolute time in connection with Einstein's criteria for the selection of a scientific theory and in analysing his attitude towards classical mechanics. The concept does not derive from the most general principles of the classical picture of the world, from what we have called the "classical ideal" of science. In the "classical ideal" science draws a world picture comprising nothing but bodies in relative motion. By motion is meant the temporal change of a body's position relative to other bodies. A necessary feature of time is "time-flow", i.e., the passage from one instant to another. Classical science imposed no limitations on the velocity of bodies, but neither did it feature infinite velocities; on the contrary, it was obvious that a body localised in one place at a given instant could not be found in another place at the same instant. Hence the "classical ideal" develops a four-dimensional world picture: in speaking of a body's position, i.e., its three spatial coordinates, one must also specify the time when the body achieved that position. It is assumed that, generally speaking, a body is never really at rest, and in any case, a stationary body would not take part in any events. This classical four-dimensional picture was unbalanced by the notion of force propagating with infinite velocity. The postulate of instantaneous action at a distance did not derive from the general fundaments of classical science but contradicted its "inner perfection", violated the natural harmony of the universe, and was something of an arbitrary complement to the "classical ideal".

Einstein's "extra-personal" ideal was to restore the world harmony, and it dominated the whole of his life and work. In the present case the task was made more difficult by the ether concept. The ether, that "offspring of classical science conceived in grief", as Planck described it, provided a basis for the concept of simultaneity and at the same time contributed to the breaking down of the four-dimensional "classical ideal" into an independent time (the flow of which embraced the whole of space and did not depend on spatial localisation) and an independent space (in which events could take place instantaneously, in zero time).

We have seen that, given a stationary ether as an absolute frame of reference for all bodies, it is possible to link two simultaneous events, even if signals are assumed to propagate with finite speed. Two signals from one source arrive at two points simultaneously if the source is equidistant from the points and the signals travel with the same speed. Two screens set up on the bow and stern of a ship will light up simultaneously if the source of light is located precisely amidships. If the ether exists and the ship's motion influences the speed of light, the synchronisation of events (the lighting up of the screens) is possible only as long as the ship is at rest relative to the ether. Imagine another ship passing by the first one just when the light is turned on. If the second ship also has two screens, the light will not reach them simultaneously as it must catch up with the screen on the bow while the sternwards screen is moving towards the light (provided, of course, that the ether exists, that the second ship is moving with respect to the ether, and that this motion affects the velocity of signals on the ship). A man on the first ship knows that the simultaneity of the lighting up of the screens is absolute since the vessel is absolutely motionless, being stationary in the ether. At the same time the man on the moving vessel makes no comment as he knows that the non-simultaneous lighting up of the screens on his ship is due to its motion.

If, however, there is no ether and the velocity of light is independent of motion, then the man on the second ship can also claim that his vessel is motionless (since motion has no effect on the velocity of light) and the beams reach the two screens simultaneously. The man on the first ship, of course, continues to maintain that his vessel is at rest and the screens light up simultaneously. When there is no absolute motion, absolute simultaneity no longer has physical meaning. Events that are simultaneous in one frame of reference are not simultaneous in another, and vice versa. Einstein's theory put an end to the fiction of a single time flow embracing the universe, and also to the idea of purely spatial instantaneous processes. Accordingly, the era of the four-dimensional, spatio-temporal conception of the world began.

The mathematical apparatus for this conception was developed in 1908 by Hermann Minkowski, who lived in Göttingen at the time. Since the time of Gauss, Göttingen was the centre of the best traditions of mathematical teaching and research. Almost one hundred years before, Göttingen scholars had reacted favourably to Lobachevsky's geometry; it was in Göttingen that Riemann had expounded his ideas of multi-dimensional geometry and developed his variant of non-Euclidean geometry. They liked mathematical subtleties in Göttingen. Even physicists would delve into mathematical constructions not necessarily designed to elucidate the physical essence of phenomena. Einstein once playfully remarked: "The people in Göttingen sometimes strike me, not as if they wanted to help one formulate something clearly, but as if they wanted only to show us physicists how much brighter they are than we."[1]

One senses in this remark the disappointment of a physicist who, while seeking the apparatus he needs, finds only works which contribute little to purely physical notions, however brilliant they might otherwise be. With the more eminent Göttingen scholars, sophistication and exactingness in mathematical thinking derived from a deep penetration into the physical sources of mathematics. Many Göttingenians voiced the idea of an experimental solution to the question, of "which of all possible, non-contradictory geometries agrees with reality?" This is true of Gauss and Riemann, and of Einstein's contemporaries, among them Hermann Minkowski, David Hilbert, Felix Klein and Emma Noether, all of whom used relativity theory to evolve some brilliant mathematical generalisations.

[1] Ph. Frank, op. cit., p. 249.

Approached from the broad historico-cultural aspect, mathematical research in the first quarter of the 20th century displayed two trends, which merge in the works of the aforementioned scholars. The elaboration of geometrical conceptions with no practical applications to speak of and strict, subtle and sophisticated definitions finally merged with physical ideas which began to serve as their mathematical apparatus. This, evidently, required a genial physicist whose mind was not overburdened with traditional philosophical and mathematical conceptions of space and time.

Hilbert once said: "Every boy in the streets of our mathematical Göttingen understands more about four-dimensional geometry than Einstein. Yet, despite that, Einstein did the work and not the mathematicians."[1] Hilbert's explanation for this was that Einstein "had learnt nothing about the philosophy and mathematics of time and space".

The idea of the physical reality of a new, non-traditional, possibly multi-dimensional and non-Euclidean geometry occurred to Lobachevsky, Gauss, and Riemann. It did not, however, become a physical theory. During the course of development mathematics "emits" certain "virtual" physical conceptions; they are absorbed by mathematics itself, like the virtual photons which are absorbed by the electron that emits them. Similarly, physics also emits "virtual" mathematical images which do not become points of departure for new mathematical schools.

On the other hand, mathematics was confronted with a physical theory capable of giving concrete physical meaning to the relationships of four-dimensional geometry. Most important was the question of objective, not phenomenological content. When Poincaré developed his very general and ingenious mathematical apparatus of relativity theory on the basis of Lorentz's theory, in which the constancy of the velocity of light was of a purely phenomenological nature, it could not have the same impact on either physics or geometry as Minkowski's ideas did, which proceeded from the objective nature of the constancy of the velocity of light

---

[1] Ph. Frank, op. cit., p. 249.

and the objective **inseparability** of space and time discovered by Einstein.

Minkowski demonstrated that the principle of the constancy of the velocity of light could be expressed in purely geometrical form. He introduced the concept of "event" as a localisation of a particle at a given instant at a given spatial point. Thus an "event" is represented as a point with four coordinates: three spatial and one temporal measured in different units. Minkowski called it a *world point.* Motion is represented by a locus of world points, called a *world line.* The totality of all possible "events", i.e., everything taking place in the universe, is a totality of four-dimensional world points—the four-dimensional space-time, which Minkowski called the *world.*

A similar four-dimensional conception of motion is found in the basic formulas of relativity theory. Minkowski, however, expressed the "world" idea in a clear-cut explicit form which contributed to the advance of the theory.

With the introduction of the four-dimensional space-time "world" in place of the conventional notions concerning the independence of space and time, Newtonian mechanics had to give way to a new mechanics "of the same type", more harmonious and consistent, possessing greater "inner perfection" and "external confirmation", and approaching closer to the "classical ideal".

Let us now see how the logical and historical conclusions of relativity came to threaten not only Newtonian mechanics, but the "classical ideal" as well. This came through relativistic dynamics, i.e., through the postulates of relativity theory concerning the acceleration of bodies under the action of forces, energy, and mass.

From the basic propositions of relativity Einstein deduced a new rule for the addition of velocity. Imagine a person travelling in a spaceship at a velocity of 150,000 kilometres per second (half the speed of light) relative to the earth. Another spaceship is approaching it with the same speed. According to the classical rule of velocity composition, the relative speed of the two vehicles is 150,000+150,000=300,000 kilometres per second, which is the speed of light. The new velocity addition rule postulated by Einstein gives a result of 240,000 kilometres per second. From Einstein's rule it follows then that in no frame of reference can a body's velocity ever exceed that of light. Let a greater force be impressed on the moving body, the velocity will increase, but the combined velocity will never exceed that of light. As the velocity tends to the speed of light the velocity increments yielded by the application of additional forces will get smaller and smaller.

Einstein accepted unequivocally the idea that the limiting nature of the velocity of light derived naturally from the general propositions and concrete observations. He voiced emphatic criticism against one popular exposition of the finality of the speed of light illustrated by motion faster than light. This was a science-fiction story called *Lumen,* by the French astronomer Camille Flammarion. Flammarion made his Lumen travel at a speed of 400,000 kilometres per second, that is, 100,000 km/sec faster than light. Thus Lumen overtakes light waves and can see those which left their source successively earlier. He witnesses the finale of the battle of Waterloo before the beginning, and in the interim cannonballs fly back into the barrels, the dead rise and join the combatants, and so on.

In April 1920, Moszkowski mentioned Flammarion's story to Einstein, who was highly critical of the picture it presented. Moszkowski defended Flammarion, saying that the story was merely intended to illustrate the relative nature of time. He quotes Einstein's answer as follows:

"These adventures and topsy-turvy perceptions are as pertinent to the notion of the relativity of time (as it derives from the new mechanics) as the idea that time passes faster or slower depending on our subjective sensations of joy or sorrow, satisfaction or boredom. Here, at least, the subjective sensations themselves are real, which is more than can be said of Lumen, whose existence is based on a meaningless premise. Lumen is made to travel faster than light. This is not just impossible, it is utterly meaningless since it has been proved by the relativity theory that the velocity of light is a limiting quantity. However great an accelerating force and however long it acts, it can never exceed this limit. We imagine Lumen as possessing sense-organs, and therefore corporeal. But at the velocity of light a body's mass becomes infinitely great, and the very idea of further increasing its speed is absurd. One may operate in one's thoughts in terms of impossible things which contradict our daily experience but not common sense."[1]

Moszkowski, however, continued to defend Flammarion's right to fantasy about motion faster than light. He suggested the following mental construction. A beacon rotating at 200 revolutions per second sends out a beam of light over a distance of 1,000 kilometres. The tip of this beam would then be circling the heavens at a speed of 600,000 kilometres per second, twice that of light.

There have been many such attempts to refute Einstein's theory, and most of them have been rightfully forgotten. The present example, too, does not refute the relativity theory. For the revolving beam does not represent the motion of an immutable body. We could turn the beacon through 180° and light up two screens 2,000 kilometres apart. But their illumination would not be events of which one was the cause or effect of the other. No physical thing can arrive at one point from another in less time than it takes light to cover that distance. An event that takes place in less time than it takes light to travel from one point to another cannot be the effect of an event at the light source.

According to Einstein, if the time interval between events at two different points is less than the time needed for light to span the distance between them, then these events are not facts in the history of any one immutable physical thing.

Relativity was advanced as a theory concerned with the behaviour of immutable physical things—non-annihilating and non-breeding particles which can interact and move relative to one another. Events constituting the history of such a particle are its localisation at different points at different instants. Such localisation means that the particle was opposite a specific intercept on a measuring rod (one end of which is at the origin of a coordinate system) at an instant when a certain recurrent process (the motion of a clock hand, for example) has completed a certain number of cycles following the event taken as the initial time.

As it advanced physics encountered new difficulties: not always can such simple physical meaning be attached to the specific location of a particle or to the specific time of an

[1] A. Moszkowski, op. cit., S. 107-08.

event in the life of that particle. From the 1930s onwards, the development of a unified theory which would proceed from the postulates of relativity and the suggested indeterminacies in the coordinates and times of "events" became one of the fundamental tasks of theoretical physics.

To prepare ourselves for an investigation of this problem we must analyse the changes which the concepts of mass and energy underwent in Einstein's works.

At velocities approaching that of light bodies offer a very strong resistance to external forces, which produce smaller and smaller accelerations as the velocity increases. It is as if the body's mass increases with the velocity, tending to infinity when the velocity tends to the speed of light. From this relationship between mass and velocity Einstein deduced the relationship between energy and mass.

A body at rest has a definite mass, called *rest mass.* Einstein postulated that a body's rest mass is proportional to its *internal energy.* This energy (in ergs) is equal to the rest mass (in grams) times the square of the velocity of light (in centimetres per second). The result is an incredibly large value, for the velocity of light is 30,000,000,000 (3×10^{10}) cm/sec, and $(3 \times 10^{10})^2 = 9 \times 10^{20} = 900,000,000,000,000,000,000$ —which gives us an idea of the tremendous energy contained in a unit of mass.

Not all bodies possess rest mass: the particles of electromagnetic radiation—photons or light quanta—have no rest mass: as light propagates with the same velocity of 3×10^{10} cm/sec in all frames of reference, photons are at rest in none.

As mentioned above, the mass of a body increases with its velocity. This is the *mass in motion,* and to it corresponds the energy of motion. It will be observed that at conventional velocities the increase in the mass and internal energy of a moving body is negligible and need not be taken into account.

The huge number with twenty zeros, which was once a measure of the remoteness of relativity from any practical applications, has today become a measure of its impact on human affairs. We have entered the age of practical utilisation of energies compatible with the *total* internal energy of matter. In atomic reactors no more than thousandths of this energy is released. But conventional power sources entail energies of the order of millionths of the total. The ultimate goal is the utilisation of practically all the internal energy of matter. This can be envisaged in processes in which internal energy (and accordingly rest mass) turns into the energy of motion (and corresponding mass in motion). In such a transformation a particle having rest mass would change into one with no rest mass. We shall see later on that such transformations were predicted when relativity joined with quantum mechanics, and they were subsequently observed experimentally. We shall also see that such transformations (transmutations) of particles of one type into particles of another type transcend the boundaries, not only of the Newtonian world picture, but of the "classical ideal" itself, which considers the motion of immutable bodies. This is the destiny of Einstein's ideas. Postulated in order to systematise the classical conceptions of the world, they led to much farther-reaching conclusions.

Chapter 16

PRAGUE AND ZURICH

> *Kepler's lifework was possible only when he succeeded in freeing himself to a great extent of the intellectual traditions into which he was born. This meant not merely the religious tradition, based on the authority of the Church, but the general concepts of the nature and limitations of action within the universe and the human sphere, as well as notions of the relative importance of thought and experience in science.*
>
> Einstein

The urgency of the situation created by Michelson's experiment, the obviously artificial nature of Lorentz's hypothesis, and the perfection and consummation of Einstein's theory—all contributed to the early recognition of the latter by a fairly broad section of the scientific community. At least one man, Max Planck, realised that a genius had come into physics, the kind of which can appear only once in a century. Einstein's fame multiplied together with the recognition, dissemination and further development of his theory, until finally, as is usually the case, it reached the country where he lived.

It was suggested then that Einstein be offered a professorship at the University of Zurich. According to the regulations, however, no one could be appointed professor at the university unless he had previously been a Privatdozent. So Einstein was invited to become a Privatdozent at the University of Bern, where in a short while he would become eligible for a professorship at Zurich. A Privatdozent is a teacher who for a very small remuneration lectures on disciplines not covered by the curriculum. This position left him time to pursue his job at the Patent Office. Einstein accepted the offer, though without much enthusiasm. He realised, of course, that he could not remain in the Patent Office forever, but at the same time he feared that the lectures would interfere with the customary routine: the easy job at the Patent Office which left sufficient time to spare for his researches.

During the winter of 1908-1909, Einstein combined his duties as Privatdozent with work at the Patent Office. In the summer of 1909 he received his first academic honours when the University of Geneva conferred upon him an *honoris causa* doctorship and invited him to participate in the celebration of the 350th anniversary of the inauguration of the university by Calvin. Participants in this occasion say that Einstein's straw hat and informal suit was practically the only bright spot amidst the embroidered frock coats of French academicians, medieval mantles of British scholars and sundry exotic attires of the two hundred representatives of universities from all over the world.

The same year the professorship of theoretical physics at the University of Zurich became vacant. The only other candidate for the position was Friedrich Adler, Einstein's former fellow student at the Zurich Polytechnic, who was then a Privatdozent at the university. He was held in high esteem by the Zurich organisation of the Social-Democratic Party. The majority of members of the Zurich cantonal board of education were also Social-Democrats, so when the vacancy appeared Adler was named as the most suitable candidate. Friedrich Adler, however, declared that his ability as a researcher could in no way compare with Einstein's and that the opportunity of obtaining a man who could benefit the university so much by raising its prestige and general level should not be lost, and Einstein was appointed professor "extraordinary" at the University of Zurich.

The position of "extraordinary" was inferior to that of a full professorship, and Einstein's income was no greater than it had been in Bern. Moreover, life in Zurich was more expensive, and Mileva soon began to take on student boarders to make ends meet. Nevertheless Einstein was happy. He found many old friends, and among them the modest and devoted friend of his student days, Marcel Grossmann.

The picture of Einstein as a university teacher can be gained from the memoirs of some of his students. His lectures included introduction to mechanics, thermodynamics and the kinetic theory of heat (1909-1910), electricity and magnetism, and a course called "Selected Departments of Theoretical Physics" (1910-1911).

Hans Tanner, who attended Einstein's lectures in 1909-1911, writes:

"When Einstein first ascended the rostrum in his shabby suit, the trousers of which were too short, with an iron watch-chain, we were quite sceptical of our new professor. However, he soon captured our callous hearts with the unique way of reading his lectures. His notes filled a slip of paper the size of a visiting-card and simply listed the points to be taken up at the lecture. Einstein's lectures thus came straight from his head and we were able to witness the working of his brain. This was much more interesting than some of the stylistically faultless, sober lectures which might even excite us but which also gave rise to a bitter realisation of the distance between teacher and student. Here we could see for ourselves the unusual ways which sometimes led to valuable scientific results. After every lecture we felt that we could even have delivered it ourselves."[1]

Characteristic of Einstein's methods of teaching and research, as well as of the contents of his ideas, was a "naturalness" of the scientific conclusions they led to. There was an inner harmony in the method and content of his lectures. It is natural of course to be dogmatic in expounding rigid theories based on certain arbitrary assumptions. An idea resting on the facts of physical reality, no matter how paradoxical it might seem, will sparkle and expand and forge ahead in front of an enraptured audience. As the paradox gradually emerges as an inevitable conclusion deriving from new basic conceptions of nature it becomes natural and "self-evident" to the listeners who see it maturing. Einstein's lectures were devoted mainly to classical physics, though after the fundaments had been revised the treatment of the subject had to be changed. The students were confronted not with a graceful architectural structure but with a building site, and Einstein was more concerned with blueprints for the new building than with the time-worn plans of the old one.

"From 1909 to 1910," Tanner writes, "I don't think I missed a single one of Einstein's lectures. They were all

[1] C. Seelig, op. cit., S. 171.

extremely interesting. As I remember, we were offered a wide choice of subject matter, ranging from classical mechanics (we had attended the lectures of other teachers and could appreciate the difference of Einstein's approach) to such new ideas of interest as Planck's quantum mechanics, which aroused lively discussions."[1]

Also in keeping with the character of Einstein's ideas was his manner during and after lectures. "We could interrupt him whenever we failed to grasp a point. We soon grew bolder and were no longer afraid of asking a foolish question. The atmosphere of informality that prevailed in relations between teacher and students was enhanced by the fact that Einstein usually remained with us during intervals. In his frank, impulsive way he would take a student by the arm and discuss a point as one would with a friend."[2]

Often after the weekly evening physics colloquiums Einstein would ask: "Who will come with me to the Terrasse Café?" The discussions would continue there, frequently departing from physics and mathematics to other scientific and social problems. One late evening, when the café was closing, Einstein took Tanner and another student home. He gave them a paper by Planck and asked them to find the error in it while he prepared some coffee. By the time the coffee was ready the students had not found the error and Einstein showed it to them. It was a case of pure mathematics which did not affect the physical conclusions. In this connection Einstein delivered a brilliant impromptu lecture on mathematical methods and physical truth.[3]

In Zurich, Einstein drew closer to his old friend from the Polytechnic, Marcel Grossmann, a friendship that later led to some valuable contribution to science. Einstein frequently consulted Grossmann, who was engaged in problems of non-Euclidean geometry.

Einstein also met Friedrich Adler frequently. They lived in the same house and often sought the seclusion of the attic for their conversations. They probably had some heated philosophical arguments, for Adler was an adherent of Mach's philosophy and he did not share Einstein's belief

---

[1] C. Seelig, op. cit., S. 172.
[2] Ibid., S. 171.
[3] Ibid., S. 173-74.

in the objective reality of the world. Like Mach, Adler also opposed the theory of relativity.

Among Einstein's friends there were also two Zurich professors: Emil Zürcher, an expert in criminal law, and Alfred Stern, an historian. It is characteristic of Einstein that he fostered intellectual contacts with people far removed from physics or mathematics. He liked to talk with lawyers, historians and physicians. This is in line with the nature of Einstein's basic ideas. His mind ascended from specific physical research to fundamental problems of physical reality, and it was along this road that he came to his most specific conclusions (some of them immediately applicable in practice). Many regarded this tendency of Einstein's as an escape from science into the domain of general philosophical ideas. Even such a vital and broad-minded scholar as Walter Nernst remarked that Einstein's theory of Brownian movement ranked higher than relativity as the latter was not a physical theory but rather a philosophical generalisation. This was a typical "pre-atomic" evaluation of relativity.

Einstein's scientific ideas and interests were of a kind which enabled him to discuss many scientific problems with non-physicists and even non-scientists. For these were men capable of grasping the more general propositions concerning space and time, they were capable of "childish" thinking not adulterated by a conviction of the "self-evidence" of traditional concepts nurtured by the routine of professional treatment. To Einstein such thinking was a point of departure for the formulation of physical concepts.

Einstein's acquaintance with the historian Alfred Stern dated back to his student days. Much later, on the occasion of Stern's eightieth birthday, Einstein wrote to him: "I hardly know another man who has retained such integrity in a time of chaotically changing opinions and values."[1]

Another close friend of Einstein's was the steam-turbine specialist, Laurel Stodola. Einstein's description of Stodola, written in 1929, is of interest not so much as a characteristic of the great heat engineer as for the insight into Einstein's own character. Here it is, almost in full:

[1] C. Seelig, op. cit., S. 185.

"Had Stodola been born in the age of the Renaissance he would have been a great painter or sculptor, for the dominant traits of his personality are a powerful imagination and an urge for creation. In the last hundred years such natures have usually turned to engineering. The creative urge of our generation has found expression in this sphere, and the passionate thirst for beauty has found greater satisfaction in it than the uninitiated can ever imagine. All along his successful career as a teacher—from 1892 to 1929—he exerted a tremendous influence on his pupils, who always speak of their teacher and his work with glowing eyes. Once, when in his capacity of a newly-baked teacher the present writer was conducting a course in theoretical physics at the University of Zurich, a wonderful image appeared in the auditorium, to the delight and dismay of the lecturer. This was Stodola, who had an interest in theoretical physics. The feeling of awe inspired by this great man was quickly dispelled by the kindness and good will that shone through his words. His modesty was overwhelming. The forcefulness and vitality of his mind contrasted strangely with the remarkable mildness and tenderness of his soul. The suffering of living creatures moved him profoundly, especially when it was due to the wanton cruelty of men. All the social problems of our time concerned him. This man, lonely, like all independent people, possessed a high sense of public duty. He suffered from the fear dominating human affairs and the sense of man's helplessness in the face of the inexhorable tragedy of world events. Success and the love of many people did not alleviate his morbid sensitivity, and he was lonely. He found solace in his love for music and the affection of his two daughters. . . . One of them, Helen, he lost. His profound grief was a reflection of the spiritual greatness of this remarkable man."[1]

Here is a portrayal worthy of Plutarch. As though cast in bronze, it is in many ways a portrait of Einstein himself. A man who never thinks of himself can produce a self-portrait by drawing the features of another man with whom he has spiritual affinity.

In June 1910, another son, Edward, was born into the Einstein family. He was very like his father, with the same

[1] C. Seelig, op. cit., S. 188-89.

features and large, clear eyes, and later on he acquired his father's love for music.

Towards the end of 1910 there occurred a vacancy in the chair of theoretical physics at the University of Prague, one of the oldest in Europe. By a decree of the Austrian government it had in the 1890s been divided into two universities, German and Czech, the former enjoying the patronage of the authorities. This was one of the steps in the policy of germanisation of the Slavic countries under the domination of the Hapsburg dynasty.

The first rector of the German University was Ernst Mach, and after he left it remained a stronghold of his philosophy. Moreover, his followers and pupils held positions of authority and did everything to support and propagate his ideas. One of the leading figures at the university was Anton Lampa, a Czech by birth, yet a zealous supporter of the policy of germanisation. The son of a janitor who worked in a building belonging to rich Germans, Lampa had had ample opportunity to compare his own family's neediness and inferior social standing with that of his father's employers. This, he decided, was not for him; his place was with the master class. He finished a German school and then the German University, where in time he attained a position of authority. Lampa devoted himself to the propagation of German culture and the eradication of all manifestations of Czech culture. It was related in Prague that Lampa would refuse to buy a postcard if the word "postcard" was printed in Czech as well as in German, and indignantly demanded a card having only the German word on it. To Einstein Lampa symbolised all that was most repulsive in the policy of germanisation.

Lampa and other officials of the German university decided that it would be a good thing for the university's reputation to recruit to its staff a professor of European standing. As a pupil and ardent supporter of Mach, Lampa probably thought that in Einstein he would find a man of like views. As mentioned before, unlike Mach, who was quick to discern the anti-positivistic purport of the relativity theory, some of his followers believed that Einstein's criticism of Newtonian conceptions of the world led him to scepticism concerning the objectivity of scientific concepts as such. Be that as it may, but Lampa named Einstein as a possible candidate, and he sought the opinions of several leading physicists concerning Einstein's qualifications. The reply from Max Planck was: "If Einstein's theory should prove correct, as I expect it will, he will be considered the Copernicus of the 20th century."

As in Zurich, there were two prospective candidates for the position, and as in Zurich Einstein's rival stood down in his favour. The reason, however, was quite the opposite to that which had motivated Friedrich Adler to stand down.

The first candidate was Gustav Jaumann, a professor at the Technological Institute in Brno, a zealous Machist and a man of inordinate vanity. The authorities at Vienna were inclined to prefer him as a native Austrian; the professors at Prague would have preferred him as an avowed Machist. But they had reckoned without Jaumann's vanity and touchiness: for when he heard that Einstein's name had been placed before his own in the list of candidates he declared in a fine display of temper that he would "have nothing to do with a university that chases after modernity and does not appreciate true merit".

The position was offered to Einstein, and he accepted it, though not without some qualms. Mileva did not like the idea of tearing up their roots and moving to a strange country. Einstein, too, was reluctant to leave Switzerland and Zurich, where his words and his music fell on the ears of friends. Still, a full professorship offered him greater independence than he had ever enjoyed before, and in the autumn of 1911 he took up his position at Prague.

One of the rules in Austria-Hungary was that a person taking up an official position was required to state his religion. The Emperor Franz Josef categorically demanded that any person holding an office should belong to a recognised Church. There was no exemption for non-believers, and Einstein duly stated his religion as "Mosaic".

Einstein found that Prague was quite unlike Munich or the cities of Italy and Switzerland which he knew so well, but he quickly came to love the old city and the beautiful views that opened up from its numerous hills.

It was a custom for a new member of the faculty to call on all of his colleagues. The necessary calls numbered some forty, and Einstein decided to take advantage of the opportunity to see the various sections of Prague. In pursuance of this plan he began to make his visits according to the location of the houses of his colleagues. He dutifully made their acquaintance and met their wives and children, but soon he came to find the calls rather a nuisance. Besides, his choice of the sections of the city he wanted to see did not coincide with the official order of precedence. Some of the professors began to suspect a lack of respect for authority, and in an institution where bureaucratic formality and ceremonial was being energetically enforced this was highly resented.

Einstein suddenly stopped the visits without having made the necessary number of calls. But he continued his sightseeing of the city. Its quaint old buildings, the town hall, the churches and turrets and the contrasting fresh greenery of its parks and gardens appealed to his sense of beauty. He strolled along the banks of the Vltava River, which divides the city, always anticipating the eternally new and wonderful sight of Karlov Bridge with its 15th-century sculptures. The bridge took him across the river to the "Prague Venice" where houses clung to the cliffs overhanging the river. From there he climbed up Hradčany Hill and into the harmony of different architectural forms embodying a millennium of labour of the Czech people. It was a natural harmony which emerged out of the natural course of history and served as a symbol of reason rising out of the chaos of human contradictions. In Hradčany Einstein saw the 12th-century Roman Church of St. George and passed under the arcades of St. Vitus Cathedral with its rational architecture, a tribute not to medieval mysticism but to 14th-century mechanics. Then down Zlata Ulička, the artisan section of medieval Prague, in which one found the genuine homes and environment of people who, by accumulating empirical knowledge, had paved the way for the Renaissance, the new world picture, and finally, the brilliant rise of the rationalist "classical ideal". Prague brought to mind many a forerunner of the "classical ideal", for there, in the 15th-century Tyn Church, stands the tomb of Tycho Brahe. It was here, in Prague, that he had bequeathed to Johannes Kepler all the records of his astronomical observations. Einstein treaded the stones of a city where discoveries lying at the foundations of the classical world picture had been made.

Among Einstein's new friends in Prague was Max Brod, a young author who endeavoured to bring out the psychological characteristics of great men in the history of ideas and discoveries. Philipp Frank writes that when Brod was working on his novel, *The Redemption of Tycho Brahe*, he was greatly influenced in his portrayal of Kepler by the impression that Einstein's personality had made upon him.[1] It is hard to say how true to life Brod's portrayal of Kepler was, but when Walter Nernst read the novel he said to Einstein: "You are this man Kepler."

Brod's Kepler is indifferent to the good things of life and mundane delights. He derives pleasure in the search for scientific truth, and he opposes Tycho Brahe, who seeks to dovetail his astronomical system to Catholic dogma. "Catholic or not," Kepler says, "the hypothesis alone is being considered, not the Emperor's favour. . . . We must defer to truth alone and nothing else." This remark, together with the realisation of the world harmony which permeates Kepler's work, is what makes the image so akin to Einstein.

It would be appropriate to compare here Einstein with Kepler and Galileo, a comparison which offers an insight into some import aspects of Einstein's world outlook.

Few thinkers can rank as high as Kepler in "athletic musculature of the mind"—at least as far as mechanics and mathematics are concerned. No other scholar of his age was so bent on discovering the causes governing the known structure of the solar system. Kepler's laws represent the first solid building stones in the foundation of modern science, and they will not be shaken even though the foundation itself is reconstructed. On this foundation rests the entire edifice of Newtonian mechanics.

Yet Kepler's influence on the spiritual life of mankind is far less than Galileo's. This is not only because Galileo's inertia concept was the key to the new science, nor because of the unity, consistency and crystal clarity of Galileo's ideas as contrasted to Kepler's vague "music of the spheres". As a scientist Kepler was inclined to solitary research. No doubt, potentially, its results were pregnant with all the spiritual and material upheavals which could be expected from the development of an unambiguous mechanical world picture,

[1] Ph. Frank, op. cit., p. 107.

rationalist criticism, and the corollaries therefrom. In the meantime social upheavals remained hidden in Pandora's box together with the new conceptions of nature, as Kepler was not a social fighter and his laws were not a banner of social struggle.

Galileo was not only the author of a crystal-clear world picture, but also a fighter for its recognition. He was not content simply to discover the truth of the world, he wanted to proclaim it to the world.

The theory of relativity as a Pandora's box of social storms can be compared with the ideas of Kepler and Galileo taken together. Einstein's universal relativity is congenial with Galileo's inertia and classical relativity; the relationships of special and general relativity are congenial with Kepler's laws. In scientific temperament, however, Einstein was a Kepler rather than a Galileo.

More than thirty years after *The Redemption of Tycho Brahe*, Max Brod published a book called *Galileo in Captivity*, which he sent to Einstein. In July 1949, he received a letter in which Einstein, among other things, expressed his ideas on Galileo's struggle against canonised dogmas.

"My idea of Galileo is quite a different one," Einstein wrote. "There can be no doubt that he was an ardent seeker of truth. But I find it hard to believe that a mature man could find any purpose in overcoming so many obstacles in order to bring a newly discovered truth to the attention of the shallow-minded populace with its paltry interests. Could the task be of such importance as to make him devote the last years of his life to it?... For no apparent reason he goes into the lion's den and undertakes a journey to Rome to fight it out with the clerics and the politicians. This does not agree with my idea of old Galileo's inner independence. In any case, I don't think I should ever undertake anything like that to uphold the relativity theory. I should reason that the truth is so much stronger than I am that any idea of mounting a Rosinante and taking up a sword to defend it would seem ridiculously Quixotic."[1]

A host of thoughts can be found in this letter. There is the rationalist conviction of the omnipotence of truth, which triumphs because of its inner perfection and agreement with

[1] C. Seelig, op. cit., S. 210.

facts. It opposes the truth to the "paltry interests of the shallow-minded populace"—an expression of Einstein's resistance to antagonistic interests affecting science and the uncertainty of positive social ideals. The main point, however, is the dissociation of social struggle from scientific exploit. Einstein wrote his letter at the very height of his struggle against war and reaction. But this struggle, though linked with his rationalist outlook, with his ideal of a cosmic harmony and aversion for the "demon of irrationality", was not a struggle for a scientific outlook. Einstein knew that social justice had to be fought for, but scientific justice, as he saw it, did not need this.

That is why Kepler's complete devotion to research and his contemplation of the truth was more akin to Einstein than Galileo's fiery social temperament. Einstein's characteristic of Kepler's ideas and personality is permeated with a feeling of profound congeniality. He had read Kepler's letters and they impressed him so much as the classical works embodying the laws of planetary motion.

"In Kepler's letters," he writes, "we find ourselves confronted with a sensitive personality, passionately devoted to the quest for deeper insight into the character of natural processes—a man who reached the exalted goal he set himself, in spite of all internal and external difficulties."[1]

Kepler's lofty goal of a causal picture of the universe was the first step towards the "classical ideal". What were the external and internal difficulties he had to overcome?

The external difficulties were due to the incompatibility of a causal explanation of the world with the dominant view. The effect of these difficulties on Kepler and Galileo was markedly different, the former inclining neither towards ideological compromise nor towards ideological struggle.

"He refused," Einstein writes, "to be paralysed or discouraged either by poverty or by the lack of comprehension among those of his contemporaries who had the power to shape his life and work. Yet he was dealing with a subject that offered immediate danger to him who professed the truth. But Kepler was one of the few who are simply incapable of doing anything but stand up openly for their

[1] *Ideas and Opinions*, p. 224.

convictions in every field. At the same time he was not one who took undiluted pleasure in personal controversy, as was plainly the case with Galileo, whose inspired barbs delight the informed reader even today. Kepler was a devout Protestant, but he made no secret of the fact that he did not approve of all the decisions by the Church. He was, accordingly, regarded as a kind of moderate heretic and treated as such."[1]

The lack of a militant social temperament not only prevented Kepler from fighting actively for the recognition of new scientific ideas. It also kept Kepler himself prisoner of some ideas essentially hostile to a causal picture of the world. Thus external difficulties turned into internal difficulties. These were largely overcome. "Kepler's lifework was possible only once he succeeded in freeing himself to a great extent of the intellectual traditions to which he was born. This meant not merely the religious tradition, based on the authority of the Church, but the general concepts on the nature and limitations of action within the universe and the human sphere, as well as notions of the relative importance of thought and experience in science."

Einstein says that Kepler had to rid himself of the animist approach in research and of reference to concepts lying beyond the scientific world picture. He also "had to recognise that even the most lucidly logical mathematical theory was of itself no guarantee of the truth, becoming meaningless unless it was checked against the most exacting observations in natural science. But for this philosophical orientation Kepler's work would not have been possible. He does not speak of it, but the inner struggle is reflected in his letters. Let the reader watch out for remarks concerning astrology."[2]

Kepler's mystical ideas were an inner brake on his work. Einstein could sympathise with Kepler's retreat from the field of social struggle for new scientific ideas (though not at the cost of compromise!), but unlike Galileo, Kepler had his internal difficulties which prevented him from achieving a purely causal understanding of the world harmony. Although disagreeing with Galileo's kind of activity in the

---

[1] *Ideas and Opinions*, pp. 225-26.
[2] Ibid., p. 226.

sphere of ideological conflict, Einstein realised its importance. Characteristic of Einstein was Kepler's immersion into an internal world of his own and inability to compromise, as well as Galileo's complete (much more complete than Kepler's) internal freedom from anything standing in the way of a causal understanding of the world harmony.

Once again I must use the musical term "harmony" in connection with Einstein: indeed, Einstein himself speaks of "the highest form of musicality" in connection with Bohr's work, and this characteristic applies to himself more than to anyone else. A realisation of the world harmony, dreams of social harmony, the harmony of a city's architectural forms, and of course, harmony in the direct sense of the word, the harmony of sounds—in this respect Prague had everything needed to appeal to a man of Einstein's type. The solemn sounds of the organ in Catholic cathedrals, the chorales in Protestant churches, the mournful Jewish melodies, the resonant Hussite hymns, folk music, and the works of Czech, Russian and German composers, all appealed to Einstein.

There were several outstanding personalities among the mass of professorial mediocrities in Prague. It was to the former that Einstein was drawn, and he cultivated an environment which catered for his scientific, intellectual and musical tastes.

Among his closest colleagues was a mathematician named George Pick. Their friendship was stimulated by Pick's interest in physical problems which he had retained since the days when, as a young man, he had been an assistant of Ernst Mach's, then a professor of experimental physics. Like Lampa, the fifty-year-old professor was a follower of Mach, and Einstein found in him an indefatigable opponent in philosophical arguments. In addition, Einstein at the time happened to be beset by considerable difficulties concerning the mathematical apparatus of the general theory of relativity, and he found it stimulating to discuss mathematical problems with Pick. It was Pick who made the suggestion that the works of the Italian mathematicians Ricci and Levi-Cività might prove of use in application to Einstein's theory. Pick was also a good violinist and through him Einstein became acquainted with a group of music-lovers with whom he took part in regular musical evenings. Pick died in a nazi death camp during the German occupation of Czechoslovakia.

Another home which Einstein frequently visited was that of Maurice Winternitz, a professor of ancient history and an expert in Sanskrit. The difference in their professional interests did not prevent them from having lively discussions on general and literary subjects. Einstein was devoted to Winternitz's jolly flock of five children, with whom he became great friends. Very often Einstein would bring his violin, and Winternitz's sister-in-law, a music teacher, would accompany him on the piano. She was very exacting, and Einstein often remarked that she was like a strict army sergeant.

Einstein's simple manners, kindness, amiability and usually inoffensive humour gained him many friends. Strange as it may seem, though, these qualities also earned him some enemies. Absence of academic vanity was taken as disrespect toward academic titles, and it shocked the Philistines within and outside the university. Einstein's plain informal suit was regarded as a sign of rebellion against academic respectability. Philipp Frank relates a rather humorous story of Einstein's university uniform.[1] An Austrian professor was required to wear his uniform, which consisted of a three-cornered hat trimmed with feathers, a coat and trousers ornamented with broad gold bands, a very warm overcoat of thick black cloth and a sword, only when taking the oath of allegiance before assuming his duties or when he had an audience with the Emperor of Austria. The uniform passed on to Frank when he replaced Einstein as professor in Prague. Frank's wife gave the coat to a former Cossack general who had fled from Russia. The rest of the uniform, including the sword, remained in the university until the nazis invaded Czechoslovakia in 1939 when the sword probably became the booty of a nazi soldier.

Some people were irritated by Einstein's kindness and sociability, which extended equally to persons of different social strata. The university snobs could not forgive Einstein for talking in the same cordial manner with the leading officials of the university and the charwoman in the laboratory. But it was his humour which most of his enemies resented. Firstly, it was not always inoffensive. Secondly,

[1] Ph. Frank, op. cit., p. 125.

any joke going beyond the standard professorial witticisms was viewed with suspicion by the zealous guardians of the ridiculous primness and swank which Lenin called (in an entirely different connection) by the French word of *pruderie*.

In 1911, Einstein travelled to Brussels to take part in his first Solvay Congress. Ernest Solvay, a poor scientist, good engineer and rich Belgian businessman, had the idea of reporting some obscure physical theories of his to a conclave of leading world physicists. As an owner of several large chemical works and a patron of science, he was in social contact with the prominent German chemist and physicist Walter Nernst. They decided between the two of them to call a conference of leading physicists in Brussels to discuss outstanding problems, exchange views on scientific advances and critically review controversial issues. Nernst drew up a list of the scientists to be invited and Solvay defrayed the costs of the conference, which included the travelling expenses of the participants to Brussels, the living expenses there and, in addition, a remuneration of a thousand francs to each conferee.

Only a small number of scientists took part in the Solvay Congress in 1911, among them Sir Ernest Rutherford of England, Marie Sklodowska-Curie, Henri Poincaré, Jean Perrin and Paul Langevin of France, Max Planck and Walter Nernst of Germany, H. A. Lorentz of Holland, and Einstein and Franz Hasenöhrl from Austria. Solvay's opening address, in which he presented a summary of his theory, did not take too much time. Fortunately, Solvay accepted the fact that he was no genius with good grace, and he subsequently sponsored several similar conferences which for many years represented the most important regular international gatherings of physicists.

Relativity was a subject of lively discussion at the 1911 Solvay Congress. In a letter to his friend, Dr. Heinrich Zangger in Zurich, Einstein wrote that the essence of relativity had not been understood. He thought in particular that Poincaré, in spite of his cleverly contrived constructions, had a poor realisation of the state of affairs in physics.

Nevertheless Einstein was deeply impressed by the congress. In his letter to Zangger he speaks with special warmth of Lorentz. "Lorentz," he wrote, "is a miracle of intellect and tact. A living work of art! In my view he is the most intelligent of all the theoreticians present."[1]

Subsequently, in 1928, in his address at Lorentz's grave, Einstein spoke of him in similar terms: "He shaped his life like an exquisite work of art down to the smallest detail. His never-failing kindness and generosity and his sense of justice, coupled with a sure and intuitive understanding of people and human affairs, made him a leader in any sphere he entered. Everyone followed him gladly, for they felt that he never set out to dominate but only to serve."[2]

Like Einstein, Lorentz was devoted to the "extra-personal". When new discoveries overthrew classical physics, Lorentz remarked that he regretted that he had not died before the old bulwarks had fallen. This was not just an obituary to classical physics. Lorentz's regret for past values was not quite so deep and it was undoubtedly followed by an acceptance of the new ideas. It is interesting to note the emotional depth of the impressions gained in an analysis of the history of science. A man to whom science was to such an extent the basis of his attitude towards life was truly a remarkable person.

Einstein's attitude towards science was also deeply emotional, but if he were asked whether scientific upheavals ever made him think of the meaning of life and death he would probably have answered that such thoughts never even entered his head. This, at least, is the purport of his replies to similar questions. With Einstein the "extra-personal" not only filled the whole of his being; it made his thoughts soar up to heights from which his own life and death became of no significance at all.

A year after the Solvay Congress Einstein left Prague and returned to Zurich, where he was offered the chair of theoretical physics at the Polytechnic from which he had graduated twelve years before. The Polytechnic, a federal educational establishment, was incomparably superior in scientific level to the University of Zurich, a cantonal institution. Thanks to the efforts of the Swiss Federal Government, the Polytechnic had become one of Europe's leading institutes of higher learning with high standards of instruction in

[1] *Helle Zeit*, S. 43.
[2] *Ideas and Opinions*, p. 73

physical and mathematical subjects. Material independence, an independent chair and the good memories of Zurich may not have been decisive considerations for Einstein, but they were for Mileva, who had been hankering after Zurich for some time.

On leaving Prague Einstein forgot to tender his official resignation to the authorities in Vienna, a cause of concern to the officials of the Ministry of Education. When several years later Einstein heard of this he hastened to carry out the prescribed requirements.

Einstein's arrival in Zurich was impatiently awaited in more quarters than the Polytechnic. Old friends and especially Marcel Grossmann were eagerly looking forward to a reunion. Einstein, too, wanted to meet his old friend whose help he continued to seek. The two friends recalled how, more than twelve years ago, Grossmann had rid Einstein of the necessity to attend lectures in mathematics. Now Einstein was reaping the fruits of this negligence which began to worry him considerably. He now knew the departments of mathematics which he needed most. They were concerned with the curvature of lines and surfaces. In Prague, Pick had suggested the geometrical concepts which could help Einstein to overcome the difficulties he might encounter in the further elaboration of the relativity theory. These suggestions, however, were inadequate. It was necessary to apply concepts of curvature not only to lines and surfaces, but also to three-dimensional space and four-dimensional space-time. Although some of the physical problems involved suggested the possible choice of mathematical methods, it was necessary, in addition to depth and clarity of geometrical perception, to have a comprehensive and systematic mathematical training.

Grossmann and Einstein discussed at length the mathematical methods suited for solving the new physical problems. Then Grossmann alone would go into the mathematical details. As in their student days, their work was punctuated with arguments concerning the relative importance of physics and mathematics. This time Grossmann enjoyed the fruits of "revenge". The time had apparently come for the application of mathematical departments in physics which had originally been developed only to accommodate and substantiate the "working" departments of mathematics. Now any mathematical department, no matter how remote at first glance, could at any moment be expected to become a "working" department, and any restriction to departments already accepted in physics could leave a researcher without the tools necessary for developing new physical theories.

Einstein's discussions with Grossmann reflected the important changes that had taken place in the relationship between mathematics and physics. As we know, in the evolution of mathematics Einstein distinguished the period when it was regarded as a semi-empirical science and the subsequent period when it became independent of physics and thus created the illusion of the *a priori* or conventional origin of mathematical propositions. In the third period, mathematics, without reverting in any way to primitive empirical notions, became associated with physical experiments designed to answer the question of the reality of mathematical constructions. The physical meaning of this will be clear when we get to the general theory of relativity, in which physical processes in space and time are treated as changes in the geometrical properties of space and time. These were the problems which Einstein and Grossmann discussed in Zurich.

Einstein lectured at the Zurich Polytechnic during the 1912-1913 winter semester (analytical mathematics and thermodynamics), the 1913 summer semester (mechanics of continuums and kinetic theory of heat), and the 1913-1914 winter semester (electricity and magnetism, geometrical optics). He also conducted weekly physical colloquiums. Max von Laue, who came to Zurich in 1912 to take up a position as professor "extraordinary", describes them as follows:

"Einstein conducted a weekly colloquium at which new works in physics were reported. Although they were held at the Polytechnic, many lecturers and students from the university attended.... After the colloquium Einstein would go, with anyone who cared to join him, to have dinner at the Kronenhaller restaurant.... One of the main topics for discussion was the relativity theory.... The most lively discussions took place in the summer of 1913, when the temperamental Paul Ehrenfest came to Zurich. I can still see

Einstein and Ehrenfest amidst a crowd of physicists clambering up the Zurichberg and I can hear Ehrenfest's triumphant cry: 'Now I get it!' "[1]

Einstein's friendship with Ehrenfest, which lasted for twenty years, until the latter's tragic death in 1933, was highly beneficial to Einstein. Ehrenfest belonged to a generation rich in talented theoreticians. He was an eminent physicist and a man of great modesty, tact and kindness. He was one of Einstein's closest friends, probably the closest among the physicists of Europe.

In the autumn of 1913, Einstein attended a scientific congress in Vienna, where he presented a popular outline of the general theory of relativity. The theory was not yet complete, and Einstein set forth only the most general considerations. These can be presented here in anticipation of a more detailed acquaintance with the purport of general relativity.

In Vienna Einstein spoke of his theory as of a new theory of gravitation. He compared gravitational theory with the development of the theory of electricity. In the 18th century, the only known thing about electricity was that it existed as charges which attracted or repelled one another with a force varying inversely as the square of the distance between them. Our present knowledge of gravitation goes essentially no further and all we know is the law of attraction of corporeal bodies. Yet in the course of 150 years the science of electricity advanced to the concepts of electromagnetic field and electromagnetic oscillations. Evidently the time has come to develop similarly more complex conceptions in the theory of gravitation. Einstein's proposition was to treat gravity as a kind of characteristic of space, a geometrical property of space.

Einstein took the opportunity of his stay in Vienna to meet Ernst Mach who, aged 75 and suffering from severe paralysis, lived in a suburb of the city. On entering the room Einstein saw a man with a grey, unkempt beard and a half-good-natured, half-cunning look on his face, whom Frank describes as looking like a Slav peasant.[2] Einstein recalled his conver-

---

[1] C. Seelig, op. cit., S. 132.
[2] Ph. Frank, op. cit., p. 131.

sation with Mach in an interview with Bernard Cohen.[1] One of the main subjects they discussed was the existence of molecules and atoms.

Later on, after discussing general relativity, we will be in a position to grasp more fully the intense intellectual activity which must have filled the years when it was in the making. All those years people meeting Einstein came away with the impression of a continuously occupied mind, which persisted in working even during friendly chats and at the family table. Also in that period, Einstein's family life was approaching its inevitable finale as his estrangement with Mileva continued to grow.

[1] B. Cohen, "An Interview with Einstein", *Scientific American*, Vol. 193, No. 1, July 1955, pp. 69-73.

Chapter 17

BERLIN

I am speaking of my predilection for lasting tranquility and silent meditation, my passionate, intrinsic love for peace and for occupations which have nothing in common with war.

Numa Pompilius
(Plutarch. "Parallel Lives")

The revolution in science and technology caused by electricity was in many ways a forerunner of the atomic revolution which took place half a century later. The beginning of the 20th century was marked by the emergence of new branches of industrial engineering, such as radio and X-ray engineering, the manufacture of electrical vacuum tubes for transforming current, etc., in which physical experiment was an essential part of the production process. The big electrical engineering firms were the first to see the advantages of setting up physical laboratories which would be free to engage in research without necessarily stipulating in advance the possible applications of its results. In fact, the unexpected results were frequently more exciting and more important than the planned ones. Any restriction to strictly planned tasks could close the way to discoveries based on new principles. It was considerations such as these which guided the General Electric Company, for example, when they invited the celebrated electrophysicist Charles Steinmetz to head their laboratories with the right to do what he pleased, the sole condition being that all anticipated and unanticipated results of his work remain within the company. More and more new institutes appeared in which theoretical research yielded new principles of technological progress. Depending on conditions and traditions, these institutes were based on university departments, laboratories of higher technical schools, divisions of scientific academies and societies or, in the United States, private laboratories.

Governments invested and encouraged investment in research establishments whose theoretical investigations were expected to yield indubitable, but unpredictable, practical results. The German Empire, bent on depriving Great Britain of her lead in science, technology and industry and on developing a "mailed fist" strong enough to embark on a recarving of markets, raw material sources and spheres of investment, saw in theoretical science a real force in the fight for industrial and military supremacy.

The financial oligarchy responded favourably to the German Emperor's intention to inaugurate a society and institute, to be named after their royal sponsor. The Kaiser Wilhelm Gesellschaft was to consist of bankers and industrialists united in helping to build research institutes. The members received the title of "senator" and the right to wear a handsome gown, and occasionally they were invited to breakfast with the Emperor. Who of his loyal subjects could resist the prospect?

The Kaiser Wilhelm Institute was envisaged as being made up of the most eminent scientists, highly paid, with no pedagogical obligations and the right to engage in any individual researches. It was assumed, not unreasonably, that the results of such investigations would be important indeed. The task of recruiting the scientists for the institute was undertaken by Max Planck and Walter Nernst.

Max Planck, the great creator of the theory of quanta, a physicist of tremendous scientific scope and keen intuition, was not only the first to appreciate the inner harmony and beauty of the theory of relativity. He realised or felt (it is hard to say whether he was guided more by logic or intuition) that for many years to come Einstein's theory would determine the main roads of physical research, which would lead to as yet unpredictable but undoubtedly valuable results in all spheres of science and culture. In academic circles Planck's scientific and moral authority was incontestable. Einstein greatly admired this tall, slim, somewhat stand-offish man whose romantic soul revealed itself whenever he sat down to play the piano or to write one of his fine papers which invariably displayed a genuinely romantic devotion to science.

Planck was respected in official circles too. His aristocratic background, belief in convention, reserved manners and soldierly bearing appealed to the military-bureaucratic society.

Walter Nernst, on the other hand, was the darling of the bourgeoisie. One of the most eminent 20th-century chemists, he was an extremely active and energetic man, a born organiser and, at the same time, a deep and original thinker.

Planck and Nernst came to Einstein personally with the following offer: Einstein was to become the director of a research institute for physics and a member of the Prussian Academy of Science. He would be made a professor of the Berlin University with a minimal burden of lectures, which he himself would plan. He would be unencumbered by obligations and free to investigate the problems of his choice, as well as to take part in the work of any other institutes and societies.

Einstein realised that acceptance of the offer would enable him to devote himself completely to his work on the generalisation of the relativity theory. Moreover, as Planck and Nernst pointed out, there were many leading physicists and mathematicians in Berlin with whom Einstein could come into contact. When Einstein remarked that, in Langevin's view, there were only twelve persons in the world who really understood relativity, Nernst responded that eight of them lived in Berlin. Still, Einstein hesitated. He did not like the idea of leaving the tolerant, easy-going environment of Zurich and coming into contact with the militant, snobbish officialdom of Germany. This, he knew, was inevitable in spite of the haven provided by the academic community.

The conversation ended in a tentative agreement. Einstein asked for a little more time to think the matter over. They agreed that Planck and Nernst would come again to Zurich for the final answer. True to himself, even now Einstein could not resist the temptation of playing a little game: if he came to meet them with a bunch of red flowers it would mean that he accepted the offer; white flowers would signify rejection.

When the two men arrived at the station again Einstein was there to meet them with a bunch of red flowers.

Mileva remained in Zurich. Separation was imminent, and when Einstein left for Berlin he went alone.

In Berlin the main form of Einstein's scientific contacts with the new community was a weekly physical seminar which was held regularly until his departure from Germany. Many of the participants in the seminar soon became his friends. Besides Nernst and Planck, there was Max von Laue, who in 1912 discovered, together with his collaborators, the diffraction of X-rays in crystals, one of the experimental cornerstones in the foundations of the new conceptions of the structure of matter. Laue was also the author of many theoretical works, among them a penetrating exposition of relativity theory. The seminar was also attended by such celebrated physicists as Gustav Hertz, James Franck, and Erwin Schrödinger whose fame was still to come (we shall meet with his name shortly in connection with the foundation of quantum mechanics during the years 1924-1926). At one period the seminar was attended by Lise Meitner, who gained world fame in the late 1930s in connection with the discovery of uranium fission.

All the former participants in the seminar speak of it in glowing terms, and the figure of Einstein is prominent in their recollections. This is due not only to the depth and clarity of his remarks. His unaffected, sincere manner, the ease with which he grasped his colleagues' ideas (truly the mark of a genius) endowed the gatherings with a lustrous brilliancy. On the other hand, the new academician hardly ever attended official meetings, including meetings of the Prussian Academy. He often ridiculed the academic meetings (and here his humour would lose its usual inoffensiveness) at which members dozed off trying to maintain a respectable and dignified air, while discussion was in progress of specialised and often trivial subjects, and where problems far removed from science could suddenly evoke spirited speeches on the part of men whose debts to science by far exceeded their contributions.

Einstein regarded the requirements of professorial etiquette as a great nuisance. In May 1914, he wrote to Adolf Hurwitz in Zurich: "Contrary to expectations, life here is not so bad; what disturbs my equanimity is that I am being drilled in all kinds of nonsense, such as the clothes I should wear so that some person or other would not think that I come from the dregs of society."[1].

---

[1] C. Seelig, op. cit., S. 247.

The early period of Einstein's life in Berlin was marked by the acquisition of new friends; at the same time he did not notice his enemies. His mind was occupied with the problems of the relativity of accelerated motions, gravitation, and the dependence of the geometrical properties of space on spatial events. He never stopped thinking of them.

Philipp Frank recalls a visit he once paid to Einstein during which they decided to visit the Astrophysical Observatory at Potsdam together. They agreed to meet on a bridge in Potsdam, but Frank, who had much to do in Berlin, said he was afraid he might be a little late. "Oh," said Einstein, "that makes no difference; I will wait on the bridge." Frank suggested that that might waste too much of Einstein's time. "Oh no," was the rejoinder, "the kind of work I do can be done anywhere. Why should I be less capable of reflecting about my problems on the Potsdam bridge than at home?" His thoughts, Frank goes on, flowed like a constant stream. Every conversation that interrupted his thinking was like a small stone thrown into a mighty river, unable to influence its course.[1] This explains why the constant and extremely intense work of Einstein's mind never prevented his natural amicability from manifesting itself.

Einstein's readiness to discuss scientific problems with others sometimes resulted in embarrassing situations. On one occasion he heard that one of his Berlin colleagues, Professor Stumpf, a well-known physiologist, was interested in problems of space perception. Einstein thought that he could take the opportunity of making a formal visit to discuss matters of mutual interest. On the chance of finding the professor at home he called in the morning. When he arrived the maid told him that the *Herr Geheimrat* was not at home and asked whether Einstein would like to leave a message. He said he would come back later in the day, in the meantime, he would take a walk in the park. When he came back at two in the afternoon the maid informed him that the *Herr Geheimrat* was taking his afternoon nap after lunch, since she had not told him that Einstein would call again. "Never mind," said Einstein, "I'll come back later." When he came back at four he was finally able to see the *Herr Geheimrat*. "You see," Einstein said to the maid, "in the end patience and persever-

---

[1] Ph. Frank, op. cit., pp. 147-48.

ance are always rewarded." The Stumpfs were happy to see the famous Einstein and assumed the conversation would be that befitting a formal introductory visit. Einstein, however, launched on the problem of space. Poor Stumpf, who had no extensive physical or mathematical knowledge, understood little of the discussion and was hardly able to wedge in a word. After Einstein had talked for about forty minutes he suddenly realised that he was actually talking to himself and that his call had lasted too long. With a perfunctory farewell he hastily departed.

Such incidents, of course, in no way disturbed Einstein's peace of mind. He was used to a certain lack of interest or understanding, even in his own professional environment. The people who really disturbed him were those who seemed specially brought up to carry out all and any designs of an aggressive state, the bearers of the "Prussian spirit" whom he remembered so well from his boyhood days in Munich. "These cool blond people," he once said, "make me feel uneasy; they have no psychological comprehension of others. Everything must be explained to them very explicitly." Events were rapidly moving in the direction which would bring the "cool blond people" to the fore. Less than a year after Einstein had taken up his residence in Berlin the First World War broke out.

In "The World as I See It" Einstein expressed his attitude towards war and militarism: "That a man can take pleasure in marching in fours to the strains of a band is enough to make me despise him. He has only been given his big brain by mistake; unprotected spinal marrow was all he needed. This plague-spot of civilisation ought to be abolished with all possible speed. Heroism by order, senseless violence, and all the loathsome nonsense that goes by the name of patriotism—how passionately I hate them! How vile and despicable seems war to me! I would rather be hacked in pieces than take part in such an abominable business. My opinion of the human race is high enough that I believe this bogey would have disappeared long ago, had the sound sense of the peoples not been systematically corrupted by commercial and political interests acting through the schools and the press."[1]

[1] *Ideas and Opinions*, pp. 10-11.

197

In July 1914, troops began marching through the streets of Berlin and crowds of enthusiastic idolisers of the Kaiser and the Reichswehr lined the pavements.

The adherents of revolutionary internationalism went underground. To Einstein it was an awful nightmare. He suddenly discovered that the academic environment was poisoned with a savage jingoism. Peaceful, inoffensive burghers with a sincere respect for world culture now suddenly took delight in martial music and calls for the annihilation of Russia, France and England, and eagerly exchanged news about the deaths of thousands of people. Vicious bigoted articles and pamphlets proclaiming the historic mission of Germany replaced Lessing and Schiller on their desks. Ostwald spoke of the subordination of Europe to the Hohenzollern empire as of the greatest task in history and signed a manifesto of German intellectuals, which was imbued with some of the worst features of German nationalism. Others, Planck among them, were utterly at a loss and could only incoherently mutter about Germany's "legitimate demands". Einstein was no longer able to maintain his free and cordial relations with his colleagues. But neither could he retreat into his shell and devote himself solely to physical problems. With the exception of a few close friends, he knew of no one who shared his ideals and his loyalty to freedom and international solidarity. The work of revolutionary groups opposing the imperialist war was remote from Einstein, but he soon got in touch with people who shared his views. These were Romain Rolland, the French author, and a group of scientists and writers who gathered about him.

In March 1915, Einstein wrote Rolland a letter in which he placed himself at the disposal of Rolland's anti-war organisation. After three centuries of intense cultural work in Europe, Einstein wrote, religious madness had been replaced by national madness. Some scientists, he said, were behaving as if they had had their brains removed. As a true exponent of rationalism, Einstein viewed the subjection of reason to animal instincts in so many scientists as a great tragedy of European intellectuals.

In the autumn of 1915, Einstein managed to reach Switzerland, where Mileva lived with the boys, whom he wanted to see so much. In Switzerland Einstein visited Romain

Rolland at Vevay, who told him that groups of opponents of war were active in all the belligerent nations. Rolland created a great impression on Einstein and he began to feel himself a member of an international community standing opposed to the evils of extreme nationalism. In Germany, too, Einstein found such men of like mind.

Meanwhile the war went on and the nationalistic passions continued to poison the scientific community. There was, for example, a circular from a group of German physicists in which they urged their colleagues not to quote the works of English physicists. They asserted that German science was especially profound and thorough in contrast to the superficial character of theories enunciated by Englishmen and Frenchmen. Such nationalistic excesses drove Einstein to seek the company of people whose reason and conscience had not been so perverted. He began to frequent the home of Rudolf Einstein, his second uncle, who lived in Berlin with his daughter Elsa, Albert's childhood friend. Elsa had come to Berlin with her two daughters after separating from her husband. She was an attractive woman, mild of manner, possessing a good sense of humour and many other traits and habits in common with Einstein. Later, after receiving his divorce in 1919, Einstein married Elsa.

In 1917 historical events confronted many scientists with problems which they had never faced before: with whom did they stand, what was their attitude towards the newly emerged social system, what kind of a picture had they in mind of the future of humanity?

A political stratification was taking place among the intellectuals of Europe, the times called for a clear definition of one's position. Einstein hailed the October Revolution in Russia as the beginning of a society based on reason and science. He characterised Lenin as a man "who completely sacrificed himself and devoted all his energies to the realisation of social justice. ... Men of his type are the guardians and restorers of the conscience of mankind."[1]

[1] C. Seelig, op. cit., S. 319.

Chapter 18

THE GENERAL THEORY
OF RELATIVITY

In 1919, Einstein's nine-year-old son Edward asked him: "Daddy, why are you so famous?" Einstein laughed and then explained quite seriously: "You see, son, when a blind bug crawls along the surface of a sphere it doesn't notice that its path is curved. I was fortunate enough to notice this."

After the appearance of the special theory of relativity, the principal purpose of Einstein's life lay in his search for a more general theory. As we have seen, Einstein regarded as artificial the preference given to systems moving uniformly in a straight line over other systems. In reference systems in uniform, rectilinear motion mechanical processes take place always in the same way and do not depend on the system's motion, on the other hand, in systems moving with acceleration mechanical processes take place differently, depending on the acceleration. Acceleration gives rise to inertia forces which cannot be explained in terms of force interactions and which indicate that the system is in motion, thus making such motion absolute in character. For this reason the Galileo-Newton relativity principle is applicable only to systems moving uniformly in a straight line.

The special theory of relativity asserts that in inertial systems all physical processes take place in the same way. This statement, we see, remains restricted to inertial systems. Acceleration disturbs the uniform flow of processes, thus demonstrating its absolute nature. Is it possible to visualise events in accelerated systems which would not violate the principle of relativity, i.e., would not provide any absolute criteria of motion? Can the relativity principle, which holds good for all inertial systems, be extended to accelerated systems?

A positive answer was suggested by a law, known since the 17th century.

All bodies possess inertia, and they all resist the action of fields of force. The measure of this resistance is a body's inertial mass. Furthermore, all bodies are responsive, as it were, to fields of force. For instance, electrically charged bodies are responsive to electric fields, and the electrical forces of attraction and repulsion act on them in various degrees. The measure of this "responsiveness" is the body's charge. In the case of electrical forces, bodies possess "responsiveness", i.e., charge, which is not dependent on their mass. A body may have large mass and small electric charge, and vice versa. In fact, a body possessing mass need not possess any electric charge at all.

There exist fields, however, in relation to which a body's "responsiveness" is always proportional to its mass. These are gravitational fields. All physical bodies are subject to the gravitational attraction of other bodies. In all cases a body's "response" to a gravitational field (its "gravitational charge" or "gravitational mass") is proportional to the body's resistance to the field, that is to say, to its inertial mass. The more massive a body, the more difficult it is to change its velocity; but the greater its inertial mass, the heavier it is, and the more it tends to gravitate towards other bodies. As a result all bodies, regardless of their inertial mass, experience the same acceleration in a given gravitational field, and near the surface of the earth they fall from the same height with the same speed (neglecting the resistance of the atmosphere).

When a system of bodies is being accelerated, the bodies resist the acceleration in proportion to their inertial masses. This resistance manifests itself in a pressure in the opposite direction of the acceleration. This pressure, or acceleration in the opposite direction of the motion, is felt by the passengers of a train when it is gathering speed. It is ascribed to *inertia forces*, which are proportional to a body's inertial mass. Acceleration caused by a gravitational field is proportional to the gravitational mass. Insofar as the two masses are proportional, we are unable to determine what has caused the observed accelerations of the bodies in our system: the acceleration of the system or a field of gravity.

Einstein illustrated the equivalence of the forces involved by comparing phenomena as observed in a lift when it is moving with acceleration in the absence of a gravitational field and when it is at rest in such a field. The lift is the counterpart of Newton's bucket introduced to demonstrate the absolute nature of acceleration.

Imagine, Einstein says, that a lift is hanging motionless in a gravitational field, the earth's, for example. A man inside feels his weight pressing against the soles of his feet and ascribes it to gravity. Now suppose the gravitational forces have disappeared and the lift is accelerating in the opposite direction of their pull. What happens? Why, nothing, so far as the man in the lift is concerned. The inertia forces of acceleration will keep his feet solidly on the floor, they will stretch a string supporting a load, etc. The man has no way of determining whether these effects are actually due to acceleration or to gravity. This is Einstein's *principle of the equivalence of acceleration and gravitation.* It follows that, since the effects of acceleration and gravitation are in no way distinguishable, there is no absolute criterion of accelerated motion.

For special relativity to be extended to accelerated motions it was necessary to show that not only the dynamic effects of motion but optical phenomena as well could be explained in terms of gravitation. Imagine that in our lift there is a hole in one of its walls. If the lift is moving with acceleration, a beam of light shining through the hole will not strike the opposite wall at the same height from the floor and will seem to bend towards the floor (since by the time it reaches the opposite wall the lift will have travelled some distance).

If the cabin is motionless in a gravitational field the beam of light is apparently not affected, it will strike the wall exactly opposite the hole, demonstrating the difference between the physical effects of acceleration and gravitation, and hence the absolute nature of acceleration.

This would indeed be the case if light were weightless. But light moves and therefore possesses mass of motion, which is attracted by the gravitational field. It follows, therefore, that light suffers an acceleration under the action of gravitational forces. This is contrary to one of the basic assumptions of special relativity. Einstein accepted this conclusion, and he restricted special relativity (and the principle of the constancy of the velocity of light) to domains in which gravitational forces could be neglected. The principle of relativity, though, could now be extended to all moving systems. The conclusion that light has "weight" (mass in motion) and the consequent bending of light rays in gravitational fields could be, and as we shall shortly see, was verified by direct observation.

A point of interest at this juncture is the correlation between the "external confirmation" and "inner perfection" of the general theory of relativity. The basic propositions of the theory were derived from the very general premise of the proportionality of inertial and gravitational mass. In classical mechanics this proportionality was an inexplicable property of gravitational fields. It is not observed in other fields, electrical, for instance. General relativity brought this proportionality within a system of interrelated laws, into a unified causal scheme of the universe. Thus the world picture approached closer to "inner perfection". Another contribution to its "inner perfection" was the removal of the restriction of relativity to inertial systems, which seemed arbitrary from the point of view of the "classical ideal".

The external confirmation was found, first theoretically and later experimentally, in the new fact of the bending of light rays. Thus the principle of relativity was extended to include accelerated systems. In other words, the generalisation affected not the classical relativity principle but Einstein's 1905 theory, and the paradoxical space-time relationships were extended to all types of motion.

The relativity of accelerated motion in large spatial domains does not derive from the principle of equivalence taken by itself. Take our two lifts, for instance. Imagine two weights hanging on strings from the ceiling of the first cabin. The forces of gravity are directed towards the centre of the earth and intersect there; hence, strictly speaking, the strings are not parallel. But in the accelerated lift we would find that the inertial forces pull the two strings strictly parallel. In small cabins the difference is imperceptible, yet it is sufficient to challenge the equivalence of gravity and acceleration in large spatial domains.

Einstein overcame this difficulty by identifying gravitation with space-time curvature. Imagine a coordinate system in which the path traversed by a body is directed along one axis, and the passage of time along the other. If the body is moving under no forces its motion on such a space-time plot will be identified by a straight line; if it is moving with acceleration the plot will be a curved line. If the world lines of all bodies, including light quanta, are curved in a field of gravity, if *all* world lines are curved, then we can speak of the curvature of space-time as a whole.

The meaning of this can be grasped from a consideration of the curvature of two-dimensional space, a surface, that is; suppose we draw several triangles on a plane and measure the sum of their angles. We find that in one region the sum is not equal to two right angles and it occurs to us then that space has probably ceased to be Euclidean. This can be visualised by imagining the surface to be warped. It is not so easy to picture to oneself the curvature of three-dimensional space or four-dimensional space-time. This is best done by picturing space-time curvature as the bending of all world lines. Since gravitation bends all four-dimensional world lines without exception, we can regard gravitation as representing the curvature of space-time. This is just what Einstein's theory of general relativity does, and to determine the force of gravity acting on a unit mass at a given point of space and at a given instant means to determine the curvature of space-time at that point, at that instant. If space-time is not curved in a given region (the gravitational field is infinitesimal) a particle's world line is straight, and it will be in uniform translational motion. If a gravitational field is acting (space-time is curved), the particle's world line is curved.

The general theory of relativity gives rise to a new conception of the universe, a new cosmology. Einstein regarded the gravitational fields of various bodies as the curving of space-time in the region surrounding those bodies. Bodies on the surface of the earth cause hardly any perceptible curvature. By curving space-time the earth makes the moon travel with acceleration. The warping of space-time by the sun bends the planets' world lines. In this case why not presume that space as a whole is also curved?

The conception of the general curvature of space can be illustrated by an analogy with a curved two-dimensional space, say the surface of the earth. We are well aware of local curvatures: hills, mountains, valleys. We also know of the earth's curvature as a whole, that this two-dimensional space is a spherical surface. Now consider four-dimensional space-time, i.e., the totality of world lines of all physical bodies. We know that the world lines are curved near centres of gravitation. Thus, if we undertake a journey around the universe the world line tracing our path will be bent by the gravitational fields of planets, stars, etc. A planet causes a small bent whereas a star makes a bigger one. In intergalactic regions gravity is negligible and the world line straightens out.

One interesting question emerges in this connection. If space-time is in fact curved, does this mean that in principle it is possible to travel around the four-dimensional spatio-temporal universe and return to the same world point, just as on earth? Einstein says No. For to return to a world point means that if we depart from some geographic locality at, say, the stroke of New Year, nineteen-umpty, we can circle the universe and return millions of years later to the same geographic point, and the same temporal point of New Year, nineteen-umpty. This is impossible, and a space-time curvature which would cause a world line to close in upon itself at the same world point cannot exist.

Einstein postulated that only space was curved, not time. Therefore, departing from a geographical locality in a journey along the shortest line around the universe one describes a closed *spatial* path to return to the same locality years later, in A.D. 10^9 or whenever. Hence, world space is finite (in the same sense as the two-dimensional surface of the earth is finite), but time is infinite. A two-dimensional space analogy is a surface curved and finite in one direction and straight and infinite in another, a cylinder, in fact.

If we trace the shortest line *around* a cylinder we come back to the same point. If we trace a line along the cylinder it will be straight and infinite. Proceeding from this analogy, Einstein's hypothesis of the curvature of space and the non-curvature of time was called the *cylindrical world hypothesis*.

In 1922, A. A. Friedman hypothesised that the curvature of world space changes with time. The universe, it seems, is expanding, a hypothesis which seems to be confirmed by astronomical observations.

Chapter 19

CONFIRMATION
OF THE RELATIVITY THEORY

> *Do not bodies act on light at a distance, and
> by their action bend its rays?*
>
> N e w t o n

The idea of the gravitational mass of light and the corresponding bending of a beam of light by a heavy body—in its gravitational field—is analogous to the question posed by Newton in his *Opticks* and quoted in the epigraph. The analogy, however, is purely superficial. Newton thought that diffraction could be explained by the repulsion of light by bodies, the degree of repulsion not depending on their mass. Newton's ideas concerning the corpuscular theory of light, cited in the epigraph to Chapter 11, comes close to Einstein's understanding: the photon theory was in fact a kind of revival of Newton's views. The idea of bent rays in a curved space, however, has no precedent, neither did it have any sources in direct experiment. In this respect it ranks among discoveries like Le Verrier's tracking-down of the planet Neptune and Mendeleyev's inclusion of undiscovered elements in his Periodic Table, in each case theoretical prediction preceded experimental proof. To Einstein the very existence of such discoveries was an irrefutable argument against any form of solipsism, consistent or inconsistent, including contemporary positivism.[1] The genesis of the idea of the bending of rays in a gravitational field offers a good illustration to Einstein's scheme of "inner perfection" and "external confirmation". The idea developed in approximately the following way.

Special relativity did away with the ether as an absolute body of reference, and with absolute time independent of a spatial reference system. Following the rejection of Newton's concept of instantaneous action at a distance,

---

[1] See "Reply to Criticisms", in *Philosopher-Scientist*, pp. 665-82.

another prop of absolute simultaneity also collapsed–the possibility of synchronising events taking into account the velocity of systems moving relative to the stationary ether. However, the removal of the infinite stationary ether left an infinite empty space which takes part in observable processes –accelerated motion in empty space gives rise to dynamic effects, the inertia forces. This contradicts the "classical ideal" with its world picture based only on the motions and interactions of material bodies. Einstein sought the ways and means of eliminating the absolute motion which violates the causal harmony of physical reality. One way, he found, was to do away with the coincidence of the gravitational and inertial masses of bodies, which lacked causal explanation. But following this path meant allowing for light to have gravitational mass. In his assumption that such mass existed Einstein was not guided by any specific experimental finding. He proceeded from a general idea emerging from the totality of experience. In this respect general relativity differs from special relativity, which also derived from general premises, but which had been prepared by Michelson's experiment.

This explains the different impact created by the two theories. Special relativity explained known facts, and its success depended on the "generality" and "naturalness" of its postulates as compared with earlier conceptions. The "external confirmation" of special relativity was based on a known fact which was unshakable. On the contrary, general relativity began by possessing great and indubitable "inner perfection" and the remarkable thing was the observation which gave it "external confirmation". The observation demonstrated, among other things, that rational thinking proceeding from the harmony and knowability of the world led to a trustworthy conception of reality.

Early in 1917, the celebrated British astronomer and physicist Sir Arthur Eddington suggested a way of verifying whether light possessed gravitational mass or not by direct observation. The importance of this for the furtherance of relativity theory can hardly be overestimated. Eddington was one of the most active developers and popularisers of Einstein's ideas. In this connection there is on record a rather humorous story. Once a colleague remarked to Eddington that he was one of three men who understood relativity theory. When a pained expression appeared on Eddington's face, the physicist said: "Professor Eddington, you shouldn't be embarrassed; you are too modest." "No," Eddington replied, "I am not embarrassed, I am only wondering who is the third."

Eddington possessed remarkable, some people say excessive, scientific imagination and ingenuity. In time these qualities produced the idea of astronomical observations which had a profound effect on the destinies of relativity.

If light possesses gravitational mass, i.e., weight, then upon passing a heavy body it should be deflected towards that body, just as a cannon-ball is deflected towards the earth and finally falls down. A light ray, of course, will not fall to the earth as, according to Einstein's theory of gravitation, its deflection by the earth is negligible, no more than 10 metres in one second (that is, over a path of 300,000 kilometres). When passing a heavier body the deflection is greater—27 times greater near the sun than near the earth. So if a beam of light from some remote star passes by the sun before reaching the earth it will be deflected and the image of the star on a photograph will be displaced as compared with a photograph taken when the sun is far away from that section of the sky. But few stars can be observed when the sun is in the sky, especially if they lie close to its disk. Such stars, whose rays pass close to the sun, can, however, be photographed during a solar eclipse. (It is also important that the sun be nearer to bright stars at the time of an eclipse.) When such an eclipse was due on May 29, 1919, Eddington began to prepare an expedition to regions where it would be total. It was decided to send two such expeditions, one to the island of Principe in the Gulf of Guinea, off the coast of West Africa, the other to the village of Sobral in Brazil.

When the British expedition arrived in Brazil it was greeted by a remark in a Brazilian newspaper characteristic of the first postwar years. "Instead of trying to establish a German theory," the paper wrote, "the members of the expedition, who are well acquainted with the heavens, should rather try to obtain rain for the country, which has suffered from a long drought."[1]

---

[1] Ph. Frank, op. cit., p. 170.

Rain greeted the expedition on the isle of Principe, in which Eddington himself took part. On the day of the eclipse the sky was overcast and the sun's corona was hardly visible through a cloud. No stars were seen. Shortly before the end of totality, however, the clouds cleared away and photographs of the stars near the corona were made.

Plates were compared with others taken half a year later, that is, when the sun was farther away, and a shift in the stellar images as predicted by Einstein's general theory of relativity was observed.

The sky over Sobral, Brazil, was cloudless and many photographs were taken. But when the plates were compared with control pictures the astronomers were disappointed: the results were at variance with prediction and with those of the African expedition. The reason was that the sun had heated the instruments, causing distortions in the pictures. Einstein was informed of the results of Eddington's expedition in September of the same year. Lorentz sent him a telegram saying that the theory of relativity could be considered confirmed. In a postcard to his mother Einstein wrote: "Good news today! H. A. Lorentz has cabled that an English expedition has proved the deflection of light rays near the sun." But Einstein, it seems, was more concerned with pleasing his mother. He himself was not at all worried about the conclusions of Eddington's expedition.

Soon Eddington reported the results of the expeditions at a joint session of the Royal Society and the Royal Astronomical Society of London. The session was opened by J. J. Thomson, president of the Royal Society, who said: "It is not the discovery of an outlying island but of a whole continent of new scientific ideas. It is the greatest discovery in connection with gravitation since Newton enunciated his principles."[1]

Eddington's report and the comments of other scientists made headline news all over the world. People felt that a great event had taken place in science. Words like "curvature of space", "finality of space", "bending of light rays" were on many lips, though few people really understood their meaning. J. J. Thomson himself said: "I have to confess that no one has yet succeeded in stating in clear language

[1] Ph. Frank, op. cit., p. 173.

what the theory of Einstein really is."[1] Many scientists, he persisted in stating, were themselves forced to admit their inability to express simply the actual meaning of the theory. Contrary to adage and, accordingly, to practice, failure to understand the theory was used as an argument against it. The notion of the finality of the universe aroused especially great objections.

It should be noted that the difference between the idea of the *end* of space and the *finite radius* of the closed paths of moving bodies and rays of light was not clearly understood. One American newspaper, characteristically enough, demanded that the principles of logic and ontology (i.e., the fundamental concepts of the real world) should not depend on the change in physical ideas. "This fails to explain," it wrote, "why our astronomers appear to think that logic and ontology depend on the shifting views of the astronomers. Speculative thought was highly advanced long before astronomy. A sense of proportion ought to be useful to mathematicians and physicists, but it is to be feared that British astronomers have regarded their own field as of somewhat greater consequence than it really is."[2]

This idea of scientists "regarding their field as of somewhat greater consequence than it really is" is not at all new. Dogmatists would always prefer to have the *fundamental* concepts of the universe (their so-called ontology) immune from any changes due to advances in specific fields of knowledge. Osiander in his foreword to Copernicus's book, in the 16th century, and Bellarmine, the head of the Italian Inquisition, in a letter to Galileo, in the 17th century, both cautioned astronomers to stick to the practical applications of the new astronomical ideas and to refrain from attaching ontological importance to their discoveries, not to undermine the world picture as a whole, nor to imagine that their discoveries constituted the truth. 20th-century dogmatists appealed to public opinion, "common sense", "self-evidence", etc. Public opinion, however, was far from unanimous. The layman could make nothing of space curvature, but he was inclined to blame himself rather than Einstein. The mass media, on the other hand, frequently found that it was Einstein's fault that it took

[1] Ph. Frank, op. cit., p. 174.
[2] Ibid., p. 142.

a knowledge of physics and mathematics to grasp the sweeping conclusions he had derived from the new theory of gravitation and abstract geometry, that the new ideas had not yet been popularly expounded and that the new theory called for courage and scope in scientific thinking. The partisans of "self-evidence" were especially discouraged by the apparent widespread acceptance of the new ideas. The layman who did not claim to understand relativity sensed the measure of its scope and boldness. The very fact that seemingly self-evident premises were being discussed seemed significant to him. In assessing in retrospect the wave of widespread, intense interest displayed towards the relativity theory and its creator, we find the symptoms of the sweeping changes in social thinking characteristic of our century. It is therefore worth dwelling in greater detail on this characteristic of the 1920s.

Chapter 20

FAME

Some physiologists think that when a man's brain expands his heart must contract. What a misconception! On the contrary, is not the apparent egoism of men, nurturing scientific discoveries, the destinies of peoples and laws in their hearts, the noblest of human feelings, a motherly feeling towards all people?

Balzac

Fame also demands sacrifices, and if one can speak of the pursuit of fame, Einstein's role was that of the prey, not the hunter.

Moszkowski

By the beginning of the 1920s Einstein's fame exceeded that of any living scientist. Leopold Infeld in his autobiographical novel *Quest* analyses the reasons for the remarkable growth of Einstein's fame after the 1919 expeditions which confirmed the general theory of relativity:

"It was just after the end of the war. People were weary of hatred, of killing and international intrigues. The trenches, bombs and murder had left a bitter taste. Books about war did not sell. Everyone looked for a new era of peace and wanted to forget the war. Here was something which captured the imagination: human eyes looking from an earth covered with graves and blood to the heavens covered with stars. Abstract thought carrying the human mind far away from the sad and disappointing reality. The mystery of the sun's eclipse and the penetrating power of the human mind. Romantic scenery, a strange glimpse of the eclipsed sun, an imaginary picture of bending light rays, all removed from the oppressive reality of life."[1]

[1] L. Infeld, op. cit., p. 289.

These sentiments bred a conscious or, more often, intuitive feeling of the social impact of Einstein's theory and the new physics as a whole. The heavens covered with stars did more than just carry the human mind away from the disappointment of reality. Their exploration held promise of the triumph of reason on earth, a triumph which involved more than just the expansion of knowledge about the universe. It could also mean a new way of life for all people. Science had sailed from the shores of "self-evidence", and it was bound to reach new lands. What riches lay untapped there was yet to be seen, but there could be no doubt that application of the new ideas would cause important changes in technology. Along with the vague expectation of a great expansion of man's productive forces there dwelt the more definite presentiment of the role of science itself in the struggle for its peaceful applications. Men anticipated a struggle for the peaceful applications of science against destructive applications, a struggle which was to reach its climax forty years later. They hoped that science would help to dispel the miasma of chauvinism and reaction which so often condensed into the clouds of war. The generation which so enthusiastically acclaimed the relativity theory and its confirmation had witnessed many an eruption of extreme nationalism, from the Dreyfus affair on, and it knew to what extremes it could lead. People knew that science was essentially international and inherently opposed to nationalism and war. There was, Infeld writes, "one further reason, perhaps even more important: a new event was predicted by a *German* scientist Einstein and confirmed by *English* astronomers. Scientists belonging to two warring nations had collaborated again. It seemed the beginning of a new era. The desire of people for peace was, it seems to me, the main cause of Einstein's mounting fame."[1]

One might add that many people knew of the baiting of Einstein by chauvinistic circles. This also served to attract widespread public attention to the relativity theory and its creator.

Already in those years there was another sphere of conflict, not so apparent but nevertheless important. Its philosophy was anti-intellectualism, which preached the feebleness and

[1] L. Infeld, op. cit., p. 289.

inadequacy of the human intellect as compared with mystical revelations. This philosophy had not yet erupted into the parade grounds of Nuremberg: with a decade or so to go, few people could foresee the mire into which the trickle of anti-intellectualism would yet lead.

The flames of war are quenched in an atmosphere of rational thinking and are fed by mysticism. Even without understanding relativity people felt that it represented a supreme achievement of the human intellect. One of the reasons for the enthusiastic acclaim given to the theory was its association with revolutionary social ideas. Not, of course, in the sense of its dependence on social movements. Relativity is a reflection of the objective laws of nature, and in this sense it is quite independent of the development of society. But like every scientific theory it is only an approximation to the laws of nature. The measure of this approximation, the form in which a theory is enunciated, its social and cultural impact—these are the things which characterise science as an historical process, and they must be interpreted in relation to the outstanding features of the age, however remote their bearing on the theory might seem.

When Engels reconstructed the chain of historical cause and effect from Newton's mechanics to the French revolution he dealt with hidden and remote, but nevertheless indubitable, historical links.

When 19th-century philosophers discerned the "algebra of revolution" in the ponderous dictums of the acclaimed philosopher of Prussian royalism, the connection seemed irrelevant, yet historically it was inescapable.

In the beginning of the 20th century the course of history became too fast for the connections between science and revolution to be as remote and indirect as before. Revolutions raged and the bearing of scientific theories on revolutionary ideas came out into the open. Only within highly specialised spheres could scholars come to conclusions of revolutionary importance without realising it or attracting the attention of the combatant social forces. Broad, epochal generalisations could not help having ideological connotations which, even if they were not readily apparent, were nevertheless intuitively felt by the scientists and the public at large. They were also felt by the enemies of revolution.

After Eddington's expedition one professor at Columbia University wrote:

"For some years past the entire world has been in a state of unrest, mental as well as physical. It may well be that the war, the Bolshevist uprising, are the visible objects of some deep mental disturbance. The unrest is evidenced by the desire to throw aside the well-tested methods of government in favour of radical and untried experiments. This same spirit of unrest has invaded science. There are many who would have us throw aside the well-tested theories upon which has been built the entire structure of modern scientific and mechanical development in favour of methodological speculation and fantastic dreams about the universe."[1]

Soon there began a direct attack on the relativity theory, which originated mainly in Germany. In the beginning German nationalists had hailed the new theory as a manifestation of "truly German" intellectual prowess. At the same time in Great Britain people tried to evade any connection between the theory and Germany. Should the results of the astronomical verification have been different, then, as Einstein once remarked, the public attitude would have differed accordingly. In an article published in the London *Times* on November 28, 1919, he wrote:

"Here is yet another application of the principle of relativity for the delectation of the reader: today I am described in Germany as a 'German savant', and in England as a 'Swiss Jew'. Should it ever be my fate to be represented as a *bête noire*, I should, on the contrary, become a 'Swiss Jew' for the Germans and a 'German savant' for the English."[2]

In spite of the confirmation of relativity theory Einstein soon became a *bête noire*, and accordingly a Swiss Jew to the Germans, and the theory itself ceased to gratify their national vanity. An unprecedented aggravation of class struggle was taking place in Germany. Terrorist organisations sprang up all over the country. The nationalist magazine *Der Türmer* published an article entitled *Bolshevistic Physics*, which said, in part: "...Professor Einstein, the alleged new Copernicus, numbers university teachers among his admirers. Yet, without mincing words, we are dealing here with an

[1] Ph. Frank, op. cit., p. 176.
[2] *Ideas and Opinions*, p. 232.

infamous scientific scandal that fits very appropriately into the picture presented by this most tragic of all political periods. In the last analysis one cannot blame the workers for being taken in by Marx, when German professors allow themselves to be misled by Einstein."[1]

A certain Paul Weyland set up a special organisation with the sole purpose of fighting Einstein and his theories. Weyland organised meetings at which he would deliver political sallies against Einstein after which he would place physicists and philosophers on the platform to refute the new theory. At about the same time Philipp Lenard, an eminent experimentalist, also joined in the attack against Einstein. He was a fierce opponent of the relativity theory and a rabid nationalist (he even had the term "ampere" replaced in his laboratory by the name of a German physicist). Lenard's statements ranged from attempts to explain the results of Michelson's experiment from the classical standpoint to calls to deal physically with Einstein. Later he undertook to find a "pure German" source of the idea of the change in the mass of moving bodies, and later ascribed priority of this discovery to the talented theoretician F. Hasenöhrl, who had been killed in the war.

Relativity became the centre of a political struggle, a fact which further contributed to its fame. Still, in analysing the reason for such widespread interest in relativity one cannot fail to consider its content and its purport. At the bottom lay the theory's connection with the "classical ideal". In three centuries the notion of the world as a totality of material bodies in relative motion came to be almost intrinsic. Now the picture was being rid of the ambiguities due to the concepts of action at a distance, absolute space, and the ether as an absolute body of reference which contradicted the very spirit of the world picture. The price of this, however, was the paradoxical rejection of the classical law of velocity addition. Thus relativity forced upon men the idea of a paradoxical physical reality—trustworthy, irrefutable and experimentally proved. This led to "paradoxical rationalism", a conception of the harmony of the universe which finds expression in simple relationships contradicting traditional "self-evidence". This complex of ideas (which forms the

---

[1] *Ideas and Opinions*, p. 196.

essence of the relativity theory, as well as of Einstein's world outlook) gradually passed on from the comparatively wide circle of people familiar with relativity to still wider circles. The general impression created by the theory was a conviction of the omnipotence of the intellect and the objective nature and harmony of the world, ideas which could not fail to appeal to people living in an age when intellect and harmony stood opposed to mysticism and chaos in one of the decisive confrontations of history. The process soon turned into something like a chain reaction: interest in the theory added to its social value (among other things it forced its author to make public statements), and this in turn served to enhance its popularity. Another factor in addition to the confirmation of the theory by astronomical observations which contributed to a feeling of its complete trustworthiness in spite of its apparent paradoxes and contributed to its tremendous public resonance, was Einstein's own attitude, his absolute conviction that observations would not fail to confirm the theory. Whatever a scientist's epistemological ideas, he inevitably steps down from a platform of agnosticism (whether phenomenological, conventionalist, or resting on *a priori* assumptions) when he is waiting for an experiment to confirm his theory. Much depends on the extent to which he is convinced of the validity of his ideas. At some stage a spontaneous, subconscious conception of the knowability of the inner structure of the world is no longer sufficient. Einstein's firm conviction that observations would support his theory emerged not only from the mathematical soundness of its apparatus, but also from a conscious, consistent, unswerving belief in the knowability of the world. When Einstein was shown the pictures taken during the eclipse he said that they were beautiful—as photographs. He was not at all impressed by the fact that the relativity theory had been confirmed, so confident had he been of its validity. When someone asked what his reaction would have been had the results been negative, he replied: "I should have been very surprised indeed."

Einstein's confidence, it should be stressed, did not rest on belief in his own infallibility as a scientist. He was not a man to admire his own intellectual achievements. Rather, his attitude was an expression of his confidence in the knowability and harmony of the world. If a world picture is in agreement with experimental findings ("external confirmation") and does not rest, as far as possible, on arbitrary assumptions ("inner perfection"), it is a good approximation to objective reality. In his case conviction of the knowability and harmony acquired the heuristic dimensions characteristic of a man of genius. It also coloured Einstein's attitude towards his work and science, towards the importance of his work and its social function.

Einstein's scientific convictions have a definite bearing on his moral philosophy. In him there was no contradiction between intellectual power and moral principles. Only a man immersed in the "extra-personal" and oblivious of self (and therefore always aware of others) could handle abstract notions with such wonderful ease, without ever falling into arbitrary constructions independent of experiments, without reducing the relation to experience to the phenomenological boundaries of "pure description". The burden of fame which fell so suddenly on Einstein's shoulders served to bring home a realisation of the scientist's responsibility for the destinies of mankind. In the final analysis, his fame was symptomatic of the unusual role which science had come to play in human affairs and which is one of the outstanding features of the 20th century.

The "motherly feeling towards all people", which Balzac spoke of in the passage quoted in the epigraph, had turned into a conscious sense of responsibility for the destinies of people in the new conditions created by the revolution in science. One might call Einstein the augur of the atomic age —though nothing could be more alien to him than posing as an augur, and in any case the very nature of 20th-century scientific and social progress leaves no place for augurs. Still, he was the first to discover that energy equals mass times the square of the velocity of light, and he realised before other scientists that the potentialities of science required scholars to take part in the struggle of social forces, insofar as they have a direct bearing on the possible practical applications of scientific discoveries. Einstein himself readily stepped into the battle of ideas—though not in its decisive sphere, which remained distant from him. But the cause to which he devoted himself was of considerable importance, namely the rallying of intellectuals to the fight against jingoistic nationalism. And even though at times his analyses of the situation were mistaken, he took his place in the ranks. Neither did he have a clear idea of the forces capable of effectively resisting war and chauvinism. His pacifist stand was vague. On one occasion in Berlin, in 1920, he remarked to a group of visitors:

"My pacifism is an instinctive feeling, a feeling that possesses me because the murder of men is disgusting. My attitude is not derived from any intellectual theory but is based on my deepest antipathy to every kind of cruelty and hatred. I might go on to rationalise this reaction, but that would really be *a posteriori* thinking."[1]

The League of Nations set up a Commission for Intellectual Co-operation with rather vague terms of reference. When Einstein was invited to sit on that commission in 1922 he responded with the following letter:

"Even though I must admit that I am not at all clear as to the character of the work to be done by the commission, I consider it my duty to obey its summons since nobody in these times should refuse assistance to efforts towards the realisation of international co-operation."[2]

In the commission Einstein encountered political attitudes which gradually made him go over from pacifism as a purely instinctive aversion for cruelty of any kind, to a clearly defined platform against war. A year later, discouraged by the League of Nations' stand in connection with the occupation of the Ruhr, Einstein resigned from the commission. He eventually saw the light and realised that instinctive pacifism was unable to oppose the forces of war. He wrote in 1923: "I have become convinced that the League [of Nations] possesses neither the strength nor the goodwill necessary to accomplish its task. As a convinced pacifist it does not seem to me to have any relation whatever with the League."

In a letter to a pacifist magazine he formulated his step even more sharply:

"I did so because the activities of the League of Nations had convinced me that there appeared to be no action, no matter how brutal, committed by the present power groups, against which the League could take a stand. I withdrew

[1] Ph. Frank, op. cit., p. 189.
[2] Ibid., p. 289.

because the League of Nations, as it functions at present, not only does not embody the ideal of an international organisation, but actually discredits such an ideal."[1]

This shows a decisive break with instinctive pacifism. As Einstein saw it, the League of Nations ought to have had not only the goodwill but also the *strength* to oppose actions constituting a threat to the peace. It had neither.

On the other hand, many people of like views, notably Marie Curie-Sklodowska, impressed upon him the idea that it would be possible to contribute, within the framework of the League, to the international co-operation of scientists. Such co-operation would serve to draw people away from nationalism. This consideration appealed to Einstein, who also thought that science was capable of overcoming bigoted nationalism. In addition, a purely negative attitude was reprehensible to him.

"The representatives of the natural sciences," he wrote, "are inclined by the universal character of the subject dealt with and by the necessity of internationally organised co-operation, towards an international mentality, predisposing them to favour pacifist objectives. . . . The tradition of science as a force in cultural training would open a much more comprehensive view before the mind and would be a powerful influence—because its outlook is world-wide—in drawing men a little away from senseless nationalism."[2]

These sentiments, bred by events during 1920s, are indicative of Einstein's new approach to science as a major force capable of contributing to peace on earth. He remained completely devoted to science, but he no longer regarded it as a haven from the attacks of bigots; on the contrary, he saw it as a powerful force in the struggle against them.

The subsequent work of the Commission for Intellectual Co-operation convinced Einstein that the solidarity of men of science could be an effective force only if it was enhanced by the direct struggle against the centres of military aggression and social reaction. In 1925, the Italian fascists appointed the Minister of Justice in Mussolini's government to be their representative on the commission. Marie Curie declared that a minister could not be accepted into a team of independent

---

[1] Ph. Frank, op. cit., p. 190.
[2] Ibid., p. 191.

intellectuals. Einstein also spoke up and added that the minister of a totalitarian state was not a suitable representative. Some members of the commission, however, expressed the fear that Italy might withdraw from the League of Nations, thereby offering Einstein an object lesson of how passive unacceptance of war goes side by side with appeasement in respect to the forces of war and reaction.

Antonina Vallentin, who frequently met Einstein and his family in the 1920s, writes in her book, *Le drame d'Albert Einstein*, of his moods during a session of the Commission for Intellectual Co-operation in Geneva. Friends, scientific interests and music were a great support for him.

"One evening, after a particularly strenuous meeting of the commission, he was sitting with Mme. Curie on a bench on the shore of the Lake of Geneva. . . . Einstein and Marie Curie sat in thoughtful silence, watching the wavering bright strip cast on the water by a lamp. Suddenly they began talking again, no trace of their previous moodiness left in their eyes. 'Why does the reflection in the water break down in this spot and not at another point?' Einstein asked. . . . Marie Curie's dryish voice took on colour corresponding to Einstein's reflective tone. The conversation drifted to formulas, figures and the laws of physics."[1]

Antonina Vallentin writes that at the height of Einstein's disillusionment with the work of the Commission of Intellectual Co-operation, he sought refuge from the painful impressions of reality in a world of musical images.

One day the commission members were chatting in a restaurant on the shore of the lake. They avoided discussing their individual differences which, they acutely felt, were so unlike scientific differences.

The strains of the restaurant orchestra rose over the hubbub of voices and the clatter of plates. The music seemed to draw Einstein away from his surroundings and the impressions of the day. He walked up to the stage, asked the violinist to lend him his violin and began to play.

"His face underwent a transformation, a smile appeared on his lips, his features relaxed, and he seemed to be dreaming, oblivious of his surroundings and unconscious of the sight he presented on the stage with the eyes of the public

[1] A. Vallentin, *Le drame d'Albert Einstein*, Paris, 1957, p. 104.

upon him. He was alone, washing away the bitterness of association."

When Einstein's friends called his attention to the lateness of the hour he returned the violin with an apologetic smile and departed.

This story might create the impression of escape from daily reality and struggle. This was not so. To Einstein music was an expression of the world harmony embodied in sound, just as science was an expression of the world harmony embodied in the laws of physical reality. All this then, far from eliminating the feeling of social discord, made it more apparent than ever and gave rise to a desire to do something about it. And we see that during the 20s and 30s Einstein evolved from pacifism to the struggle against military psychosis, chauvinism and reaction.

In the 1920s Einstein's Berlin home was a place of pilgrimage for men and women of different professions, interests, views and motivations seeking answers to physical, mathematical, philosophical, moral, religious, political, and purely personal questions. This unending stream was swelled by legions of sightseers, for by then Einstein had become one of Berlin's major tourist attractions and his house at 5 Haberlandstrasse was a tourist's must. Out of some of these visits friendships developed. Many of these people have contributed reminiscences of Einstein which provide us with an insight into his views on important problems. Einstein possessed an intrinsic democratic streak and he was capable of expounding some new and unpublished idea on the spur of the moment to a student who had come to ask for a minor favour. Many of those ideas can be found in Einstein's scientific papers or letters. The value of personal memoirs of people who knew him lies in the intimate details of his life, habits and appearance which they contain and which are so dear to us and will undoubtedly remain so for many years to come. Some of these reminiscences deserve to be cited here. Now that we are familiar with the main aspects of Einstein's world outlook, thinking and habits, these details fall into a comprehensive image. They are not, of course, derivable from the internal image of the man, in the same way as Einstein believed it to be possible in principle to derive all the details of the world picture from its basic principles. But Einstein was a man in whom the personal and the daily commonplace receded to the background and was subordinated to the basic "extra-personal" content of his life. In this respect he was an example of his own ideal of scientific knowledge which he expounded in his *Autobiographical Notes*.

One can hardly overestimate the part played by Elsa Einstein in creating the domestic atmosphere most suited to her husband's habits. She did not attempt to set up a wall between him and other people and was not fussy. Her intelligence, sociability, good taste, and respect for the opinions of others helped to create in the Einstein domicile at 5 Haberlandstrasse an atmosphere that agreed well with Einstein's conflicting but internally harmonious interest in people and desire to work in seclusion.

A few words about Einstein's home. The landlord, a native of Russia, had for long been an ardent admirer of Einstein. To have him as a tenant was the summit of his proudest dreams. Einstein rented a nine-room flat in which he lived with his wife, his two stepdaughters, Ilse and Margot, and for a short while, his mother. After the death of Hermann Einstein, Pauline had lived with some relatives, moving later to Berlin, where she died in 1920.

The house was situated in a comparatively new section in the west of Berlin frequently called the Bavarian quarter because its streets are named after Bavarian places. Its broad streets, well-kept trees and new houses made it popular with well-to-do families. Einstein's house resembled thousands of others in Berlin. It fronted on a small square in the centre of which stood a statue of St. George and the dragon.

The simple furnishing, the flowered bright wall-paper, the family pictures, the portrait of Frederick the Great with his two dogs, and the piano in the corner were characteristic of thousands of other homes in the city. Only the library offered an idea of its owner's profession. Any visitor who sought a reflection of Einstein's personality in the furnishings of his home was disappointed, unless he happened to gain entrance to the professor's study. In a little corner turret there was a small room separated from the rest of the apartment by a staircase. This was Einstein's study. In a window alcove was a round table covered with a red-and-white cloth and littered with papers and pamphlets and tobacco ashes. Two chairs with straw seats, a couch and against the walls shelves filled with scientific books and maga-zines and two fat bibles. On a shelf stood a statuette repre-senting an old Jew with an immense head of hair. Einstein's hair had begun to thin rapidly and Elsa advised him to eat a lot of onions to strengthen it. Einstein followed her advice. Margot, his stepdaughter, made the statuette and inscribed the name Rabbi Zwiebel on it ("zwiebel" means "onion" in German). "By eating onions," she told Einstein, "a person can acquire such a head of hair and a beard down to his waist." Einstein became very fond of the figurine.

The statuette, which could be taken as a symbol of the simple, friendly atmosphere pervaded with gentle humour that reigned in the family, kept company with miscellaneous objects left by previous tenants of the flat. These did not bother Einstein, who easily accepted the tastes of others. On his desk was a picture of Newton and next to it a little telescope. When visitors asked him whether he ever used it Einstein would reply: "No, my friend, I do not stargaze. The telescope belonged to the grocer who used to live here. I kept it just for a plaything." When asked where he kept his own tools he would tap his forehead with a smile. Asked by a visitor about his laboratory, Einstein pointed to his foun-tain pen.

Einstein usually got up at about eight o'clock. In bathrobe and slippers, while waiting for the bath-tub, he would pick out a tune on the piano. His wife would announce, "Ready, Albertle," and he would go into the bathroom, often forget-ting to shut the door behind him, which Elsa would hasten to do. After breakfast he would fill his pipe and retire to his study.

People frequently asked Einstein how many hours he devoted to his work. He was at a loss to answer such a question, for to him working was thinking. He sometimes asked a friend, "How many hours a day do you work?" And when the friend replied, "Oh, eight or nine," he would shrug his shoulders and exclaim: "I cannot work so long. I cannot work more than four or five hours a day. I'm afraid I am not a very diligent man!"

With Einstein safe in his study, Elsa would start to sort out the mail. Letters came from all over the world, in all languages—hundreds of letters, which the concierge brought up by the basketful, from scientists, statesmen, public and

DEUTSCHES REICH

Frau
Pauline Einstein
Sanatorium Rosenau
Luzern (Schweiz)

Abs. A. Einstein
Haberlandstr. 5
Berlin

27. IX. 19

Liebe Mutter!

Postcard from Einstein to his mother. September 27, 1919

civic leaders, workers, unemployed, and students. There were countless appeals for help or advice and offers of services. One young lady offered her services as a "cosmic contemplator". Inventors wrote of new machines, parents informed him of children christened Albert, a cigar manufacturer wrote of a new brand which he had named Relativity.

Elsa sorted out the letters. Some remained unanswered, some she answered herself, the rest she showed to Einstein. This work often took up the better part of the day, and sometimes the evening as well.

In spite of Elsa's screening, the mail was an eternal source of annoyance to Einstein. He complained in 1920: "I never could say 'No'. Now, with endless newspaper articles and letters pleading and inviting and demanding, I dream at night that I'm roasting in Hell and our postman is a devil who shouts at me and hurls packets of new letters at my head for my not having replied to all the previous ones. Add to this my mother's illness and the 'period of fame', i.e., countless purposeless meetings. As a result I have turned into a bundle of the simplest reflectory responses."[1]

On another occasion Einstein remarked. "The postman is my greatest enemy. I shall never escape from his clutches."[2]

Einstein's hobby was sailing. In a sail-boat, he said, he did not have to be in fear of callers. He did not care for other sports. "I don't like physical exercise," he said "I'm too lazy, and sailing is the only sport that suits me."[3]

Einstein never paid much attention to his clothes. He usually wore a brown leather jacket, a present from Elsa. On colder days he would put on a grey English woollen sweater, also a gift from Elsa. He attended formal dinners in an old-fashioned dark suit, he could only be induced to wear a dinner-jacket on very special occasions and at the unanimous demand of his family. Other interesting details concerning Einstein's habits and mode of expression and thinking can be found in many memoirs devoted to him.

Dr. Moritz Katzenstein, a surgeon who treated the Einsteins and whom Einstein called his best friend in Berlin, tells how they went sailing together on the lakes which abound around the German capital. Katzenstein says that the

[1] C. Seelig, op. cit., S. 272.
[2] Ibid., S. 282.
[3] Ibid., S. 283.

main traits of Einstein's character were a fine sense of humour and a vivid imagination. "He was quite unlike the North-German type, always overburdened with duties which the Italians, in their days of freedom, called 'bestia seriosa'."[1]

Another friend of Einstein's, Rudolf Ehrmann, also a doctor and a companion in excursions to the suburbs of Berlin, offers the following rather professional characteristic:

"Many contemporaries know his angelic eyes in which little imps start to dance when he laughs and the frank sincerity with which he looks upon the world. He is much less known from the physical aspect. Einstein was above medium height, he had white skin, a well-developed musculature.... He had an aversion for medicine but liked medical men.... He liked to talk to doctors because of the ease with which they come into contact with people of different social standing. In the company of doctors he felt an affinity to his own interests, for Einstein was, in his own right, a champion of a healthier and better human race."[2]

Another frequent companion of Einstein's in Berlin was Emanuel Lasker, one-time world chess champion. Lasker left no memoirs, but some remarks of Einstein's about his friend offer an insight into traits of Einstein's own character.

"Lasker," he wrote, "was undoubtedly one of the most interesting men I have ever met. Rarely is independence of thought linked with such a profound interest in the important problems which concern mankind. I am not a chess-player and cannot judge of the power of his intellect in that game. I have always disliked the competitive spirit of that inspired game."[3]

A significant confession! Einstein regarded chess as an exercise of the intellect, but his own thoughts revolved around problems which were solved by discovering the truth, not by gaining ascendancy over an adversary. Einstein was of a profoundly ontological frame and he could not accept a mode of thinking which seeks criteria within itself instead of seeking the goal of Spinozan rationalism—a trustworthy description of physical reality. Einstein's philosophy made him unreceptive to any form of competitive struggle or to

[1] *Helle Zeit*, S. 46.
[2] Ibid., S. 59.
[3] C. Seelig, op. cit., S. 331.

manifestations of the "merely-personal" in mentality and research.

Another man who has written extensively about Einstein is Leopold Infeld, already quoted in this book. Infeld first met Einstein in 1920, while in his fifth year at the University of Cracow. Infeld wished to complete his studies in Berlin under Planck, Laue and Einstein, but natives of Poland, and especially Jews, were unwelcome visitors in the eyes of Prussian officialdom. All doors seemed shut to him, until finally he mustered his courage and decided to appeal directly to Einstein. Here is how Infeld describes the meeting:

"Shy, deeply touched, in a holiday spirit of expectation at meeting the greatest living physicist, I pressed the bell of Einstein's flat at 5 Haberlandstrasse. I was shown into a waiting room full of heavy furniture and explained to Mrs. Einstein why I had come. She apologised and explained that I would have to wait because a Chinese minister of education was just then talking to her husband. I waited, my cheeks burning with excitement.... Einstein opened the door of his study to let the Chinese gentleman out and me in. Einstein was dressed in a morning coat and striped trousers with one important button missing. It was the familiar face which one saw at that time so often in pictures and magazines. But no picture could reproduce the shining glow of his eyes.

"I completely forgot my carefully prepared speech. Einstein looked at me with a smile and offered me a cigarette. It was the first friendly smile directed toward me since I had come to Berlin. Briefly I told him my situation. Einstein listened carefully.

" 'I should be very glad to give you a recommendation to the Ministry of Education. But my signature does not mean anything.'

" 'Why?'

" 'Because I have given very many recommendations and'—here he lowered his voice to a confidential tone—'they are anti-Semites.'

"He thought awhile, walking up and down.

" 'The fact that you are a physicist makes it simpler. I will write a few words to Professor Planck; his recommendation may mean much more. Yes, this will be the best thing.'

"He began to search for his writing paper which was on

his desk before him. I was too shy to point it out. Finally he found it and wrote a few words. He did it without knowing whether I had the slightest idea of physics."[1]

Among Einstein's visitors in Berlin were Soviet statesmen. Einstein was deeply impressed by Grigori Chicherin, the People's Commissar for Foreign Affairs, and their talks provided Einstein with a wealth of information and ideas about the revolution and socialism. Einstein expressed his great sympathy with the Soviet state in conversations with A. V. Lunacharsky, the People's Commissar for Education, who wrote an article, "A Meeting with Greatness," for a Moscow magazine. The reader, I hope, will not object if I quote at some length from the article.

Lunacharsky's article begins with the following incident. There was once a deranged lady by the name of Eugenia Dickson, known mainly for an attempt to assassinate Krasin, the Soviet ambassador in Paris, with a revolver which wouldn't shoot and was apparently not even loaded. At one time she had been after Lunacharsky with stories that the former tsarist minister Milyukov was the father of her (nonexistent) baby and had murdered the child with the purpose of provoking a new Beilis trial, that the tsarist agent provocateur Azef was the father of another non-esixtent baby, and finally, that Azef was in hiding under the alias of Einstein and posing as a physicist.

Later on, when Lunacharsky met the Einsteins in Berlin, Elsa told him the sequel to the story. Eugenia Dickson wrote a letter to Einstein in which she threatened to expose him. This was followed by a series of threatening letters posted from various railway stations between Paris and Berlin, until one day the poor demented woman rang the bell at the house in Haberlandstrasse and demanded that she be shown in to Azef-Einstein. When she saw Einstein she exclaimed that she had indeed been mistaken and that he was not Azef. Nevertheless, she entreated Einstein, as the alleged father of the dead baby, to save her from being placed in a mental institution and also asked for money. The whole affair was taken up by the Berlin police and an official was stupid enough to tell Elsa that the possibility of a liaison could not be ruled out.

[1] L. Infeld, op. cit., pp. 91-92.

This account of Lunacharsky's tallies on the whole with Seelig's account, taken from Ehrenfest's words.[1]

In the beginning of 1925, Ehrenfest came to the railway station of Leipzig to meet Einstein, who was expected from Berlin on a morning train. Einstein, however, arrived only in the evening. He told Ehrenfest that he had had to go to a jail to see a woman being held for planning to assassinate him as the man Azef. Margot had met her in the doorway and it struck her that the woman, who was quite obviously not in her right mind, might be going up to the Einstein flat. She called up from a street telephone booth to warn her mother of the visitor, who was eventually taken to a prison. When Einstein visited the woman, she declared that he was not Azef ("Your nose is much shorter"). Einstein used his influence to set her free and brought some things at her request. The whole incident may not have been so simple and amusing as it seemed when related to Lunacharsky by Elsa and later by Einstein to Ehrenfest. Garbedian, in any case, writes of a serious attempt on Einstein's life:

"Einstein's activities in political affairs won him many new friends, and, as was inevitable, some bitter enemies. One of the latter managed to get by the watchful eye of the faithful Otto [the concierge], and one day Mme. Marie[sic!] Erguewsewa-Dickson, a Russian widow of an American, who had been living in Paris since the Russian Revolution, surreptitiously entered the Einstein apartment in Berlin. Murder was in her heart, and at the end of the hatpin which she brandished venomously, but she had figured without Mrs. Einstein who could rise to any emergency to protect her beloved husband. The scientist's wife disarmed the threatening visitor, and summoned the police; and did it all so competently and quietly that Professor Einstein did not learn of the danger to his life until a long time afterwards."[2]

Now back to Lunacharsky's article. His purpose in introducing the incident is to present a literary portrait of Einstein. Lunacharsky writes of the tremendous impression (which he defines as "a feeling of great sympathy mixed with a

[1] C. Seelig, op. cit., S. 307-08.
[2] H. G. Garbedian, *Albert Einstein. Maker of Universes,* Funk and Wagnall, New York, 1939, p. 199.

degree of reverence") which Einstein's very presence caused on others.

"There is a dreamy expression in Einstein's near-sighted eyes, as if long ago he had turned the greater part of his vision to his inner thoughts and kept it there. One feels that most of Einstein's vision is constantly occupied with his thoughts and calculations. That is why his eyes have that dreamy, even melancholy look. Nevertheless, Einstein is a jolly fellow in company. He enjoys a good joke ... and readily breaks into peals of rollicking, childish laughter which momentarily change his eyes into those of a child. His remarkable simplicity is so charming that one feels like hugging him or squeezing his hand or slapping him on the back— which in no way detracts from one's esteem for him. It is a strange feeling of tender affection for a man of great and defenceless simplicity mingled with boundless respect."

Of Elsa, Lunacharsky writes:

"She is no longer young, with thick grey hair, but a lovely woman with a chaste beauty that is much more than physical beauty. She is all love for her great husband, always ready to shield him from the harsh intrusions of life and to ensure the peace of mind necessary for his great ideas to mature. She is filled with a realisation of his great purpose as a thinker and with the tenderest feelings of companion, wife and mother towards a remarkable, exquisite, grown-up child."

Chapter 21

TRAVELS

> The ideals which have lighted my way, and
> time after time have given me new courage to
> face life cheerfully, have been Kindness,
> Beauty, and Truth. Without the sense of
> kinship with men of like mind, without the
> occupation with the objective world, the
> eternally unattainable in the field of art and
> scientific endeavours, life would have seemed
> to me empty.
>
> *Einstein*

Einstein, as mentioned before, did not sympathise with
Galileo's stubborn efforts to uphold the truth of the heliocentric system. As far as his own ideas were concerned, he
would have preferred to rely on the convincingness of the
truth itself, which does not need the scholar's feeble efforts
to assert it. At the same time he declared that life would
have been empty without the sense of kinship with men of
like mind. There is no contradiction between these two attitudes. Einstein never doubted the validity of his conception
of the world and its basic principles. To him it was simple
and knowable by virtue of its naturalness and harmony—the
"inner perfection" which appealed to the intellect irrespective
of difficult calculations and observations. Einstein always carried his work to the point of utmost logical and mathematical
refinement. He spent years working out intricate mathematical
constructions and he realised their controversial nature and
incomprehensibility to the layman. But in addition to their
being involved, controversial and esoteric, Einstein's theoretical constructs included simple and clear principles which
allowed for exoteric, simple, clear exposition. These principles
had to be revealed to people, and their inner harmony and
convincingness would do the rest.

In the 'twenties Einstein was especially sensitive to the
necessity of advancing such simple, lucid and indubitable

scientific principles. The poisonous ideas of revenge, the ideological bankruptcy and futility of the League of Nations, the merging of nationalistic rabble-rousing with attacks against the foundations of scientific thinking were the facts of life which gave weight to the idea of the social effects of science.

Reaction had to be opposed, not by mathematical computations, but by the rational spirit of physical theories and the overall picture of universal harmony. In this sphere it was in broad sections of the public that Einstein found the men of like mind whose kinship he sought. Contact with them could not be effected within the scope of physical journals.

In 1615, Galileo travelled to Rome to defend the helio-centric concept and the classical relativity principle before a congregation of cardinals. In the 1920s Einstein travelled extensively in order to present the new world picture to the collective intelligence of mankind.

It is worth noting that Einstein's opponents were annoyed by the expansion of the audience to which he appealed. In Germany a brochure entitled *The Mass Suggestion of the Relativity Theory* appeared, in which its author wrote:

"As soon as the erroneous character of the relativity theory became evident in scientific circles, Einstein turned more and more to the masses and exhibited himself and his theory as publicly as possible."[1]

In the early 'twenties the Einsteins visited Holland, Czechoslovakia and Austria, they travelled to America, stopping in England and France, and finally undertook a long journey which took them to Japan, Palestine and Spain.

In Leiden, Holland, Einstein delivered a lecture on "Ether and the Relativity Theory" to an audience of fifteen hundred. It was a popular exposition of the fundaments of physics and it was characteristic of his appeal to men of like mind outside of his own profession. Its leitmotiv was the idea of the rational scheme of the universe, an idea whose social resonance was appreciated by friends and foes alike. The latter wrote concerning Einstein's views:

"For a long time efforts were made to convince us of the sensational fact that the ether had been got rid of, and now

[1] Ph. Frank, op. cit., p. 205.

Einstein himself reintroduces it; this man is not to be taken seriously, he contradicts himself constantly."[1]

The enthusiasm of Einstein's followers and, more important, the remarkable swelling of their ranks after the Leiden lecture, demonstrated that the issue at stake was not restricted to physics; it was nothing less than the defence of a rational, scientific world outlook in the face of reaction.

In his Leiden lecture Einstein took a historical approach to the ether concept. The ether had been introduced in response to the desire to develop a unified picture of physical reality. The concept of action at a distance contradicted the idea that bodies owe their states of motion to the action of forces. It was necessary, therefore, to postulate a medium whose action could cause bodies to gravitate towards one another. Then came the wave theory of light, which required a medium in which mechanical vibrations could propagate wavelike and be responsible for optical phenomena. In the 19th century optical experiments indicated that the medium did not participate in the bodily motions and that all bodies moved relative to the ether. But then Michelson's experiment failed to detect the different velocities of light in different directions within a moving body as a result of motion through the ether. On this basis the special theory of relativity postulated that motion relative to the ether has no physical meaning, insofar as there is no possible means of observing it.

The general theory of relativity, however, opens the door for a partial rehabilitation of the ether by ascribing a physical meaning to the concept. Ponderable bodies—sources of gravitational fields—change the metric properties of space, which are treated as physical properties. But if space possesses definite observable physical properties, then we can regard it as a material medium, and even call it "ether". Only this "ether" would lack its classical properties, which cause physical bodies to move with respect to the ether or the ether to be entrained by moving bodies. In introducing the ether concept in such form Einstein stressed that, insofar as according to the general theory of relativity space possesses physical properties, then in this sense the ether can be said to exist.

[1] Ph. Frank, op. cit., p. 205.

The ether concept, however, did not survive and scholars preferred to speak of gravitational field as being responsible for changing the properties of space.

Einstein's 1920 trip to Leiden was the first of a series of regular trips to the city. In Leiden lived Lorentz, whom Einstein held in high esteem, and Paul Ehrenfest, whose company he sought. The doors of the Ehrenfests' home were always open to Einstein and Ehrenfest and his Russian wife Tatyana Afanasyeva-Ehrenfest became bosom friends of Einstein and Elsa. In 1923, Ehrenfest succeeded Lorentz at the University of Leiden, and he invited Einstein to take up a non-staff professorship there. Einstein commuted between Berlin and Leiden, always staying with the Ehrenfests where he was sure to be treated with his favourite dishes. The Ehrenfests were always delighted to hear Einstein exclaim joyfully as he entered their house: "What does a man need besides a violin, a bed, a desk and a chair?"

The year after the Leiden lecture Urania, a scientific society in Prague, invited Einstein to deliver a lecture. In Prague he was the guest of Philipp Frank and his wife. It was difficult to find an apartment in Prague and the Franks lived in the office at the Physics Laboratory, the same room that had once been Einstein's office. This enabled Einstein to escape the pack of correspondents who were after him. Einstein and Frank visited the Czech university and then made a round of several cafés. This was Einstein's idea as he wanted to get a closer look at the life of the city in whose streets he had once walked so much.

In the evening Einstein lectured in the overcrowded hall of the Urania society. After the lecture a number of guests gathered to spend the evening with Einstein. Several speeches were made. When Einstein's turn came he said, "It will perhaps be more pleasant and understandable if instead of making a speech I play a piece for you on the violin." He played a sonata by Mozart in his simple, precise and therefore doubly moving manner.[1]

From Prague Einstein went to Vienna where he gave a lecture in a huge concert hall seating some three thousand persons.

[1] Ph. Frank, op. cit., p. 210.

In Vienna Einstein was told the details of the sensational case of Friedrich Adler, who during the war had shot the head of the Austrian government at a dinner in a fashionable hotel. He was arrested and condemned to death, but the Emperor commuted his sentence to life imprisonment. The idea was propounded that Adler was not in his right mind when he committed the assassination. Confirmation of the idea was to be found in a rather remarkable way. Following Mach, Adler opposed the theory of relativity and while in prison he had written a work which he believed presented cogent arguments against Einstein's views. The court sent the manuscript to expert psychiatrists and physicists who were to determine whether any conclusion could be drawn from it, to the effect that the author was mentally deranged. One of the experts was Philipp Frank. He writes that the experts, especially the physicists, found themselves in a very difficult situation. If Adler was pronounced mentally deranged this would surely mitigate his sentence. On the other hand, this would necessarily be highly insulting to the author, since he believed that he had produced an excellent scientific achievement.[1]

In Vienna Einstein lived with the well-known Austrian physicist Felix Ehrenhaft. The two were constantly in argument but in spite of this or possibly for that very reason, Einstein liked to meet him. Ehrenhaft's wife was an outstanding organiser of education for women in Austria. She wanted Einstein to look his very best at the lecture and sent one of the two pairs of trousers that he had brought with him to be pressed by a tailor. Einstein, however, turned up at the lecture wearing the unpressed pair.

Also in 1921, Einstein received an invitation to accompany Chaim Weizmann, the leader of the Zionist movement, on a trip to the United States. The purpose of the trip was to collect funds for the establishment of a Jewish university in Palestine. When Einstein arrived in New York Harbour he was greeted by a huge crowd. The ship had hardly been made fast when a crowd of reporters swarmed on board, surrounding Einstein, his wife and Weizmann in a close circle. Reluctant as he was to face the ordeal of an interview, he had to answer the questions. When asked to explain the content of

[1] Ph. Frank, op. cit., p. 212.

the relativity theory in a few sentences he said, "If you will not take the answer too seriously and consider it only as a kind of joke, then I can explain it as follows. It was formerly believed that if all material things disappeared out of the universe, time and space would be left. According to the theory of relativity, however, time and space disappear together with the things."[1]

He was asked whether it was true that only twelve people in the world understood relativity. Einstein denied that he had ever said such a thing. This remark had in fact been uttered by Langevin who was alleged to have said it at the dawn of relativity. Einstein thought that every physicist who studied the theory could readily understand it, and that his students in Berlin all understood it.

Mrs. Einstein was also asked a question: whether she understood the theory. To this she replied, "Oh no, although he has explained it to me so many times, but it is not necessary for my happiness."[2]

Of the lectures given in the United States the most important were four delivered at Princeton University. They were published and for a long time remained a classical exposition of the relativity theory. On the way back from the United States Einstein stopped in London at the invitation of Lord Haldane and gave a lecture at King's College.

The big audience in the hall gave Einstein a cool reception: he was a world-famous scientist, to be sure, but he represented German science. It was the first time he was not greeted with applause. Einstein spoke of the international role of science, of contacts between scientists, of the British people's part in the advancement of science, and of Isaac Newton. He thanked his English colleagues, remarking that without their contribution he would probably never have received the most important confirmation of his theory. The lecture presented a programme of international co-operation of scientists. It swayed not only the audience present but the whole of the British scientific community as well. The public resonance and social impact of Einstein's ideas had been once again reaffirmed.

[1] Ph. Frank, op. cit., pp. 217-18.
[2] Ibid., p. 218.

In London the Einsteins were the guests of Lord Haldane. Their room in his palatial residence was bigger than the whole of their Berlin apartment. Einstein's embarrassment turned into dismay when he found that a footman had been assigned to him. When he saw the liveried monument he whispered to his wife: "Elsa, do you think they will let us out if we try to run away?" They slept in a spacious bedroom with heavily curtained windows. Next morning Einstein rose early, as was his custom, and tried in vain to open the curtains. Behind him his wife asked laughingly, "Albertle, why didn't you call the footman to do it?" "Oh no," he replied, "he frightens me." Finally by joint effort they managed the curtains and went down to the hall to have breakfast. That evening a dinner was given in honour of the distinguished guest. Among the guests was the Archbishop of Canterbury. He wanted to know the effect relativity would have on religion, and he asked Einstein as much. To his relief Einstein replied briefly and to the point, "None."

Einstein returned to Berlin in June 1921. The honours that had been bestowed upon him in the United States and England added fuel to the social storm that raged around his personality and the relativity theory. In Germany the forces of reaction were rising.

In June 1922, Walter Rathenau, the German Minister of Foreign Affairs who advocated friendly relations with Soviet Russia, was murdered. On the day of his burial classes were cancelled in all universities. Only Philipp Lenard in Heidelberg demonstratively invited his political supporters to attend a regular lecture. A group of workers dragged Lenard out of the auditorium. Attacks against Einstein and the relativity theory became part of a much greater plot against democracy, peace and progress. Lenard launched a series of hysterical racialist attacks against the relativity theory. Together with the nationalistic terrorist organisations he saw the relativity theory as a triumph of the hated rationalist thinking. The workers and democratically-minded intellectuals saw it as a force opposed to reaction. What people had felt intuitively in 1919-1920 was being confirmed by the whole of the political storm that raged around Einstein and relativity.

After Einstein's trips the ideological differentiation increased and became more apparent. In March 1922,

Einstein went to France at an invitation from the Collège de France, which had been moved by Paul Langevin. He was met by Langevin and Charles Nordmann, a French physicist who contributed much to the dissemination of Einstein's ideas in France.

Langevin and Nordmann had been informed that nationalistic and monarchistic circles were preparing a hostile demonstration at the railway station. Accordingly they decided to hustle Einstein into town through a side entrance. It turned out, however, that the crowd outside the station consisted of students who had gathered under the leadership of Langevin's son to hail Einstein and prevent any possible hostile demonstrations.

At 5 p.m. on Friday, the 31st of March, a restricted audience of scientists and a small number of students gathered in the largest hall of the Collège de France to hear Einstein's lecture. Many people were surprised that "All Paris" was not present, but Langevin had seen to it that tickets were given only to persons who were known to have an actual interest in the subject.

In his lecture Einstein spoke of the conflict between the classical principle of relativity and electrodynamics. Electrodynamics had forced the question: does the principle of relativity and the idea that uniform rectilinear motion cannot be detected by any physical effects on a mechanical system remain valid for light phenomena? The constancy of the velocity of light means that motion retains its relative nature when optical processes are taken into account: the velocity of light does not change in inertial motion and provides no internal manifestations of motion. Einstein pointed out the objective character of this basic proposition of relativity. Referring to mathematicians who had memorised formulas but failed to grasp the essence of relativity, he said: "Their mistake is that they see only the formal relationships without stopping to consider the physical realities which correspond to the mathematical symbols." By physical reality Einstein means the possibility of verifying speculative constructions based on logical conclusions by direct observation. That this is in principle possible is a testimony to the existence of an external objective physical reality, which lies behind the causes of sense-impressions. The correlation of speculative constructs with sense-impressions is proof of the objective value of the former.

Spatial distance is a concept that must correlate with observation. But only a distance traversed by a physical object is suitable for such correlation. Since a physical object cannot travel with infinite velocity any correlation with sense-impressions must involve a concept combining spatial distance and time interval. Such a concept has physical meaning. There are no "instantaneous" spatial distances in the objective world, instead there are space-time separations.

On April 3, a discussion in a close circle of scientists was held in the physical auditorium of the Collège de France. Einstein spoke of the impossibility of synchronising clocks which are observed in systems moving relative to one another. His main opponent was Paul Painlevé, an outstanding mathematician, who spoke enthusiastically of Einstein's genius but attacked the basic assumptions of the theory of relativity. He gave examples which contradicted the conclusions of the theory. However, as Einstein demonstrated, acceleration figured implicitly in his examples, which therefore did not fall under the special theory of relativity.

Three days later, on April 6, Einstein expounded his views on Kantian philosophy at a session of the French Philosophical Society held in the Sorbonne. He engaged in an argument with the philosopher Henri Bergson, who defended the idea of a special "inner", intuitively realised time. When Emile Meyerson asked Einstein what he thought of Mach's philosophy, Einstein answered that Mach was "a poor philosopher".[1]

Einstein did not speak at the French Academy. His name was offensive to many of the "immortals" as it was identified too much with the struggle for freedom, peace and social progress. Other Academicians saw in relativity theory a threat to canonised classical science. As Einstein remarked, "Everything that they learned up to the age of eighteen is believed to be experience. Whatever they hear about later is theory and speculation."[2]

[1] *Bulletin de la Société Française de philosophie.* Sèance du 6 Avril 1922, p. 92; E. Meyerson. *La déduction relativiste.* Paris, 1925, p. 62.
[2] Ph. Frank, op. cit., p. 238.

Men adhering to reactionary scientific or political views (and as a rule the two attitudes come together) dug up all kinds of formal pretexts. Since Einstein was not a member of the Academy, some said, he could not sit among the members and would have to sit in the audience. Thirty members stated that they would leave the room if Einstein came. All this petty bickering reached Einstein's ears, and in order to spare his friends any unpleasantness and annoyance he himself declined to participate in a session of the Academy.

"Exactly the same groups that protested violently against the reception of Einstein because he was a German," Philipp Frank writes, "became the most zealous proponents of a policy of 'collaboration' with Germany after the nazis had seized power. These French 'patriots' prepared the French defeat of 1940 and the German domination of the continent."[1]

Einstein returned to Germany, but soon he was off again. Repeated invitations came from Japan, where preparations were going on for his lectures and meetings with him. In the autumn of 1922, the Einsteins arrived in Marseilles where they boarded a Japanese ship and sailed east, through the Mediterranean and across the Indian Ocean, stopping at Colombo, Singapore, and Shanghai. Everywhere Einstein's arrival was hailed by broad sections of the public.

Einstein arrived at Kobe in the end of November, and there too he was greeted by a large crowd. Lectures, meetings, receptions and visits followed in succession, made all the more difficult as every word had to be translated. At his lectures hundreds of people listened patiently to the unfamiliar German speech and then to the Japanese scientist who translated it. With the translation the first lecture lasted more than four hours. Einstein pitied the people who listened so patiently to him, and when he gave his next lecture in another city he shortened it so that it lasted only two and a half hours. But he had reckoned without the Japanese character. His Japanese companions explained to him with some embarrassment that the audience had considered the shortening of the lecture as a slight.

In Japan Einstein received the news that he had been elected to the Russian Academy of Science. The letter of

---

[1] Ph. Frank, op. cit., p. 239.

Einstein playing his violin. *L. Pasternak*

Einstein and Elsa

The Einstein villa at Caputh

recommendation signed by A. F. Joffe, P. P. Lazarev and V. A. Steklov said, in part: "...the remarkable achievements of physics in the last fifteen years are largely due to his ideas."

Each new city saw a repetition of the receptions, meetings and presentations which invariably followed an intricate pattern of ritual. Among the gifts was a four-volume *Encyclopaedia of Tea* with descriptions of different tea drinking ceremonies.

Einstein was deeply impressed by Japan. "Japan is wonderful," he wrote to Solovine. "Refined manners, an interest in everything, an artistic sense and intellectual naïveté coupled with common sense. A refined people in a picturesque country."[1]

At a meeting with Japanese children Einstein told them to bear in mind that the knowledge they gained at school was an inheritance to which they must add and which they must one day faithfully hand on to their children; for "thus do we mortals act immortally in the permanent things which we create in common."[2]

After a stay of several weeks, Einstein and Elsa, loaded with good wishes and gifts, left Japan for Palestine. The British High Commissioner, Sir Herbert Samuel, invited them to live at his house and undertook to be their guide. Here, too, Einstein had to submit to the established ceremonial. For when the High Commissioner left his residence a cannon was fired, and when he rode through the streets he was accompanied by mounted troops. A ceremonial formality prevailed at all receptions, dinners and luncheons. Einstein accepted it all with ironic humour, but Elsa was very irritated.

" 'I am only a simple housewife,' she complained one day to her husband. 'I don't care for all these nonsensical displays!'

" 'Be patient, my dear', he answered soothingly, 'we are on our way home.'

" 'It's easy enough for you to be patient. You are a famous man. If *you* make a mistake in etiquette or act according to your own feelings, it is overlooked. But I am always being teased in the newspapers. Just because I'm so near-sighted,

---

[1] *Solovine*, p. 45.
[2] H. G. Garbedian, op. cit., p. 218.

they said that by mistake I ate the green leaves of the flower at my plate instead of my salad.' "[1] Elsa invented all kinds of pretexts so as not to participate in the ceremonies.

Einstein lectured at the University of Jerusalem, in Tel Aviv and in other towns. Everywhere he found big, responsive audiences to whom he expounded his scientific, philosophical and political beliefs.

In March 1923, the Einsteins sailed from Palestine to Marseilles. From there they went to Spain, where Einstein delivered several lectures at the University of Madrid and visited several towns. After a brief stay in Spain they returned to Berlin.

In July 1923, Einstein went to Sweden to receive the Nobel Prize that had been awarded to him in November 1922, shortly after he had left on his Orient trip. In Göteborg he lectured at a meeting of Scandinavian scientists which was attended by the King of Sweden.

That Einstein deserved the Nobel Prize had been apparent for some time, but the committee of the Swedish Academy which handled the question was undecided. Relativity had many opponents. It was customary for the Nobel committee to award its prizes for specific discoveries with practical applications. The Swedish Academy and the Nobel committee were apprehensive of the political resonance that might be caused by awarding the prize for the theory of relativity, they feared the inevitable reaction to this on the part of Lenard and others like him. Therefore the statement of the award was formulated in general terms: "The prize is awarded to Einstein for the photo-electric law and his work in the field of theoretical physics."[2]

Lenard was quick to respond with a sharp protest to the Swedish Academy.

Einstein handed over half the premium that goes with the Nobel Prize to Mileva and dedicated the other half to charity.

Back in Germany Einstein devoted more time than ever before to popular lectures on scientific problems, as well as on more general issues, which were widely attended. He also

[1] H. B. Freeman, *The Story of Albert Einstein*, Random House, New York, 1958, p. 128.
[2] Ph. Frank, op. cit., p. 245.

took part in charity concerts. One time he travelled to a town in Central Germany to take part in a charity concert. A young inexperienced writer had been sent to report the event.

"Who is this Einstein who is playing tonight?" he asked a lady next to him.

"Good heavens, don't you know? It is the great Einstein!"

"Ah, yes, of course," returned the young reporter, busily writing.

The next day the newspaper reported the successful appearance of the "great musician, Albert Einstein," and called him a musical celebrity and violin virtuoso second to none.

The Haberlandstrasse apartment rang with hearty laughter, and Einstein laughed more than any one else. He cut out the report and carried it with him and he would show it to acquaintances, remarking:

"You think I am a scientist, eh? Hah! I am a famous fiddler, that's what I am!"[1]

Einstein made several trips to Davos, Switzerland, where he read lectures to ill students. In 1927, on one of his visits he was forced to become a patient himself. He had lately taken to sculling in a heavy boat; the outcome was that he developed a dilation of the heart. In the hotel at Davos he would not let an old porter help him, and carried his suitcase upstairs himself. The effort proved too much, and Einstein went down with heart trouble and was forced to spend some time in bed. Elsa decided that if her husband was to continue his work he needed someone to help him. She was recommended Helen Dukas, who remained Einstein's secretary until the end.

It was 1929. Einstein's fiftieth birthday was approaching. As the date drew nearer more and more photographers and reporters began to besiege Einstein. He escaped from their clutches by seeking refuge in a small cottage on the shore of a lake near Berlin a few days before his birthday. Only the family attended the celebration, Einstein, being comfortably dressed in his usual old trousers and sweater. Mrs. Einstein and her daughters brought down the holiday dinner, which consisted of Einstein's favourite mushrooms,

---

[1] M. Freeman, op. cit., pp. 124-25.

gefilte fish, stewed vegetables, salad, fruit and cake. Coffee and drinks were prohibited as Einstein was still convalescing after his illness, but when Elsa objected to his smoking, he put his foot down and allowed himself an occasional pipe. Whenever Elsa asked him, "How many pipes have you had so far today?" he would invariably reply, "One."

The municipal council of Berlin decided to mark Einstein's fiftieth birthday by presenting him with a country house. The officials, however, proved remarkably careless in handling the affair. Twice they offered him plots over which the council's authority did not extend. Finally they asked Einstein to pick out a plot of land of his own choice. Elsa found such a plot in the village of Caputh, near Potsdam. A contract was drawn up with the owners and an architect and builders were invited. Meanwhile the motion for the purchase of the land by the municipal council was challenged by nationalist members. The subject was postponed. The matter gradually developed into something of a scandal, with Einstein finally losing all patience and refusing to accept the gift. In a letter to the municipal council he wrote, "My dear Mr. Mayor, human life is very short, while the authorities work very slowly. I feel therefore that my life is too short for me to adapt myself to your methods. I thank you for your friendly intentions. Now, however, my birthday is already past and I decline the gift."[1]

Work on the house had already begun and Einstein had to pay for it, and the land as well, with his own money.

In this connection Mrs. Einstein remarked to Philipp Frank: "In this way, without wanting it, we have acquired a beautiful home of our own situated in the woods near the water. But we have also spent most of our savings. Now we have no money, but we have our land and property. This gives one a much greater sense of security."[2]

The quiet village of Caputh stands upon a small hill surrounded by woods. Einstein's house stood outside the village, several minutes' walk from lake Havel. Riding at anchor at a small landing stage was Einstein's little yacht *Tummler*. It was a tranquil rural landscape filled with fresh air.

[1] Ph. Frank, op. cit., p. 269.
[2] Ibid., p. 270.

244

In 1930 Einstein received an invitation to deliver a series of lectures as visiting professor at the California Institute of Technology in Pasadena. He hoped that this time he would be able to confine himself to purely scientific matters. The development of theoretical physics in the late 'twenties provided plenty of food for discussion.

But already in New York harbour things began to go wrong, at least as far as Einstein was concerned. The ship had hardly dropped anchor when a hundred reporters swarmed on board. Before he knew it he had already promised one reporter an hour-long interview. Others showered him with questions: "Can you explain relativity theory in one sentence?", "Where is your violin?", "Does religion contribute to peace?" ("Not yet," he answered), "What do you think of man's future?", and so on and so forth. The photographers, too, lost no time, and the pictures in next day's papers showed a rather pale and embarrassed man with straggly grey hair wearing a black overcoat who was obviously doing his best to evade the cameras. The five-day stay in New York had turned into an unending succession of speeches, receptions, interviews and sightseeing tours.

Before leaving for California Einstein visited Riverside Church, at the edge of the Hudson River. Over its entrance stand the statues of the greatest scholars of all times and peoples. Out of the six hundred statues there was one of a living man–Albert Einstein. The thought weighed heavily on him and even his usual ironical attitude towards his own fame failed him.

Pasadena, too, had its share of functions and speeches, but these were more than offset by a comprehensive programme of scientific reports, colloquiums and informal meetings. The inevitable sightseeing tours were not as onerous as in New York. In Arizona, Einstein visited an Indian tribe. He was formally adopted as a member of the tribe by the name of Chief Great Relative and presented with an Indian outfit.

At the Mount Wilson Observatory the Einsteins were shown the giant telescope. "What do you need such a huge instrument for?" Mrs. Einstein inquired. "For the purpose of establishing the structure of the universe," was the director's reply. "You don't say," she responded. "My husband usually does this on the back of an old envelope."[1]

Einstein left America in the spring of 1931 with the promise to return to Pasadena the following year. He took with him many souvenirs, including the Indian chief's dress, Hawaiian baskets, and a piece of petrified wood from Arizona. He had declined to accept a genuine Guarneri violin. "Only a real master should play on such an instrument," was his comment.

Einstein revisited Pasadena again in the end of 1931. He spent the winter with the physicists there, returned to Berlin in the spring of 1932, and was back again in Pasadena by the autumn.

Einstein's third visit to Pasadena was preceded by an incident which caused his American friends some embarrassment. On his previous trips all passport and visa formalities had been handled by the U.S. Embassy without his having to call. This time the ambassador happened to be away, and the papers came to an official, who summoned Einstein and started to question him concerning the purpose of his visit and his political affiliations. Einstein was indignant. If that was the case, he declared, he would not go to the United States at all, and he left the embassy. There was a turmoil in American diplomatic circles in Berlin. The telephone line between Berlin and Washington was busy all night. Finally, the next morning Einstein's passport was delivered to him by a special messenger.

The embassy official's zeal had probably been due to one letter, a copy of which had been received at the embassy. An American women's organisation had protested to the State Department against Einstein's visit to the United States, accusing him of pacifism and communism. The whole affair had caused considerable consternation in the United States and Einstein received a pile of telegrams entreating him to disregard both the embassy official's lack of discretion and the patriotic ladies' letter. Elsa, too, urged him to overlook the matter, which might cost the unfortunate official his job. It was the latter thought that made Einstein unbend, and the next day they left for America. However, he could not resist writing to the patriotic American women:

[1] C. Seelig, op. cit., S. 291.

"Never yet have I experienced from the fair sex such energetic rejection of all advances; or if I have, never from so many at once.

"But are they not quite right, these watchful citizenesses? Why should one open one's doors to a person who devours hard-boiled capitalists with as much appetite and gusto as the Cretan Minataur in days gone by devoured luscious Greek maidens, and on top of that is low-down enough to reject every sort of war, except the unavoidable war with one's own wife? Therefore give heed to your clever and patriotic womenfolk and remember that the Capital of mighty Rome was once saved by the cackling of its faithful geese."[1]

[1] *Ideas and Opinions*, p. 7.

Chapter 22

THE NAZI REGIME IN GERMANY

When the time comes to preserve life, then we have to fight back.

Einstein (1933)

The great rationalists of the 18th century sought for the objective logic of nature, and they found it in the universal causality of things, in the determinism governing the phenomena of nature. But they went further in that they demanded that human affairs also be guided by logic and reason, and hence by right and justice. They attacked the whole repertory of irrationality, its blind faith in dogmas, its intolerance, and its arguments of the stake and the block as opposed to those of logic and reason.

In the 1930s the demon of irrationality reared up to its full height. Its goal was revenge in its fight against reason. One of the ingredients of Hitler's programme was the elimination of objective and logical criteria of science. Science should proceed not from experiment and the logical connections of mental constructs agreeing with experience; it should proceed from the will of a dictator and the criteria decreed by him. One such essential criterion was the racial background of a scientific conception. Theoretical thinking as a whole could not satisfy this criterion. As the nazi minister of education Bernhard Rust declared: "National socialism is not an enemy of science, but only of theories."[1]

The evident rationalism of relativity, which is based on a firm belief in the objective reality of the physical universe, was offensive to nazi dogma. Lenard and Stark lost no time to take revenge for the inglorious failure of their erstwhile attacks against relativity and Einstein. In 1933, Lenard wrote in the *Völkische Beobachter:*

"The most important example of the dangerous influence of Jewish circles on the study of nature has been provided

[1] Ph. Frank, op. cit., p. 281.

248

by Herr Einstein with his mathematically botched-up theories consisting of some ancient knowledge and a few arbitrary additions. This theory is now dashed to pieces, as is the fate of all products that are estranged from nature. Even scientists who have otherwise done solid work cannot escape the reproach that they allowed the relativity theory to get a foothold in Germany, because they did not see, or did not want to see, how wrong it is, outside the field of science also, to regard this Jew as a good German."[1]

Two years later, in an inaugural address at the opening of a new physics institute, Lenard said:

"I hope that the institute may stand as a battle flag against the Asiatic spirit in science. Our Führer has eliminated this same spirit in politics and national economy, where it is known as Marxism. In natural science, however, with the overemphasis on Einstein, it still holds sway. We must recognise that it is unworthy of a German to be the intellectual follower of a Jew. Natural science, properly so called, is of completely Aryan origin, and Germans must today also find their own way out into the unknown."[2]

Proof of the racial defectiveness of the theory was found, besides the racial background of its author, in its "abstract nature": that is, it was not directly associated with sense-impressions as "Aryan physics" should be. Even so, in practice the nazi purge of science was based not so much on such vague considerations as on the racial background of the parents and grandparents of the scientists concerned and their "common" associations with racially inferior colleagues and views. Fortunately, when the purge of German universities and science was launched in full scale Einstein was already out of reach of the storm troopers and the secret police.

As mentioned before, Einstein since 1930, had been "visiting" professor at the California Institute of Technology. In the spring of 1932, shortly after the election of Hindenburg as President of Germany, Einstein returned to Berlin. At the villa in Caputh friends discussed the latest events: Brüning's resignation, the appointment of Papen as Chancellor, and the emergence of Schleicher on the scene. Einstein saw

[1] Ph. Frank, op. cit., pp. 279-80.
[2] Ibid., p. 280.

that the financial magnates were paving the way for Hitler to power. When, in the autumn of 1932, he set out with his wife for California, where they were to spend another winter, he said to her as they left the villa in Caputh:

"Before you leave our villa this time, take a good look at it."

"Why?" she asked.

"You will never see it again."

When Hitler came to power Einstein was already in California. At the height of the "purge" of German universities, in the winter of 1932-1933, Einstein travelled from Pasadena to New York and communicated with the German consul. The latter told Einstein that he need have no fear of returning to Germany, where the new government would do justice to all. If he was innocent, nothing would happen to him. Einstein, however, declared that he would not return to Germany as long as the nazi regime remained in power. After the official part of the conversation was over, the consul said to him privately: "Herr Professor, now that we are speaking as man to man, I can only tell you that you are doing the right thing."[1]

In the spring of 1933 Einstein returned to Europe and took up residence in the Belgian seaside resort Le Coq sur Mer, not far from Ostende.

Queen Elisabeth of Belgium, who was interested in Einstein's theories and held their creator in high esteem, and the Belgian royal family and government did everything to protect Einstein from possible attempts on his life from across the nearby border. It was arranged that bodyguards were to watch him day and night. In the summer of 1933, Philipp Frank, while passing through Ostende, decided to try and find Einstein. He went to Le Coq and inquired of the inhabitants whether they knew where Einstein was living. But the authorities had given strict orders to the inhabitants not to give any information to anyone about Einstein's residence, and Frank's inquiries immediately alerted the bodyguards. When he finally saw Mrs. Einstein she was terribly frightened as she had been warned that a suspected assassin was at large.[2]

[1] Ph. Frank, op. cit., pp. 281-82.
[2] Ibid., p 290.

However annoying these precautions might have been to Einstein, they were nevertheless justified. He stood high in the list of scientists who could well expect a visitation from nazi agents from nearby Germany, and his closest friends also did their best to look after him.

In Le Coq Einstein occupied a small villa on the seashore, which he shared, besides Mrs. Einstein, also with his step-daughter Margot and his secretary Helen Dukas. Before escaping from Germany, Margot had been able to arrange for a part of Einstein's personal archive to be transferred abroad through the French legation.

Antonina Vallentin visited Le Coq in the spring of 1933. She wrote in her book:

"Spring was late that year. The grey, wintry sky was oppressive. The silvery dunes looked as if they had been swept by the wind. The leaden sea battered the shore.... The small house echoed all sounds like a seashell: the crunching of footsteps, the clatter of dishes, the staccato of the typewriter."

She found Einstein in quite his usual mood. He was as engrossed as ever in his scientific thoughts and viewed his adversities with his old ironic humour. "When he laughed it was like a great big laughing tree shaking its mighty branches."[1] Vallentin showed Elsa a large album published in Germany with pictures of opponents of the nazi regime. On the first page was a photograph of Einstein with a list of his "crimes", starting with the theory of relativity. At the end of the list was the note: "Not yet hanged (*noch unge-hängt*)."[2]

Elsa was in constant fear of a provocation of some kind. She told Frank of a recent visit of a former nazi storm trooper who urgently demanded that Einstein should receive him. The man was quite convinced that Einstein was a leader of an anti-fascist emigrant organisation and offered to sell him secret documents for a substantial sum.[3] All sorts of unpleasant surprises, including kidnapping and assassination, could be expected.

[1] A. Vallentin, op. cit., pp. 178-79.
[2] Ibid., p. 161.
[3] Ph. Frank, op. cit., p. 292.

During his conversation with Frank, Einstein remarked that in getting rid of his Berlin environment he had also experienced a certain psychological liberation. Mrs. Einstein, however, did not sympathise with such statements, remarking that Einstein had spent many happy hours in Berlin and he had been well satisfied with the gathering of outstanding physicists there. "Yes," Einstein said, "from a purely scientific point of view life in Berlin was often really very nice. Nevertheless, I always had a feeling as if something was pressing on me, and I always had a presentiment that the end would not be good."[1]

In the meantime Einstein had resigned from the Prussian Academy. He knew that the nazis would compel the Academy to expel him in any case. This would place many German scientists, Max Planck for one, in a most embarrassing situation. To protest against Einstein's expulsion would lay them open to persecution. Agreement with it would disgrace them. In order to spare his friends such a trial Einstein wrote to the Academy that under the present government he could no longer serve the Prussian state and therefore resigned his position.

At first the Academy was rather at a loss what to do. Nernst declared that the Academy, which was proud of such French members as Voltaire, d'Alembert and Maupertuis, should not demand of a member to be also a nationally-minded German. Under pressure from the nazis, however, the Academy finally published a statement accusing Einstein of being engaged in activities detrimental to Germany and spreading stories of atrocities there instead of opposing them. "A good word for the German people from you in particular," the Academy wrote to Einstein, "might have produced a great effect abroad." Einstein replied that a "good word" on his part for "the German people" would have been equivalent to a repudiation of all those notions of justice and liberty which he had stood for all his life. Such testimony, he wrote, would undermine the principles which had won for the German people a place of honour in the civilised world. "By giving such testimony in the present circumstances I should have been contributing, even if only indirectly, to moral corruption and the destruction of all

[1] Ph. Frank, op. cit., p. 291.

252

existing cultural values. It was for this reason that I felt compelled to resign from the Academy, and your letter only shows me how right I was to do so."[1]

Max Planck's class prejudices made it impossible at the time for him fully to comprehend the true meaning of events in Germany. He sincerely believed that the excesses of the new regime were only temporary attendant phenomena. He even advised one professor, who had decided to leave Germany for good, to take leave of absence for a year. By then, he was sure, all the unpleasant features of the new government would have disappeared. On one occasion he tried to intervene personally with Hitler in an attempt to retain "non-Aryan" scientists at the Kaiser Wilhelm Institute. To Planck's surprise the Führer spoke in his usual hysterical manner about his "great goal" of destroying the enemies of the Reich which he would never give up. Planck was fated to witness the downgrading of German science, and Einstein was glad that he had not added to his friend's burden.

In March 1933, the police visited the villa at Caputh and confiscated Einstein's property. (According to the political police, it was obviously going to be used to finance the communist movement.) Soon after that Einstein's writings, including his articles on relativity, were publicly burned together with other "non-Aryan and communist literature" in the square before the State Opera House in Berlin.

Nevertheless, even during the nazi regime some professors continued to teach relativity. They did not speak of it by name, nor did they ever mention Einstein, and mostly set forth the formulas and conclusions without going into the basic concepts. Some physicists nursed a plan of getting rid of Lenard and his anti-relativistic notions of science. They thought that a search in the archives of Bratislava, where Lenard's ancestors had lived, might reveal materials that would prove that he himself had some non-Aryan blood in his veins.

[1] *Ideas and Opinions*, p. 209.

Chapter 23

PRINCETON

In 1938, the Bavarian artist Josef Scharl, who had painted a portrait of Einstein in 1927, escaped from a nazi prison and came to Princeton. In Princeton Scharl asked an old man why he admired Einstein so greatly even though he knew nothing of his theories. "When I think of Professor Einstein," the old man replied, "I feel that I am no longer alone."

When Nernst and other German scientists were persuading Wilhelm II to set up a special research institute in Berlin to engage in the most important problems of natural science, they had before them the example of analogous institutions in the United States. The need for such institutes was dictated by the achievements of science and technology, and they appeared in many countries, under different auspices, according to the prevailing conditions and traditions. In Germany the financial affairs of the Kaiser Wilhelm Institute were the concern of the Kaiser himself. In the United States research institutes not associated directly with industrial firms were nevertheless financed by many top businessmen. Scientific advance in the 1920s called for a greater degree of organisational autonomy for fundamental research. In 1930, Louis Bamberger and Mrs. Felix Fuld, his widowed sister, asked the advice of Abraham Flexner, who had done so much for the reform of American education, concerning the organisation of a new research institute. Dr. Flexner remarked that the United States already had an adequate number of ordinary-type research institutes and he suggested the organisation of a new kind of establishment. Flexner himself became its chief organiser and it was named the Institute for Advanced Studies.

It was Flexner's idea to engage a group of outstanding scientists who would be free of educational or administrative duties as well as of material concerns and could devote themselves to the most general and fundamental problems. These men would form the nucleus of the institute around which talented younger scholars would group. In letters explaining the purpose and objectives of the new institute special stress was laid on the complete freedom of action of the scientists invited to join it. As Flexner once expressed it, "It should be a haven where scholars and scientists may regard the world and its phenomena as their laboratory without being carried off in the maelstrom of the immediate."[1]

Flexner decided that for a beginning the institute's nucleus should comprise scholars devoted to mathematical sciences. The institute was installed in a part of Fine Hall, the Gothic-style mathematics building on the beautiful campus of Princeton University. In 1940, the institute moved from Fine Hall and the university campus to a more isolated building some half hour's walk from Princeton.

In Pasadena, in January 1932, R. A. Millikan, the famous physicist, suggested that Flexner discuss plans concerning the Institute of Advanced Studies with Einstein, who was in California just then. Flexner relates that at first he hesitated to approach Einstein, but when he finally did he immediately fell under the spell of Einstein's unaffected sociability.

When they met again later at Oxford, England, Flexner extended Einstein an invitation to work at the institute. They agreed to continue the talks.

By then it was clear to Einstein that he could no longer remain in Germany. He told Flexner, however, that he hoped to be able to spend a part of the year in Berlin, but there seemed a slim chance of this.

Einstein moved to Princeton and assumed his duties at the Institute of Advanced Studies. In one respect he was not altogether satisfied with his position at the institute. It was wrong, he used to say, to be paid for research work, which constitutes an inner compulsion, and without having any pedagogical duties. On the other hand he regarded as really only his own the time in between lectures, seminars, examination sessions, meetings, and so on. In this respect his duties in Berlin had been incomparably lighter than in Prague or Zurich. In Princeton they were virtually nil. He collaborated with several young scholars whose interests paralleled his

[1] Ph. Frank, op. cit., p. 321.

255

own. These included: Walter Mayer, his assistant from 1929 to 1934, whom he brought with him from Berlin; Nathan Rosen (1934-1935); Peter Bergmann (1937-1938) and Valentin Bargmann (1938-1943) (the similarity of their names gave rise to endless jokes and misunderstandings in Princeton); Ernst Strauss (1944-1947), John Kemeny (1948-1949), Robert Kraichnan (1950), and Bruria Kaufmann (1951-1955). Einstein's collaborator in 1936-1938 was Leopold Infeld, whose reminiscences have been quoted extensively. Einstein associated much less with the older generation of his Princeton colleagues.

The feeling of some embarrassment which Einstein experienced at receiving remuneration for purely scientific work had deep, though possibly subconscious, roots. He always felt that some other occupation besides research should provide the means of subsistence. The example of Spinoza, who had been a diamond grinder, was attractive to him. At the worst he might prefer being paid as a professor and indulge in research in his free time, which would be completely his own. This was an expression of his desire for independence. In spite of the repeated avowals of the sponsors of the Institute of Advanced Studies concerning the scientists' complete independence, Einstein would have preferred to ensure his independence by some modern version of Spinoza's circumstances.

This, however, was impossible. The problem of the unified field theory occupied Einstein so much that he could not forfeit the opportunity that presented itself for devoting all his time to it. Every morning he went to Fine Hall (and, after 1940, to the new building of the institute), met his colleagues there and discussed their progress, difficulties and promising lines of investigation. Then he would retire to his own study where he worked on much the same problems.

There were many distractions, however, for people from all over the United States continually pestered him with requests for advice, help, or public statements. As a rule they got what they wanted. The upshot of it all was that a man who always sought solitude was compelled to meet and have contact with more people than any other of the great world scientists, though this was due not only to external circumstances but to the nature of Einstein's world outlook as well.

On one occasion Einstein had to speak in London at a meeting devoted to helping and finding work for scientists fleeing from Germany. He suggested that the job of a lighthouse keeper would be an excellent thing. This was no jest. Einstein really regarded the solitude of a lighthouse as being the ideal place for research. He frequently complained to friends about the daily petty affairs which distracted him from scientific work. Another and more important consideration was Einstein's requirement of complete independence in scientific work.

"He told me many times," Leopold Infeld writes, "that he would not have minded working with his hands for his daily bread, doing something useful like making shoes and treating physics only as a hobby; that this might be more attractive than earning money from physics by teaching at the university. Again something deeper is hidden behind this attitude. It is the 'religious' feeling, bound up with scientific work, recalling that of the early Christian ascetics. Physics is great and important. It is not quite right to earn money by physics. Better do something different for a living such as tending a lighthouse or making shoes, and keep physics aloof and clean. Naive as it may seem, this attitude is consistent with Einstein's character."[1]

Long before he moved to the United States Einstein sensed the approaching tragedy of science being exploited for aggressive and destructive purposes. The war of 1914-1918, with its new explosives, air raids, tanks and poisonous gases, was a bitter lesson. One could foresee still more destructive applications of the achievements of physics and chemistry. Einstein would have liked to have severed all ties with official science, but apart from other considerations, he already realised the scientist's responsibility for the applications of science. This attitude led subsequently to active interference in scientific and technological research and an appeal to the state which had truly tragic consequences.

To Einstein a lighthouse would also have been an ideal place to escape the innumerable visits and requests which left him hardly any time for work. Einstein's love for people was not of an abstract kind. He was not the man to let his concern for the destinies of humanity overshadow his con-

[1] L. Infeld, op. cit., p. 286.

cern for the plight of individual men. This was a burden to him, for his mind rose far above the daily commonplace and the urge to work was always strong within him.

"Though only scientific ideas and physics really matter to Einstein," Infeld writes, "he never refused to help when he felt that his help was needed and could be effective. He wrote thousands of letters of recommendation, gave advice to hundreds. For hours he talked with a crank because the family had written that Einstein was the only one who could cure him. Einstein is kind, smiling, understanding, talkative with people whom he meets, waiting patiently for the moment when he will be left alone to return to his work."[1]

Einstein's desire for seclusion was not due to the aloofness of a mind overburdened with scientific problems awaiting solution. The feeling was much deeper. An insight into his attitudes is found in his essay, "The World as I See It":

"My passionate sense of social justice and social responsibility had always contrasted oddly with my pronounced lack of need for direct contact with other human beings and human communities. I am truly a 'lone traveller' and have never belonged to my country, my home, my friends, or even my immediate family, with my whole heart; in the face of all these ties, I have never lost a sense of distance and a need for solitude—feelings which increase with the years. One becomes sharply aware, but without regret, of the limits of mutual understanding and consonance with people. No doubt such a person loses some of his innocence and unconcern; on the other hand, he is largely independent of the opinions, habits, and judgements of his fellows and avoids the temptation to build his inner equilibrium upon such insecure foundations."[2]

A lone contemplator seeking solitude and an ardent champion of social justice. An open heart and a sincere, vibrant joy from contacts with people and an impatient desire to be alone in his inner world. The Einstein image seems contradictory indeed. And yet one senses a profound harmony in these contradictions.

In the first place, the word "contemplator" is applicable to Einstein with some essential reservations. Even an adherent

[1] L. Infeld, op. cit., p. 287.
[2] *Ideas and Opinions*, p. 9.

of "pure description" never remains completely on phenomenological positions. Einstein–a master of "cruel experiment" who subjected nature to a third-degree interrogation
in order to bring out the active aspects of scientific notions
–was not a contemplator in the usual sense. What is relativity
if not a rejection of observable self-evidence and a penetration into a world of processes which can be assessed only
by means of active experimental verification? To Einstein
cognition is an invasion of nature. It serves to reshape
human life on a basis of reason and science. The search for
the objective rationality, harmony, laws and causality of
the world develops into a desire to see human society based
on reason. Out of a passionate search for the world harmony
there develops the "passionate *sense of social justice and
social responsibility*". This, however, did not necessarily
require daily contacts and associations with people. Already
in the 1920s Einstein's desire for solitude, of which he spoke
himself and which was apparent to his friends, went together
with numerous social activities.

Such activities did not break through his solitude in his
immediate environment in Princeton. In the greater world
Einstein's social interests and sympathies brought him both
friends and foes; they did not concern his immediate environment very much. As a whole the scientific community had
not yet reached the stage in which scientific and social interests merge; scientists were still hardly aware of the new social values of science. In this respect, as in respect of purely
physical problems, Einstein was already in the 'twenties and
'thirties abreast of the mode of thinking which has come to
characterise physicists in the latter half of the century.

All through the Princeton period Einstein gradually drifted away from the more immediate problems which concerned the majority of physicists. He was preoccupied with
complex mathematical constructions designed to provide the
basis of a unified field theory in which the interactions of
particles and their very existence would derive from common
general laws. Most physicists disagreed with Einstein's
approach to the problem; it was utterly incomprehensible to
the uninitiated, and on the whole it failed to satisfy Einstein
himself. Nevertheless, regardless of the complexity of the
suggested solutions, the overall pattern, based on the concept of a rational unified world governed by uniform physical

laws, was definitely attractive. And even though a formulation of this pattern, as Einstein saw it, involved the elaboration of physical and mathematical constructions of truly baffling complexity and magnitude, the idea appealed to people far removed from the scientific profession.

A realisation of this very broad audience, which accepted the idea of the world harmony without going into the details and subtleties of the problem, grew steadily within Einstein. On the other hand, the intimate circle of like-minded men grew smaller and smaller. In this respect Einstein was keenly sensitive of his aloneness.

Shortly after the Einsteins' arrival at Princeton Elsa had to hasten back to Europe, to the bedside of her elder daughter Ilse, who was dying in Paris. Ilse's death was a terrible blow, Elsa suffered acutely, and suddenly became very old. With Margot at her side, Elsa returned to Princeton carrying the urn with her elder daughter's ashes.

Meanwhile their house was nearing completion at 112 Mercer Street. Elsa supervised the interior decoration and furnishing of their new home, but she never recovered completely from the blow caused by her daughter's death. She developed grave heart and kidney trouble, and when Margot came back from a short stay in New York she found her mother in bed and very weak. "She has practically given up the fight," Einstein told his stepdaughter. He was pale and depressed and his eyes were filled with grief.

Elsa's condition continued to deteriorate. In a letter to Antonina Vallentin she wrote: "I would never have thought that I meant that much to him, and I am very happy to know this now."[1]

That summer Einstein rented a beautiful old lakeside house not far from Montreal, Canada. He resumed his yachting. Elsa felt better in the fine old woods surrounding the house. All her thoughts continued to be with her husband. "He is in fine trim," she wrote to Antonina Vallentin, "and has lately solved some important problems. It will be a long time, though, before all that he has done will be understood and utilised. He himself thinks that this is the greatest and best of his achievements."[2]

[1] A. Vallentin, op. cit., p. 190.
[2] Ibid., p. 191.

Elsa never recovered, and she died in 1936.

Einstein continued to lead much the same life as before. He walked in the streets of Princeton with its red brick houses reminiscent of old England. In his study he continued to work on the mathematical apparatus of the unified field theory. But he had changed a lot. Nothing could make up for the loss of Elsa. Once in Princeton Elsa had remarked: "We all change with the years for we are controlled by our environment or desires or other influences, but Albert as a little boy was exactly as he is now as a man." Now he too had changed, and he felt his loneliness more acutely than ever before.

The feeling of aloneness and melancholy reflected in many of Einstein's letters to friends written in acknowledgement of congratulations on his seventieth birthday in March 1949. He had just recovered from a serious abdominal operation. The suspected malady had fortunately proved groundless, but he was rather weak. His condition, to be sure, did not affect his customary humour, joviality and interest in people and, even more so, it did not prevent him from concentrating on the fundamental problems of the unified field theory. Nevertheless, there was a streak of sadness in his attitude. He wrote to Solovine in the end of March 1949:

"I was touched by your affectionate letter, which contrasted sharply with the countless other letters that have been showered upon me in connection with this sad occasion. You seem to think that I look back upon my life work with serene satisfaction. Viewed more intimately, however, things are not so bright. There is not a notion of which I could be sure. I am not even sure that I am on the right road. Contemporaries view me as a heretic and a reactionary who has, so to say, outlived himself. Of course, this is due to the vogue, as well as to a lack of vision, but neither am I myself satisfied. To be sure, it could hardly be otherwise if you have a critical mind and are honest and if humour and modesty create an equilibrium that is not affected by external influences."[1]

This letter is indicative of Einstein's mood at the time of writing. But it also reveals certain traits of his personality which were always characteristic of him. Although essential-

[1] *Solovine*, p. 95.

ly a reflection of Einstein's dissatisfaction with the results of his work on the unified field theory, the letter also gives us an insight into his character as a scientist in general. As mentioned before, Einstein never posed as an augur proclaiming absolute truths. By their very content his scientific ideas were opposed to absolute conceptions. In complete harmony with this were his critical mind, honesty, modesty and sense of humour—all qualities opposed to dogmatism of any kind. That is why the impact of Einstein's theory was so great, enunciated as it was at a time of a general reappraisal of values.

A reappraisal, however, does not mean the rejection of values, and relativity is not to be understood absolutely (if we may use the pun). A critical mind coupled with modesty and humour cannot fall into scepticism or a nihilistic negation of all and everything; an anti-dogmatic mind does not make a dogma of negation and it creates eternal values not in the sense of their being unchangeable but in the sense of their perpetuation in ever-changing forms.

Einstein's outlook was essentially deeply optimistic, although it inevitably bore the imprint of hesitation, doubt and uncertainty—all of which serve to distinguish a living inquisitive mind from a hidebound one. On the whole, Einstein favoured an unambiguous lucid representation of the world. He saw the nebulosities and obscurities of the world picture and he didn't like them. He would not be satisfied with a vague, foggy picture, feeling that it should be definite, unambiguous, and precise. Herein lies the psychological basis of the conflict between the strict picture presented by relativity and the uncertainties of quantum physics. The logical aspect of the conflict will be discussed in the following two chapters.

In the late 'forties and early 'fifties Einstein's psychological tone was considerably affected by the loss of some of his best friends. Every new departure tended to revive the memory of friends and associates who had departed in the 1930s. In Princeton Einstein frequently thought of his friend and fellow-scientist Paul Ehrenfest, who had committed suicide in 1933. Einstein regarded Ehrenfest's suicide as an expression, in part, of the conflict between the problems which science poses before the scientist and the answers he can find. The immediate cause of Ehrenfest's suicide was purely personal. The deeper cause lay in a tragic dissatisfaction which haunted him in his later years.

Einstein's characteristic of Paul Ehrenfest as man and scientist is presented in an obituary written in 1934. Men of high qualities, Einstein writes, will depart this life by their own free will fairly often. This generally stems from an incapacity or an unwillingness to resign oneself to the new and more difficult outward conditions of life. "To refuse to live out one's natural life because of *inner* conflicts that are felt to be intolerable—that is even today in persons of sound mind a rare occurrence, possible only in the case of the noblest and morally most exalted personalities. It is to such a tragic inner conflict that our friend Paul Ehrenfest has succumbed. Those who knew him well, as was vouchsafed to me, know that this unblemished personality in the main fell victim to a conflict of conscience that in some form or other is spared no university teacher who has passed, say, his fiftieth year."[1]

This conflict is bred by a scholar's inability to tackle the problems with which science confronts him. Ehrenfest possessed a remarkably clear understanding of these problems. However, he regarded his own constructive abilities as being much inferior to his critical abilities. "In the last few years," Einstein says, "this situation was aggravated by the strangely turbulent development which theoretical physics has recently undergone. To learn and to teach things that one cannot fully accept in one's heart is always a difficult matter, doubly difficult for a mind of fanatical honesty, a mind to which clarity means everything. Added to this was the increasing difficulty of adaptation to new thoughts which always confronts the man past fifty. I do not know how many readers of these lines will be capable of fully grasping that tragedy. Yet it was this that primarily occasioned his escape from life."[2]

With Einstein the discrepancy between the demands of science—for a unified field theory—and the possibility of an unambiguous, clear-cut answer was not so tragic as was the rift between problem and solution with Lorentz, and even more so, Ehrenfest. Einstein possessed an inborn optim-

[1] *Later Years*, p. 236.
[2] Ibid., p. 236.

ism nurtured by an unshakable confidence in the harmony and knowability of the world. The difficulties of developing the general theory of relativity, overcome in 1916, and the far greater—and unsurmounted—difficulties of developing the unified field theory were a source of considerable mortification, but beneath this lay the unshakable conviction that no matter how difficult and tortuous the ways of science, they nevertheless lead to a trustworthy knowledge of the real world harmony.

Behind the outward appearance of unruffled calm Einstein too was beset by great soul-racking storms. They were never apparent to the outsider, but they frequently raged beneath the surface. Einstein was far from being the type of serene divinity that Goethe is sometimes represented to have been.

When Einstein wrote of the "mathematical torment" he experienced in developing the unified field theory and his inability to bring it up to a point where it could be verified by observations, he was indeed tormented by a realisation of the questions that had to be answered and his inability to answer them. At Princeton Einstein frequently had occasion to recall Ehrenfest's tragedy. In a conversation with Antonina Vallentin he again brought up the question and spoke of the conflict with the new generation which had shaken Ehrenfest.

"He spoke with feeling and with resignation," Vallentin says, "for it was a conflict which he himself had gone through. The drama which had originated in the happy years when he was in constant contact with contemporary scientific thinking was now becoming more and more intense. It was not the usual conflict of generations in which one represents bold imagination, while the other stands for outmoded ideas and is like a block of stone at the side of a disused road. His was the drama of a man who, in spite of his age, pursues his own road, which gets more and more deserted and which friends and young people regard as being wrong and leading to nowhere."[1]

It was this feeling that made Einstein's thoughts return to departed friends. Among them was Marie Curie-Sklodowska of whom Einstein wrote after her death: "It is the

[1] A. Vallentin, op. cit., p. 200.

moral qualities of its leading personalities that are perhaps of even greater significance for a generation and for the course of history than purely intellectual accomplishments. Even these latter are, to a far greater degree than is commonly credited, dependent on the stature of the character."[1]

Reminiscences of departed friends and their emotional dramas were not just a source of placid, resigned sorrow. These emotional dramas were testimony to great moral integrity, unswerving devotion to the truth and compassion for people—qualities which fostered confidence in the future of science and human society.

"It was my good fortune," Einstein continues, "to be linked with Mme. Curie through twenty years of sublime and unclouded friendship. I came to admire her human grandeur to an ever growing degree. Her strength, her purity of will, her austerity toward herself, her objectivity, her incorruptible judgement—all these were of a kind seldom found joined in a single individual. She felt herself at every moment to be a servant of society and her profound modesty never left any room for complacency. She was oppressed by an abiding sense for the asperities and inequities of society. This is what gave her that severe outward aspect, so easily misinterpreted by those who were not close to her—a curious severity unrelieved by any artistic strain."[2]

In the beginning of 1947 Paul Langevin died, and yet another symbol of lofty moral integrity was added to the martyrology of science. "He was one of my very best friends, a veritable saint and extremely gifted," Einstein wrote in a letter to Solovine.[3]

Einstein's thoughts would pass on from departed friends and associates in the service of science to Elsa—he could not forget her.

During those latter years Einstein was also fated to witness the gradual passing away of his only sister Maja, the little girl so like her brother on the old photograph taken in Munich.

In 1939 Maja and her husband, the son of the teacher Winteler of the cantonal school at Aarau, moved to Princeton

[1] *Ideas and Opinions*, pp. 76-77.
[2] Ibid., p. 77.
[3] *Solovine*, p. 83.

from Florence, Italy. They could no longer stand the oppressive atmosphere of the fascist regime. Maja's husband went to Switzerland temporarily, while she visited her brother.

Many people in Princeton were struck by the great likeness between brother and sister. "Her manner of speaking and the sound of her voice," Frank writes, "as well as the childlike and yet sceptical formulation of every statement are unusually similar to her brother's mode of expression."

In 1947 Einstein wrote to Solovine: "Subjectively my sister feels well, but she is nearing the end of the road of no return. She has gone downhill faster than most of her contemporaries."[1]

In subsequent letters Einstein writes of the deterioration of Maja's health. He spent much time at her bedside reading aloud the works of ancient classics and other books. Maja passed away in the summer of 1951. Of Einstein's intimate family circle, only his stepdaughter Margot and his secretary Helen Dukas remained in the two-storeyed cottage at 112 Mercer Street not far from the Institute of Advanced Studies.

The house would have been undistinguishable from many other houses inhabited by the Princeton professors if not for the numerous photographs which have made it familiar to people all over the world.

The path to the door passes through a gap in a hedge of clipped bushes. Inside, a wooden staircase to the left of the entrance leads up to the second floor along a wall decked with dried stalks of maize.

Einstein's study overlooks a garden with several fine old trees. The window occupies almost the whole wall opposite the door. Shelves of books line the left and back walls. In a small space left of the window hangs a portrait of Gandhi. On the right of the entrance one door leads to a terrace, and another to Einstein's bedroom. Hanging on this wall are several excellent canvases by Josef Scharl and portraits of Faraday and Maxwell.

In front of the window stands a big desk and next to it a small table with several pipes and an Australian boomerang on it. Near the entrance is a round table and

---

[1] *Solovine*, p. 85.

an armchair in which Einstein liked to work with his writing paper on his knees and scattering the written sheets about him.

Every morning Einstein would leave the house and set off for the Institute of Advanced Studies. His way lay down Mercer Street and into shady lanes which took him to the beautiful Princeton campus, with attractive clumps of nut-trees, plane trees, maples and lindens. There are many fruit-trees there, especially apple trees, and in autumn the lanes are strewn with fallen apples. Some of the lanes pass through tunnels made by the crowns of plane trees and lindens meeting overhead.

The attitude towards Einstein in the United States differed widely in various circles. Reactionaries called him a "Red". Clergymen and "fathers of families" protested in the press against public speeches by a "refugee" who sought to "deprive Americans of their personal God". The overwhelming majorities of Americans, however, took a keen interest in Einstein's pronouncements and sought in his words answers to many burning problems.

The people of Princeton were in this respect a mirror of the United States and the world. The atmosphere around Einstein was truly remarkable. On the one hand, the figure of Einstein walking down the long shady road to and from the institute soon became part of the Princeton landscape. At the coffee-house, where the owner and visitors knew Einstein's tastes and habits, it was quite customary for Princetonians to exchange the time of the day with him just as with any other local citizen. On the other hand, the people of Princeton saw in him "one of the legendary figures of the 20th century."[1]

In this respect they were hardly unlike the schoolgirl from British Columbia who wrote to Einstein: "I am writing to you to find out whether you really exist."[2] The girl's impression of a well-known and even commonplace personality mixed with the image of a legend is not unlike the man in the street's impression of Einstein's ideas: as of something tremendous in loftiness, scope and paradoxicality, and at the same time based on ordinary human intuition.

[1] Ph. Frank, op. cit., p. 356.
[2] C. Seelig, op. cit., S. 344.

Many outstanding scientists have lived in Princeton but none of them were at the same time so "ordinary" and so legendary a figure. This brings us back to the question of Einstein's popularity as a characteristic trait of the 20th century.

The years which Einstein spent in Princeton make possible a definite answer to this question. Einstein's scientific interests were not shared by most physicists and were unknown to the public at large. Nevertheless, all his work at Princeton served to confirm what people had felt ever since the 'twenties: that Einstein's purpose was to present a rational, objective world picture shorn of any anthropocentrism and mysticism whatsoever—to discover the kingdom of reason in nature. People have always felt that the rational ideals of science are inseparable from rational social ideals. The legendary man who sought to discover the kingdom of harmony in the cosmos and build it on earth would be an ordinary man like any other. The people of Princeton who saw Einstein daily had an idea of his historic exploit. People who had never seen Einstein but had an idea of his work guessed the traits of his personality.

Chapter 24

EINSTEIN'S ATTITUDE TOWARDS QUANTUM MECHANICS

You believe in the dice-playing god, and I in the perfect rule of law in a world of something objectively existing.

Einstein
Letter to Max Born (1944)

While Einstein was in Berlin seeking the inroads to the general theory of relativity, in Copenhagen a new school of theoretical physics was emerging. It came into the public limelight when Niels Bohr applied quantum ideas to explain the structure of the atom.

The development of atomic physics began with Mendeleyev's Periodic Law. During the forty years that had passed since its discovery in 1869, many attempts were made to offer a physical interpretation of the observed periodic recurrence of analogous chemical properties in elements arranged according to increasing atomic weights. This was made possible by the discovery of discrete sub-atomic particles.

Rutherford demonstrated in 1911 that the atom consists of a central nucleus (accounting for only a fraction of the total volume) around which revolve negatively charged electrons. This initial scheme later became more complex. The nucleus was found to consist of positively charged protons and neutrons with no electric charge. The electron orbits are distributed in layers, close-lying orbits forming electron shells surrounding the nucleus. The heavier the atom the more nuclear particles it contains, and accordingly, the more electrons circling around the nucleus. In going over from lighter to heavier atoms we find that the electrons make first one shell, then two, and so on. The outer shell contains first one, then two, etc., electrons, until it is filled; then the next shell begins to increase, starting with one electron. Each successive shell requires a definite number of electrons to fill it. Thus, in a row of atoms of increasing weight there periodically occur atoms with the same number of electrons in the external shell. Since the chemical and some physical properties of elements depend on the number of external electrons, these properties periodically recur.

The trouble is, however, that the notion of an electron spinning about in an orbit does not agree with the laws of electrodynamics. Such an electron is bound to emit electromagnetic waves, rapidly losing its energy. As a result the electron would lose velocity and spiral down towards the nucleus and finally fall on it. Atoms, however, are quite stable structures.

The contradiction was resolved by Bohr, who postulated that an electron can move only in certain orbits corresponding to specific energy values of the moving electron. While in orbit the electron does not radiate electromagnetic waves. Radiation occurs only when it jumps from one orbit to another. The energy dissipated by the atom equals the difference between the energies corresponding to the higher and lower electron orbits, and it is carried away by electromagnetic radiation, which consists of Einstein's light quanta, or photons. An electron jumping from one orbit to another causes the emission of a photon.

Einstein was greatly impressed by Bohr's brilliant intuition which helped him advance his postulates long before they could be derived more or less directly from more general assumptions; moreover, they were based on extremely fragmentary and apparently not interrelated experimental data. Well into the 1920s the idea of quantised radiation and light quanta remained shaky ground for the advance of physics. It had undermined the classical foundations of physics, but no new fundamental laws of mechanics or electrodynamics had yet been developed to replace them.

"It was," Einstein writes in his *Autobiographical Notes,* "as if the ground had been pulled out from under one, with no firm foundation to be seen anywhere, upon which one could have built. That this insecure and contradictory foundation was sufficient to enable a man of Bohr's unique instinct and tact to discover the major laws of the spectral lines and of the electron shells of the atoms together with their significance for chemistry appeared to me like a miracle–and appears to me as a miracle even today. This is the highest form of musicality in the sphere of thought."[1]

We have already spoken of the meaning attached to "musicality" in this context. For Bohr's theory, with its paradoxical postulates of electrons orbiting without radiating energy, was an excellent example of physical intuition.

Einstein understood the nature of this intuition. His evaluation of Bohr's theory sheds light on the basic features and style of his own mode of thinking. He was not at all sympathetic with the new theory, which was essentially contrary to his ideal of physics. Niels Bohr recalled Einstein's first reaction to the new atomic model in a lecture at the Moscow Institute of Physical Problems, in 1961. "I could probably have arrived at something like this myself," Einstein had said, "but if all this is true then it means the end of physics."[2]

There is a wealth of meaning and generalisation in this remark. "I could probably have arrived at something like this myself." Quantum theory led physics to a new picture of electron motion in the atom. It was a paradoxical picture, and Einstein saw or intuitively sensed that an explication of Bohr's paradoxical postulates would lead to more general paradoxes which would overthrow or circumscribe the ideal, harmonious, rational world picture that emerged from the philosophical treatises of Descartes and Spinoza, was reliably supported by Newton's mechanics (which at the same time imbued it with the alien concept of absolute motion), and finally developed into the harmonious form of relativity. To Einstein the meaning of physics lay in the elaboration of this picture. Hence his remark concerning Bohr's theory: "If all this is true then it means the end of physics". At a time when Bohr's atomic model was being debated from many aspects (such as its applicability to atoms more complex than hydrogen) Einstein saw the true meaning of the new theory: it spelt the collapse, or at least a restriction, of the ideal which in the eyes of the creator of relativity theory constituted the mainstay of physics.

Bohr, on the other hand, was attracted by the very aspects of the photon theory and his own constructions which tended

[1] *Philosopher-Scientist*, pp. 45-47.
[2] *Nauka i Zhizn* (*Science and Life*), 1961, No. 8, p. 77.

to violate the strict canons of the classical ideal. His intuition led him not so much to the destruction of the classical ideal as to a kind of blurring and washing out of its contours. Such intuition labelled Bohr as the Rembrandt of physics (true, in connection with later ideas of his which tended to blur the clear-cut, precise patterns of classical science). Bohr could also be likened to those 19th-century artists who, following Goya, turned from the ideal of clarity in painting inherited from the previous two centuries.

In the 1920s Bohr's postulates of discrete, preferred orbits and the non-radiation by electrons moving in those orbits ceased to be regarded as paradoxical. A new general theory was developed which provided a rational explanation for them. The theory itself, however, was more paradoxical than anything ever known to science, for it introduced the concept of waves associated with particles.

The crisis in quantum physics in the 1920s due to the inability of scientists to offer a more general theory capable of explaining Bohr's atomic model ended in a series of discoveries which marked a new epoch in physics.

In 1924, Louis de Broglie introduced the concept of *waves of matter* (de Broglie waves, as they are now called). According to de Broglie, the motion of material particles, the electron in the present case, is associated with a wave process. The orbit which an electron can occupy must contain an integer number of these waves. This is the "allowed" or "preferred" orbit. The particle's motion is subject to the laws of wave propagation. Thus originated the science of wave mechanics. In 1925, Erwin Schrödinger wrote an equation for calculating the amplitude of certain oscillations—the wave function. Solution of this equation gives a discrete series of energy values which give the energy of an atom in different states corresponding to the movement of electrons in certain orbits.

What is the wave function? What is the physical meaning of the quantity whose variations determine an electron's behaviour?

The answer was given by Max Born: what is essentially involved is the *probability* of encountering an electron. If we compute the wave function for a specific point and a specific time, the solution (or rather the square of its absolute

The Einsteins' home at 112, Mercer Street, Princeton, N. J.

value) is a measure of the probability of the electron occurring at that point at a given time.

Max Born and Pascual Jordan correlated the *intensity of the de Broglie waves* (a purely wave concept) with the *average number of electrons* in a unit volume of space (a purely corpuscular concept). The connection between the wave and corpuscular concepts takes the following form.

We spoke of the *average* number of electrons in a given volume–average over a large count. In the same way we can say that in tossing a coin the *average* occurrence of heads out of ten flips is five. The probability, then, is one-half: that is to say, the chances of the coin falling heads up is equal to half the number of flips.

Born and Jordan assumed that the intensity of de Broglie waves varies with the average number of electrons. But the average number of electrons in a given volume is also dependent on the probability of each electron occurring within the volume. Hence, the wave intensity can be interpreted as the *probability* of finding the electron in the given volume. As long as we restrict ourselves to undulatory concepts in discussing de Broglie waves we have no trouble: Schrödinger's equation very accurately determines the wave intensity at any point and time. But when we go over to the corpuscular concept and treat electrons as particles the equation no longer determines a fact, an observed result, but only its probability.

The intensity of wave motion is determined by the amplitude of the oscillations. The average amplitude, however, is zero, for deviations to one side (with a plus sign) are as frequent as deviations to the other side (with a minus sign); as on the surface of a choppy sea, the crests are balanced by the troughs. The square of the amplitude is taken in order to characterise the intensity of oscillations: then the values with the minus sign take on a plus sign (the square of a negative quantity is a positive quantity), and the average is no longer zero. That is why the measure of the intensity of de Broglie waves is the *square* of the absolute value of the amplitude of the wave function. It is a measure of the probability of finding an electron at a given point and time. This probability is determined by Schrödinger's equation, which gives the de Broglie wave intensity at a given point and time.

Thus quantum mechanics, which emerged in 1925-1926, operates with laws which, generally speaking, determine not the motion of a particle—its position and velocity at a given instant—but only the probabilities of a position and velocity. The more exactly the coordinates of a particle are known at a given instant the less exactly can its velocity be determined, and vice versa. This statement is an expression of the *uncertainty principle*, which was formulated by Werner Heisenberg in 1927.

Uncertainty relations are illustrated by means of "imaginary" or "thought" experiments. Consider, for example, an electron passing through a fixed narrow aperture. The electron's position can be measured at any given instant, and the smaller the aperture the greater the accuracy with which the position can be determined. The possibility of measurement is essential for the concept of "position" as applied to the electron. The experiment, however, precludes the possibility of a precise determination of the electron's *velocity* at the same instant. The electron's motion is accompanied by the propagation of de Broglie waves, which interact with the edges of the aperture and change their direction; as a result the electron's velocity undergoes a change, and the narrower the aperture the greater the change. If we wish to determine the electron's velocity with greater accuracy, we must be satisfied with a correspondingly less accurate determination of its position. In other words, the notion of the simultaneous "sharp" determination of an electron's position and velocity lacks physical meaning. If we take this relationship into account and do not insist on unlimited accuracy we can apply the classical concepts of position and velocity to the electron.

We cannot simultaneously and unambiguously assign an electron a specific position and velocity. But we can assign it the probability of this or that position or velocity occurring at any instant of time. This probability is given by Schrödinger's equation.

Laws which determine the probability of events instead of the actual events, are called statistical laws. At one time they restricted Laplace's determinism, that is the idea that the coordinates and velocities of all the particles in the universe at any given instant can unambiguously determine the state of the universe at any subsequent instant, together with all subsequent events in its history. First the statistical laws of thermodynamics had restricted Laplacian determinism. Now it was restricted from another quarter: the notions of particles are not subject to the laws of dynamics, the state of a particle's motion at any given instant determines merely the probability of certain coordinates or velocities occurring at a subsequent instant.

This point of view aroused the objections of many eminent theoretical physicists, whom Max Born later called "grumblers". The first broad discussion of the issue took place at the 1927 Solvay Congress. Being one of the "grumblers", Einstein was the most active and profound critic of quantum mechanics (or rather of its probability interpretation). At the congress and subsequently in writing Einstein tended proof to the fact that uncertainty relations do not provide a complete picture of physical reality. Bohr, Heisenberg, Born and others parried the blows aimed against the assertion of statistical laws as the basic world laws. The argument was made the more difficult by attempts of the creators of quantum mechanics (supported by positivistic philosophers) to represent the transition from dynamic to statistical determinism as recognition of *indeterminism* in nature. Furthermore, some men declared that the only reality the physicist can speak of is the instrument readings, measurements and observations, obtained in the course of physical experiments.

Incidentally, the idea of "waves of probability" was to some degree Einstein's. In his light-quantum theory he had in effect brought together the wave and corpuscular conceptions of light. Light consists of waves possessing energy, such that in a unit volume of space there is a definite quantity of light-wave energy. The space through which a ray of light travels is characterised by a certain energy density of electromagnetic waves. But light consists of particles, photons. In the corpuscular conception the space through which a ray of light passes is characterised by an average photon density. Thus the average photon density (which varies as the *probability* of encountering a photon: the greater the probability the more photons are encountered) is equivalent, in going over to the wave conception, to the energy density, i.e., to the intensity of oscillation of the electromagnetic field. These oscillations, which propagate through space as electromagnetic waves, determine the probability of encountering a photon. This notion was derived logically from Einstein's photon theory. The quantum mechanics developed in 1925-1926 dealt initially with electrons. The probability of encountering an electron, the probability of its location in a given volume is determined not by electromagnetic waves but by de Broglie's "waves of matter", which Born treated as waves of probability.

Schrödinger's wave equation determines the motion of an electron (it can be used to determine the probability of locating an electron); in optics an analogous wave equation determines the motion of photons. In this sense Einstein's photon theory already contained the basic contradictions of quantum mechanics. Light consists of particles. On the other hand, completely trustworthy experiments indicate that light is electromagnetic oscillations. Furthermore, Einstein's conclusion that electromagnetic wave intensity is proportional to photon density brings one to the idea that wave intensity corresponds to the probability of locating a photon at a given point: electromagnetic waves are in fact waves which have a high probability of meeting a photon. Einstein did not accept the idea of waves of probability, as this would mean that a law governing merely probabilities of events are the most general laws of the microcosm. Yet in the final analysis it was his own theory that led to this conclusion.

Evaluating the photon idea in retrospect, we find that it contains an even more radical departure from the foundations of the classical world picture. Unlike Planck, Einstein spoke of the discontinuity of energy in an electromagnetic field not only in connection with emission or absorption but in intermediate states as well. Field is by its very nature discrete ("beer is not only sold in pint bottles but it also consists of indivisible pint portions"). A natural generalisation of this idea is the notion that all fields are discrete, that we can describe a field acting on a particle to an accuracy which cannot go beyond some indivisible quantity. Classical physics proceeds from the notion that the behaviour of particles is determined by their interactions (Mach's principle), that is, by fields of force generated by the particles and acting on them. If we rid classical mechanics of other forces acting on particles (say, for instance, the inertia forces caused by the absolute acceleration of a system), that is, if we bring it closer to the "classical ideal", we obtain a universe in which fields of force determine everything that takes place in it.

If these fields cannot be determined with unlimited precision, then the ideal picture will be covered with tiny dots. The "classical ideal" is restricted by certain minimum energy values, by certain minimum forces determining particle motion. Thus the photon theory turned out to be something of a time bomb planted under the "classical ideal". And even though it threatened the "ideal" only within very small field domains, this was sufficient to remove the erstwhile absolute confidence in a picture in which everything could be determined with any precision whatsoever, to the extent that any infinitesimal change in the state of a particle could be explained by some field action.

This connection between an infinitesimal change in a particle's state of motion and field intensity is a cornerstone of physics, and not only Newtonian, but also as reformed by Einstein. Einstein regarded interactions between particles as responsible for all natural events. They are described by equations connecting variable fields with infinitesimal changes in a particle's state of motion. These equations are called *differential equations*. An example is the equation of motion of a particle in a field of gravity. Any infinitesimal change in its velocity is determined by the field's intensity.

Before the development of quantum conceptions it was thought that the law linking a particle's behaviour with the action of other particles or fields would always be valid, no matter how small the change in the particle's state of motion (for example, its acceleration in a gravitational field). Now we find that a field's intensity cannot be less than some minimum value and that it can increase only in finite increments. Before, we spoke of the discrete nature of matter, of atoms as the smallest portions of matter. Now we find that interactions between bodies, on the one hand, and changes in their states of motion, on the other, are discrete; they lose their unambiguous relationships when the quantities considered are less than the minimal limiting values of the variables expressing field intensity and changes in the state of motion.

Compare two pictures. One is painted with colours mixed on a palette. On the canvas different hues merge imperceptibly into one another. The other picture is done with pure unmixed colours and is made up of a number of small blotches of different colours. This was the manner of some impressionist artists (pointilists) who thought that colours blended in the eye instead of on the palette offered a truer representation of the subject. The classical world picture corresponds to the landscape painted in the manner of the old masters; the quantum picture corresponds to the impressionist method of pointilism. Which of the two reflects physical reality?

In the pre-quantum era the answer differed depending on whether matter or motion were involved. Matter was recognised as discrete, the ultimate picture therefore consisting of separate colour dots corresponding to the atoms. The picture of motion was continuous, and the laws of motion connected infinitesimal increments and velocities with infinitesimal forces.

On the basis of numerous indubitable facts quantum mechanics arrived at a discrete picture of field and motion. These conclusions could already have been made on the basis of the photon idea. But in 1917 Einstein made yet another step in the direction of the statistical-probability conception of particle motion. Out of the photon concept and Bohr's model he developed the laws of radiation originally discovered by Planck. The laws governing atomic radiation are of a statistical nature, they determine the probability of radiation in every given case. Wave radiation and particle radiation (always indeterminate) seem incompatible, and Einstein regarded this as the weak point of his radiation theory.

"The weakness of the theory," he wrote, "lies in the fact that, on the one hand, no closer connection with the wave concepts is obtainable and that, on the other hand, it leaves to chance the time and the direction of the elementary processes."[1]

Elementary processes, such as the emission of a photon when an electron jumps from one of Bohr's orbits to another, are in fact a matter of chance, and only when the number of radiated photons is large will the result agree with the probability as determined by the statistical law.

[1] *Physikalische Zeitschrift*, 1917, 18, p. 127.

These considerations—the absence of closer connections with the wave concepts and the chance nature of radiation—were to Einstein the symptoms of the great threat to the very existence of physics. Bohr was not at all worried. He knew that light behaves like particles in photo effects, for example, in photoelectric cells in which photons strike electrons out of the surface of a metal plate. Bohr also knew that light behaves like waves in passing through narrow apertures or gratings, where refraction phenomena caused by waves skirting the edges develop. Hence the inevitability of a new approach to light, regardless of whither it may lead.

In the *Living Philosophers* volume devoted to Albert Einstein, Bohr writes of their first meeting and their first argument about the nature of the laws governing the behaviour of photons:

"When I had the great experience of meeting Einstein for the first time during a visit to Berlin in 1920, these fundamental questions formed the theme of our conversations. The discussions, to which I have often reverted in my thoughts, added to all my admiration for Einstein a deep impression of his detached attitude. Certainly, his favoured use of such picturesque phrases as 'ghost waves (*Gespensterfelder*) guiding the photons' implied no tendency to mysticism, but illuminated rather a profound humour behind his piercing remarks. Yet, a certain difference in attitude and outlook remained, since, with his mastery for coordinating apparently contrasting experience without abandoning continuity or causality, Einstein was perhaps more reluctant to renounce such ideals than someone for whom renunciation in this respect appeared to be the only way open to proceed with the immediate task of coordinating the multifarious evidence regarding atomic phenomena, which accumulated day to day in the exploration of this new field of knowledge."[1]

During his visit to Moscow in 1961 Bohr returned to the subject of his early discussions with Einstein. When Einstein expressed his doubts in connection with the need to give up the ideals of continuity and causality, Bohr had replied:

"What do you hope to achieve? You, the man who introduced the conception of light as particles! If you are so con-

[1] N. Bohr, "Discussion with Einstein", in *Philosopher-Scientist*, pp. 205-06.

cerned with the situation in physics in which the nature of light allows for a dual interpretation, then ask the German Government to ban the use of photoelectric cells, if you think that light is waves, or the use of diffraction gratings, if light is corpuscles."

"My arguments," Bohr added, "were neither convincing nor weighty, which, however, was characteristic of the state of affairs."

Today it has become evident that Einstein's stand was not merely an expression of fidelity to the old positions of physics; rather it was due to an intuitive feeling that the new positions were not yet final and that more general and more precise basic physical principles might yet appear.

Bohr continues his reminiscences:

"Einstein remarked bitterly:

" 'There you are: A man like you comes and one would expect that two like-minded persons had met, yet we are unable to find a common language. Maybe we physicists ought to agree on certain general fundaments, on certain general propositions which we would regard as positive before embarking on discussions?'

"I objected with some heat:

" 'No, never! I would regard it as the greatest treachery on my part if, in embarking on a new domain of knowledge, I would accept any foregone conclusions.' "[1]

This is where their roads parted. Einstein continued to meditate on the general fundaments of physics out of which specific problems could be derived. He continued to seek these fundaments in the classical ideal of science. Bohr saw adventure in discovering new laws of physical reality which did not fit precisely into the pattern of the classical harmony.

Einstein's comment, "if all this is true then it means the end of physics," is a remarkable statement. Einstein considers Bohr's point of view to mean the end of the physics as it was known then. He does not reject it entirely but considers it to be possible, at least in principle ("*If* all this is true. . . .").

Here is a courageous mind which reached a point when it had to question the pivotal idea of its own creations as well as the fundamental ideas of all preceding science. Here

[1] *Nauka i Zhizn (Science and Life)*, 1961, No. 8, p. 73.

is a mind which conceded the possible validity, more, the beauty ("higher musicality") of a theory with which it did not sympathise and which threatened its scientific ideal. In the final analysis, such unlimited tolerance is a manifestation of complete liberation from the "merely personal", even to the extent when one's "merely personal" ideal of science is sacrificed for the benefit of the objective, "extra-personal" world picture. Einstein was devoted to the classical ideal of a world picture in which the interactions of particles describe all world events with absolute precision. This devotion, however, was not greater than his devotion to objective truth. Paraphrasing Aristotle, he could have said, "Newton is dear to me, but dearer still is truth", "Newton" being understood as a symbol of the classical harmony, of a "Newtonian type of mechanics". We could say the same of Descartes or Spinoza with equal justification. To Einstein Newton was a symbol of the classical ideal in science. He spoke of "Newton's programme" (in which everything is determined by interactions between bodies) and "Maxwell's programme" (in which the motion of a body at every point is determined by the field acting upon it) as the pivotal programmes of physics. We could recall here the words of Robert Mayer quoted in the epigraph to Chapter 9 (such reminiscences are inevitable, as Einstein is an embodiment of all that is immortal, living and anti-dogmatic in the history of science): "Nature in its simple truth is greater and more beautiful than any creation of human hands, than all the illusions of the created spirit."

We could also quote a significant passage from a letter to Solovine: "We cannot overlook the fact that the bodies we use for measuring objects react upon those objects," and the final remark: "Without sinning against reason we could never arrive at any conclusions."

Comparing this with his remark in connection with Bohr's theory, we may conclude that Einstein did not rule out the possibility of encroachments on the "classical ideal". His words about the "end of physics" do not refer to the objective world picture as such but to the physics of the "Newtonian programme" and the "Maxwellian programme".

Einstein's attitude towards quantum-statistical ideas was complicated, but on the whole it fitted with the remarks cited by Bohr. He saw the connection of those ideas with his own work, he saw the threat to physics inherent in them, anticipated that the crisis would be overcome by subsequent researches, and hoped to discover the basic dynamic laws determining not the probability of processes but the processes themselves, as was the case in classical thermodynamics.

De Broglie's theory could inspire hope in such a non-statistical explanation. Today, looking back in retrospect, we see in electromagnetic waves something reminiscent of the waves of probability. In the first quarter of the century scholars had sought to reduce the statistical laws of particle motion to laws of dynamics or at least to the existence of pilot waves to guide such motion. The analogy between de Broglie's waves and electromagnetic waves facilitated acceptance of the new theory and at the same time accustomed the mind to the idea of the reality of "waves of matter". Photons are in some way connected with electromagnetic waves, though it is hard to say just how. Electromagnetic waves were presumed to represent changes in the intensity of a real field. De Broglie's waves, it seems, should also be regarded as propagating oscillations of some real field. These hopes and hypotheses, however, soon gave place to the idea of "waves of probability".

Einstein's attitude towards the idea was, as mentioned before, complicated. He flatly rejected the positivistic conclusions and ideas of "indeterminism", and this aspect of his critical argumentation was refutable. His specifically physical considerations and "thought experiments" designed to refute the physical constructions of Heisenberg, Bohr, Born and other adherents of "probability waves", however, drew some sound counter-arguments from them. Only today can a general idea, or rather an intuitive speculation concerning a theory that would be more general and precise than quantum mechanics, be embodied in comparatively specific form and correctly evaluated. Let us investigate this aspect of the matter.

In 1932 Einstein had a meeting in Berlin with Philipp Frank, who stood by the "orthodox" statistical version of quantum mechanics and the erroneous positivistic conclusions derived therefrom. Frank quotes Einstein as follows in this connection:

"A new fashion has now arisen in physics. By means of ingeniously formulated theoretical experiments it is proved that certain physical magnitudes cannot be measured, or, to put it more precisely, that according to accepted natural laws the investigated bodies behave in such a way as to baffle all attempts at measurement. From this the conclusion is drawn that it is completely meaningless to retain these magnitudes in the language of physics. To speak about them is pure metaphysics."[1]

Hearing Einstein talk in this way, Frank sought to identify the above-mentioned conception with the basic premises of relativity theory. Relativity, for example, rejects the concept of "absolute simultaneity" on the grounds that no real or imaginary experiment is capable of demonstrating the possibility of synchronising events investigated in different reference frames moving relative to one another. Hence, Frank concluded, the concepts rejected by relativity were rejected because they could not be observed. He said as much to Einstein: "But the fashion you speak of was invented by you in 1905?"

"A good joke should not be repeated too often," Einstein replied, going on to explain that relativity theory describes objective processes and real material things and establishes the connection between different descriptions of one and the same reality. It has nothing in common with positivism and the "new fashion".

In fact the positivistic conclusions drawn from the quantum-statistical nature of microcosmic laws do not derive from quantum mechanics. It is a long distance from the theory to its epistemological interpretation, which is what Einstein spoke of. We find in quantum mechanics a natural "curve of knowledge" which, when interpreted absolutely, leads to this epistemological interpretation. Today, from the standpoint of the physics of the 1960s, we can see that the important aspect in this "curve" is not so much its departure from classical ideas as its *insufficiently drastic* departure, as far as the quantum mechanics of the 1920s is concerned.

This calls for a preliminary explanation. Compare relativity with quantum mechanics. Relativity proceeds from the consideration that such concepts as "motion with respect to

1 Ph. Frank, op. cit., p. 260.

the ether", "absolute simultaneity" and others cannot be experimentally verified. But we find such an impossibility of experimental measurement already in Lorentz's theory. Length contraction of all bodies in the direction of motion made it impossible to register motion with respect to the ether by any experiments, whether real, like Michelson's, or imaginary.

Relativity goes farther. It rejects the existence of a real, objective motion with respect to the ether (insofar as there is no way of detecting it) and all physical properties associated with such motion. When observability is *identified* with reality the difference between the conceptions of Lorentz and Einstein disappears. Recognition of *objective* reality makes this difference extremely important. Einstein's relativity breaks completely with motion through the ether and related classical concepts and declares them meaningless.

Let us take a look at quantum mechanics from this point of view. It restricts the application of such concepts as "position" and "velocity" to electrons by imposing certain conditions. But quantum mechanics cannot be expounded without those classical concepts. It is quite meaningless without them. And in fact it does not claim that in small space-time domains particles do not possess coordinates or velocity. Quantum mechanics does not break so drastically with classical notions. It does not throw away the concepts of the position and velocity of a particle with the same finality with which relativity theory threw away the classical notions of absolute space, time and motion.

This does not mean that relativity has gone farther away from classical physics than quantum mechanics. On the contrary. But though quantum mechanics has not completely rejected the concepts of position and velocity of a particle, these concepts played a much more fundamental role in classical physics than Newton's absolutes, which were actually in contradiction with the classical ideal. A more revolutionary quantum mechanics would not "purge" the classical ideal, it would destroy it.

Initially quantum mechanics merely restricted the classical ideal. At the price of the indeterminacy of velocity it is possible to determine a particle's position with some accuracy; reciprocally, at the price of indeterminacy of position it is also possible to determine velocity with some accuracy. In the early 'thirties, however, it was established that in very small domains it is impossible to determine a particle's position sharply even when its velocity is indeterminate. Then new processes were discovered which tended more drastically than ever before to remove classical conceptions from the subatomic picture.

This physical school (which will be examined in the following chapter) goes beyond quantum mechanics. Niels Bohr clearly defined the basic premise of the latter at the International Physical Congress held in Como in 1927. He sets forth his arguments in his "Discussion with Einstein", written in 1949:

"It is decisive to recognise that, *however far the phenomena transcend the scope of classical physical explanation, the account of all evidence must be expressed in classical terms.*"[1] (Bohr's italics.) This is an extremely important formula as it reveals the positive classical aspect of quantum mechanics. The latter stipulates that classical concepts are applicable to all observable physical phenomena, subject to reduced accuracy.

If there exist phenomena to which classical concepts are *totally inapplicable,* such phenomena will force a restriction of quantum mechanics, making it a theory describing only some real processes. In 1927, however, there were no known physical phenomena to which classical concepts would be completely inapplicable. Therefore criticism of quantum mechanics was directed not against its "protective" (with respect to classical concepts) aspects, but against the thesis concerning the *conditions* of such application. The criticism was levelled from the standpoint of *unconditional* application of classical concepts, from the standpoint which allowed for the existence of "hidden parameters" precisely determining events in the microcosm and which could be unconditionally expressed in terms of classical concepts.

Einstein did not attend the congress at Como. He voiced his objections to Bohr and other exponents of the new theory at the Fifth Solvay Congress which took place that year at Brussels. The debate was continued at the following Solvay Congress in 1930. Einstein suggested a variety of ingenious thought experiments with different combinations of

[1] *Philosopher-Scientist*, p. 209.

apertures, boxes, balances and other gadgets to convince Bohr. The latter, however, demonstrated that these constructions did not contradict the postulates of quantum mechanics. The discussion between Einstein and Bohr continued whenever they met. Paul Ehrenfest frequently took part in these discussions, acting as a mediator between the two men.

Einstein's critique of quantum mechanics was expounded in general form, without "thought constructions", in a paper, "Can Quantum-Mechanical Description of Physical Reality Be Considered Complete"[1] written in 1935 in collaboration with Podolsky and Rosen. Bohr responded with a paper under the same title.[2] The argument brought out with increasing clarity the differences between the prevailing understanding of quantum mechanics and Einstein's position.

Einstein's philosophical stand was crystal clear. In a letter to Solovine in 1938 he gave the following characteristic of the connection between the difficulties encountered by quantum mechanics and positivism. After speaking of the "harmful influence of subjective positivistic views" he goes on: "The conception of the objective reality of nature is regarded as an obsolete prejudice. and the quantum theoreticians are making a virtue out of necessity. Men are more influenced by suggestion than horses, which is why they have a fashion for every period, the majority being quite unaware of its origin."[3]

"A virtue out of necessity." In this case the "necessity" consisted of an urgent need to apply classical concepts to microcosmic theory, and describe the motions of elementary particles subject to the restrictions imposed by the indeterminacy of conjugate variables, which allow only the probability of the precise values of the variables for each instant and point to be indicated. The restriction of classical concepts is necessitated by the diversity of facts supporting both the wave and corpuscular nature of particles.

As far as Einstein was concerned, "necessity", or in his own terminology, "external confirmation", was not enough to solve a problem. A concept had to derive from general physical principles. Uncertainty relations and the statistical

[1] *Physical Review, 47,* 777 (1935).
[2] *Physical Review, 48,* 696 (1935).
[3] *Solovine,* p. 71.

character of quantum-mechanical laws derived from the notion of *a priori* impossibility of cognising objective reality, from the inseparability between object and subject in the process of cognition, from the limits of the causal explanation of the world. Necessity became a virtue. The orthodox statement of quantum mechanics ceased to be a result of "necessity", a tentative explanation of certain phenomena requiring further elaboration. It was regarded as an expression of preordained qualities of knowledge—a result of "virtue". To Einstein, however, any restriction on the causal explanation of the world, indeterminacy or a denial of the objective nature of reality constituted a departure from the unshakable and experimentally verified fundaments of science. He sought the "inner perfection" of quantum mechanics which would enable its relationships to be derived from a more general picture of objective reality and a more general conception of causality.

Einstein saw that the statistical probability of relationships in quantum mechanics did not contradict experience. To him, however, this fact did not obviate the possibility of "precise determinism" with regard to the microcosm. Einstein considered that it was possible to imagine a picture of elementary processes whose course could be precisely determined. Whether this is so in principle constitutes the controversial issue of theoretical physics.

In 1950 Einstein wrote to Solovine:

"From the point of view of direct experience exact determinism does not exist. On this we are in complete accord. The question is whether or not a description of nature should be deterministic. There is also the particular question of whether it is possible to form a conceptual image of individual objects which would in principle exclude statistical interpretation. Only on this score do opinions differ."[1]

Einstein's ideas concerning the non-statistical laws of behaviour of elementary particles were intuitive and he never formulated them in a specific hypothesis. He did not look forward to a rehabilitation of pre-quantum physics. At the time, criticism of quantum mechanics from non-classical positions could not take any concrete form and remained a vague and largely intuitive trend of thought. Einstein's

---

[1] *Solovine*, p. 99.

criticism of quantum mechanics is of the same trend in many of his statements on this question.

In his article "Physics and Reality"[1], published in 1936 in the *Journal of the Franklin Institute,* Einstein wrote that while to believe that quantum-mechanical description can be exhaustive was logically possible without contradiction, it was so very contrary to his scientific instinct that he could not forego the search for a far more complete conception. Replying to this in his "Discussion with Einstein", Bohr once again expressed, in somewhat different form, the fundamental idea of quantum mechanics: "In quantum mechanics we are not dealing with an arbitrary renunciation of a more detailed analysis of atomic phenomena but with a recognition that such an analysis is *in principle* excluded."[2]

By a "more detailed analysis" is meant here the determination of dynamic variables, such as position and velocity, to any accuracy. Quantum mechanics restricts this accuracy by the condition: the sharper one variable the less sharp the other. The following question, though, remains unsolved: is there in principle a limit to the application of the concepts of position and velocity in the microscopic and submicroscopic world?

When Bohr visited Princeton in 1937 his discussion with Einstein took the form of a rather humorous contest concerning which side Spinoza would have taken had he lived to see the development of quantum mechanics. To Einstein, Spinoza's outlook was the most general expression of the idea of the unity, determinacy and objective and material nature of the world. Einstein embodied this idea in his criteria of "inner perfection" and "external confirmation". Quantum mechanics, he found, did not satisfy them. Now we know that quantum mechanics displayed this insufficiency only after the discovery of phenomena embodying entirely new principles, a circumstance which can undermine any theory.

"Every element of the physical reality," Einstein, Podolsky and Rosen write, "must have a counterpart in the physical theory." If that is the case, then a physical theory provides a *complete* description of reality and, following the well-

---

[1] *Ideas and Opinions,* p. 290.
[2] *Philosopher-Scientist,* p. 235.

known court oath formula, it speaks "the truth, *the whole truth*, nothing but the truth". Yet in his 1949 autobiography Einstein speaks of the criteria for choosing a theory which would have *relative* "inner perfection" and "external confirmation". They guide science along a road which infinitely approaches the truth, but they do not guarantee "the *whole* truth". In some of his remarks concerning quantum mechanics Einstein implies the criterion of absolute completeness in the description of physical reality. Today, when we can view quantum mechanics from the standpoint of a more general and exact theory, we find that it offers a *relatively* incomplete description of physical reality. This incompleteness, which is present in any mechanics where the motions of immutable particles are fundamental processes and is inherent in any mechanics "of the type of Newton's", has become apparent only today. Only now are we in a position to outline, if only hypothetically, the contours of a new world picture which would be more comprehensive and exact than the one presented by the "Newtonian-type" mechanics. Formerly the physical arguments aimed at demonstrating the incompleteness of the quantum-mechanical description of the world were restricted to an intuitive presentiment of broader conceptions. This is seen in the passage from Einstein's letter to Max Born quoted in the epigraph. By the "dice-playing god" Einstein means the concept according to which the statistical laws are fundamental laws of physical reality.

"In our scientific expectations we have progressed towards antipodes. You believe in the dice-playing god, and I in the perfect rule of law in a world of something objectively existing which I try to catch in a wildly speculative way. I hope that somebody will find a more realistic way, or a more tangible foundation for such a conception than that which is given to me. The great initial success of quantum theory cannot convert me to believe in that fundamental game of dice."[1]

"God does not play dice!" Einstein again speaks of "god" in this somewhat ironical context, and again it is a pseudonym for the objective *ratio*—the most general laws of reality. These

[1] M. Born, *Natural Philosophy of Cause and Chance*, Clarendon Press, Oxford, 1949, p. 122.

laws are not statistical, they determine not the probability of events but the actual events themselves. The idea of deeper and more general laws acting behind the scenes of thermodynamics was, as we have seen, the point of departure for Einstein's work on Brownian motion. Einstein realised (we have mentioned this) that the statistical laws of thermodynamics, that is, the laws governing the behaviour of large ensembles, are not reduced to the laws of displacement and interaction. But he was interested in the inseparability of the higher forms of motion from the simplest and most general.

Now it was a question of the statistical laws governing the movement of individual particles. These laws could not be explained in terms of the dynamic laws of motion of other kinds of bodies, as was the case in thermodynamics. Nevertheless, Einstein could not accept statistical laws as fundamental.

Einstein was not satisfied with attempts to grasp the universal dynamic laws of reality "in a wildly speculative way" and he expected that in future a "more tangible foundation for such a conception" would be found. Consequently he was unable to put forward to Born any specific arguments and he spoke only of a subjective intuition which made him believe in the universal dynamic orderliness of the world. In 1947 he wrote to Born:

"I cannot substantiate my attitude to physics in such a manner that you would find it in any way rational. I see of course that the statistical interpretation (the necessity of which in the frame of the existing formalism has been first clearly recognised by yourself) has a considerable content of truth. Yet I cannot seriously believe it because the theory is inconsistent with the principle that physics has to represent a reality in space and time without phantom actions over distances. ... I am absolutely convinced that one will eventually arrive at a theory in which the objects connected by laws are not probabilities, but conceived facts, as one took for granted only a short time ago. However, I cannot provide logical arguments for my conviction, but can only call on my little finger as a witness, which cannot claim authority to be respected outside my own skin."[1]

[1] M. Born, op. cit., 1949, p. 122.

Not much later Einstein again wrote to Born, whom he wanted to see very much:

"I can understand why you consider me an old sinner. I also feel that you fail to comprehend how I have found myself on my lonely road. You would not accept my point of view, of course, but it might amuse you. I would also be glad to have an opportunity to put my finger on your positivistic philosophical platform. I am afraid, however, that I may not be able to do this in our lifetime."[1]

When, at Seelig's request, Born commented on this letter, he wrote that he did not sympathise with positivism and that Einstein was an adherent of *classical* determinism. The latter statement must be elaborated upon.

Einstein did not recognise statistical laws as being fundamental laws of physical reality. His idea was that fundamental laws must determine events themselves, not just their probabilities. In a letter to Seelig he writes that field, which determines events at every point in space, is an elementary concept.

"My views concerning the foundations of physics are at variance with those of my contemporaries, and I cannot claim to speak for theoretical physics. I do not believe in the necessity of the statistical nature of the fundamental laws and, contrary to the almost universal opinion, I do think that it is at least plausible, if not conclusive, that the concept of field is an elementary one."[2]

In a letter to James Franck Einstein wrote:

"I can imagine that God created a world without any laws of nature. A chaos, in short. But the notion that statistical laws are final and that God draws lots is highly unsympathetic to me."[3]

Writing to Infeld in 1948, Einstein mentioned a discussion with a physicist who defended the orthodox view on quantum mechanics. Einstein writes that he was charmed by his interlocutor's scientific ingenuity.

"But I found it very difficult to talk to him since the weight of various arguments was not the same to him as to me. He could not understand my adherence to logical simplicity or my

[1] C. Seelig, op. cit., S. 395.
[2] Ibid., S. 396.
[3] Ibid.

lack of confidence in the value of theoretical criteria, no matter how impressive, when questions of principle are at stake. Like all of those who think that quantum theory approaches the core of the problem, he finds my position strange and detached."[1]

This letter alone is sufficient for an understanding of the meaning of Einstein's "logical simplicity". It is an ontological characteristic of reality, it asserts the existence of the objective *ratio*, the objective determinacy of natural processes. To Einstein this determinacy bodies forth in the "classical ideal" purged of the arbitrary postulates of absolute simultaneity and absolute space.

In this respect the theory went farther than its maker. In the practical sphere Einstein's equivalence of mass and energy brought forth the atomic age, in the sphere of physical theory it produced the concept of particle transmutation. This had no effect on the fundamental purpose of Einstein's work, which was to develop a theory in which the motion of immutable bodies would remain the fundamental concept.

Leopold Infeld writes in his memoirs:

"It was distressing to see Einstein's isolation and aloofness from the main stream of physics. On several occasions this man, probably the greatest physicist in the world, said to me in Princeton: 'Physicists consider me an old fool, but I am convinced that the future development of physics will depart from the present road.' Today Einstein's objections against quantum mechanics have lost none of their force. In fact today, I think, he would have been less alone in his views than in 1936."[2]

Indeed, during the 'fifties, when Infeld wrote these words, and especially in the 'sixties, physics has been increasingly approaching the limits of the world picture which was created in the 17th and 18th, elaborated in the 19th and completed in the present century. In the 17th-18th centuries men thought that to explain the world meant to draw a picture of the motions of particles in space; such a picture, which gives the positions and velocities of all particles, would, they thought, provide an exhaustive explanation of physical reality. 19th-century scientists realised that particle

[1] *Uspekhi Fizicheskikh Nauk*, 59, Issue 1, p. 174.
[2] Ibid., p. 173.

motion was not enough to explain the essense of phenomena and that there existed complex processes which could not be explained by means of mechanical models. In the 20th century, Einstein demonstrated that the laws of motion of particles and all natural bodies differ from the classical laws of Newton; quantum mechanics went on to specify that particle motion is a complex process which does not allow for a simultaneous sharp definition of a particle's position and velocity. This was a restriction of the "classical ideal". Discoveries in the sphere of elementary particles and the generalisation of quantum mechanics and relativity theory, which will be discussed in the following chapter, prepared a more radical ground for the rejection of this "ideal". A clear understanding of the necessity of such a rejection depended largely on the clarification of the principles of quantum mechanics which developed out of the discussions between Einstein and the adherents to the orthodox probability interpretation.

For one thing, these discussions stimulated Bohr and other adherents to the orthodox conception to an elaborate clarification of their position. In his lecture at the Moscow Institute of Physical Problems, Bohr had this to say after describing his first meeting and first discussion with Einstein:

"We met frequently after that conversation and we often argued. Today beginners know the answers to many of the questions which had once caused heated discussions. But today, when Einstein is no longer with us, I would like to say how much he did for quantum physics with his eternal, indomitable desire for perfection, for the classical consummation of theories, for a unified system on the basis of which the whole physical picture could be developed. In every new step of physics which, it seemed, derived unambiguously from the previous one, he found contradictions which served as stimuli for the further advance of physics. At each stage Einstein would challenge science, and if not for those challenges the development of quantum physics would have been much slower."[1]

Secondly, the critical platform was clarified in the course of these discussions. It became apparent that within a certain domain of processes quantum mechanics displays no inner

[1] *Nauka i Zhizn* (*Science and Life*), 1961, No. 8, p. 73.

contradictions. In this respect it differs from Newtonian mechanics, which had several inherent contradictions, such as instantaneous action at a distance, absolute time, and inertia forces as a criterion of absolute motion, which contradicted the "classical ideal", that universal basis for all mechanics of "Newton's type".

Quantum mechanics proceeded from the postulate of the existence of a classical object, and nothing in it contradicted the basic postulate or introduced arbitrary assumptions. From here, hence, unlike Newtonian mechanics, progress was possible only provided entirely new facts were presented, provided a new world were discovered in which there was no place for the initial postulates of quantum mechanics.

Such facts accumulated in the physics of elementary particles. They did not, however, enter the arsenal of Einstein's criticism of quantum mechanics, and at first his criticism seemed to lack heuristic value. It was considered purposeless like the search for the unified field theory. From this followed the conclusion concerning the almost complete futility of Einstein's scientific work at the very stage when his genius could have been expected to reach its zenith. It is difficult to accept such a conclusion.

The idea that Einstein's criticism (as well as his search for a unified field theory) was fruitless collapses with a change in the criteria of what we have called heuristic value. Unambiguous, positive physical theories possess apparent and immediate heuristic value. But there is also a great deal of heuristic value, though not necessarily apparent, in conceptions that are still in the making and have not yet achieved unambiguous positive form, conceptions that leave to the future, questions instead of answers.

Today the objective meaning of the *questions* contained in Einstein's criticism of quantum mechanics is fairly clear. Heisenberg and Bohr spoke of the interaction between a moving elementary particle and a body concerning which there exist no doubts as to its position and velocity. Such a body, for example an aperture through which the particle passes, most certainly remains motionless during the experiment. We ignore the fact that, in the final analysis the aperture itself is made up of particles which are lacking position or velocity. Once we extend quantum-atomistic conceptions to the aperture, quantum mechanics loses meaning, for it comprises statements relating, firstly, to quantum objects (the particle), and secondly, to classical objects (the aperture). Quantum mechanics possesses not only negative content; it not only rejects the possibility of a simultaneous sharp determination of a particle's coordinates and velocity. Quantum mechanics, as stated before, also possesses positive content; it declares that in certain conditions, and subject to certain qualifications, it *is possible* to determine a particle's position and velocity. It is this positive content of quantum mechanics that has been challenged in all more radical (in the sense of their rejection of classical conceptions) theories, starting with the 1930s when the first doubts were voiced concerning the possibility of exact determination of field variables independently of Heisenberg's conditions ensuring and restricting this possibility.

A world without classical objects goes beyond the realm of quantum mechanics. In describing such a world classical conceptions must be revised even more radically than in the case of quantum mechanics.

The notion that prevailed for many years that Einstein's criticism of quantum mechanics was levelled from *classical* positions is a major historical misunderstanding. The real objective meaning of his criticism is that it pointed to the limits of quantum mechanics beyond which there lay even more revolutionary theories.

This was not a *misunderstanding* in the literal sense. It was an *historical* misunderstanding; that is to say, it was impossible for the conception to display its real meaning before new concepts acquired more or less explicit form. We shall soon deal with the concepts which enable us to view in retrospect the true meaning of Einstein's position with regard to quantum mechanics. True, it is a question not only of the history of science but also of the evolution of Einstein's ideas. For many years he kept within the boundaries of the "classical ideal" of science, i.e., he sought to draw a world picture consisting of nothing but the motions and interactions of immutable bodies. A genuine criticism of quantum mechanics, not from "behind" but from "ahead", from more radical positions, from positions of even greater indeterminacy of dynamic variables, is possible only *beyond the limits of Mach's principle and the "classical ideal" of science.*

Einstein defined very precisely the sphere of application of quantum mechanics:

"In the field of *mechanical* [Einstein's italics] problems, i.e., wherever it is possible to consider the interaction of structures and of their parts with sufficient accuracy by postulating a potential energy between material points— [quantum mechanics] even now presents a system which, in its closed character, correctly describes the empirical relations between statable phenomena as they were theoretically to be expected."[1]

Here a definition of mechanical processes is given. Einstein regards them as motions caused by interactions among particles, the interactions being dependent on the spatial distribution of the particles. This is a picture in which particle motions are dependent in some way on their positions, and correspondingly, on the forces due to interactions between bodies, i.e., it is the "classical ideal", the world picture obeying Mach's principle, and all processes in the world are explained by the motions and interactions of masses.

[1] *Philosopher-Scientist*, p. 666.

Chapter 25

RELATIVITY, QUANTA, AND UNIFIED FIELD THEORY

The time is out of joint;—O cursed spite,
That ever I was born to set it right!

Shakespeare. *"Hamlet"*

The phrase in the epigraph is the key to Hamlet's inner tragedy, presented with such force of artistic generalisation that even the remotest conflicts and emotions find reflection in it. The moral harmony of the world was shattered on the terrace at Elsinore. Hamlet, who saw the world harmony in the implementation of the moral ideal, came up against jarring disharmony, treachery and crime. A heavy burden rested on his shoulders, and he saw the restoration of the world harmony in revenge. Hamlet realised the difficulty of his task and he knew that a straightforward, resolute action could not "set the time right".

For Einstein the ideal harmony was Spinoza's world, a unified world with the mutual, relative motions of interacting bodies, such that the motion of each of them is determined by its interactions with the others. Einstein restored this classical ideal when he extended the relativity principle discovered in the 17th century to the new phenomena discovered in the 19th. The harmony, however, was restored only for inertial motion, which fits in with the classical ideal. As long as accelerations are not introduced into the world picture it contains nothing that would not be the cause of interactions between bodies. By dint of tremendous intellectual effort Einstein was able to remove absolute accelerated motion from the world picture. Here he had to stop.

There was left the difference between electromagnetic and gravitational fields, and this did not fit into the world harmony. On the other hand, features which also did not fit into the initial scheme of the ideal world harmony were discovered in the motions of elementary particles. Both Newtonian mechanics, which departed from this scheme, and Einstein's mechanics, which restored the harmony, proceed from the continuity of the motion of particles whose positions and velocities are determined by the initial conditions and their interactions. In the 1920s it was found that, generally speaking, a particle's position and velocity cannot be simultaneously sharply defined for any given moment of time.

Quantum mechanics was neither a subjective nor an objective tragedy of Einstein's. First of all, Einstein did not see the removal of Newton's absolutes and Lorentz's ether as a single master stroke resulting in a millennium of ultimate truth. As pointed out before, special relativity had contributed more than any previous theory to the overthrow not just of Newtonian dogma, but of the very spirit of dogmatism as such. Secondly, to Einstein goes the credit for the photon idea, that is, the source of the theory which ascribes wave properties to particles and corpuscular properties to waves. Finally, Einstein in effect linked criticism of quantum mechanics with the prospects of further advances in physics, not with a reversal to classical notions.

Towards the end of his life Einstein had evolved from recognition to negation of Mach's postulate as a universal principal of nature. He spoke of the limitations, not only of Newtonian mechanics, but of all theories "of the same type". The enunciation of a new theory overstepping the limits of the "classical ideal" could not be a subjective tragedy to a thinker who had contributed so greatly to bringing physics to that ideal. And when physics continued to advance, Einstein did not see this as a failure of the world harmony. At the beginning of this book an attempt was made to reveal the scope and vitality of Einstein's rationalism. By the very nature of his world outlook Einstein, who never claimed to have the final say in any respect, simply could not conceive of a tragedy of lost positions. That is why quantum mechanics was not a subjective tragedy to him.

Neither was it an objective tragedy for his ideas, because it was precisely the consistent and natural development of Einstein's conceptions which tended to carry the world picture beyond the confines of the "classical ideal".

Immediately after the enunciation of general relativity the problem of the unified field theory was placed on the order of the day. Gravity can be identified with space *curvature*. Could not other fields of force be identified with other geometrical properties of space? Could it not be possible then to reduce all fields of force to unified geometrical relationships and bring them under the head of a unified field expressed in terms of certain geometrical properties of space? At the time when these questions were first posed two types of fields were known, gravitational and electromagnetic. Attempts were made to "geometrise" the latter and represent it as a change in the geometrical properties of space. These attempts occupied Einstein's thoughts for almost thirty years.

In the spring of 1942 Einstein wrote to his friend Hans Mühsam, an old doctor who lay paralysed in Haifa at the time:

"I am an old man known mainly as a crank who doesn't like to wear socks. But I am working at a more fantastic rate than ever, and I still hope to solve my pet problem of the unified physical field. I feel as if I were flying in an airplane high in the skies without quite knowing how I will ever reach the ground.... I hope to live to see better times and to catch a glimpse of something like the promised land."[1]

Two years later he wrote to Mühsam:

"I may still live to see whether I am justified in believing in my equations. It is no more than a hope, as every variant entails tremendous mathematical difficulties. I did not write to you for so long because, despite my conscience pricking and a sincere desire to write, I am in an agony of mathematical torment from which I am unable to escape. To save time I don't even go anywhere, and I have put off all other things *ad calendas Graecas....* As you see, I have become a miser, though in my lucid intervals I realise the futility and foolishness of my greed for time."[2]

Einstein thought that the unified field theory would enable quantum-statistical laws of the microcosm to be derived from deeper and more general non-statistical physical laws governing the facts themselves and not merely their probabilities.

"I am working with my young men," he wrote to Solovine in 1938, "on an extremely interesting theory which, I hope,

[1] *Helle Zeit*, S. 50-51.
[2] Ibid., S. 51.

will enable us to overcome the current mysticism of probability and the departure from the idea of reality in physics."[1]

Twelve years later, in another letter to Solovine, Einstein confessed that the unified field theory did not yet lend itself to verification as mathematical difficulties made it impossible to achieve unambiguous solutions, while general philosophical and logical arguments failed to impress most physicists.

"The unified field theory is now finished.... In spite of the vast amount of work put into it I am unable to verify it in any way. This situation will prevail for many years, all the more so as physicists do not accept logical or philosophical arguments."[2]

Is it possible that almost thirty years of unparalleled mental effort of a genius could have been in vain?

Before attempting to answer this question it is necessary to trace another trend in the development of physics since the 1930s.

The quantum mechanics enunciated during 1924-1926 was a non-relativistic theory. It did not take into account processes predicted by relativity, such as the change in the mass of an electron depending on its velocity. In 1929, Dirac wrote a relativistic wave equation describing electron movement which took account of relativity adjustments such as the change in mass, providing a more accurate description of the motion of fast, high-energy electrons. The calculations, however, yielded negative values for the electron's energy. This physically unacceptable conclusion led Dirac to assume that his wave equation also described the behaviour of a particle differing from the electron in charge. This positively charged particle was discovered in due course and called the positron.

It was found that an electron can fuse with a positron with the emission of two or three photons. Reciprocally, photons can turn into electron-positron pairs. The concept of particle transmutation, according to which particles can change into one another, introduced a new element into the classical picture. Classical science dealt with qualitative changes of matter, reducing them to the regrouping of atoms, that is, to

[1] *Solovine*, p. 75.
[2] Ibid., p. 107.

the movement of indestructible, immutable particles. When the transmutation of elements was first discovered it was explained by a regrouping of the component parts of atoms and atomic nuclei: electrons, protons and neutrons. In the case of transmutation of elementary particles, however, no regrouping or motion of smaller sub-particles is involved. In the contemporary world picture transmutation is regarded as an elementary process not reducible to other processes.

Elementary transmutations apparently stand outside the pale of processes described by relativity theory. Here motion does not exist in the classical sense of displacement and change of spatial configuration with time. Thus at first glance the idea of velocity of a particle and other mechanical concepts seem to be meaningless. There is no sense in speaking of the relativity of motion, in the sense of displacement, if there is no motion. On the other hand, the transmutation of elementary particles is a process which is predictable by relativity theory. When electrons and positrons turn into photons their rest mass disappears. Photons have no rest mass. Transmutation of photons into electrons and positrons involves a transformation of mass in motion into rest mass. This is a very general and fundamental law. When bodies travel at velocities comparable with the speed of light the increase in mass due to the motion becomes substantial. In the case of the transmutation of electrons and positrons into photons the rest mass turns completely into mass in motion. Such effects could be called *ultra-relativistic.*

Here we come to an extremely important point which is essential for a correct analysis of Einstein's work in the latter part of his life, the 1930s-1950s. From Einstein's autobiographical notes, letters and discussions with friends one can see that the years devoted to the unified field concept and opposition to orthodox quantum mechanics constituted a significant period in his life work. It was a period in which he approached a unified conception embracing the whole of the universe, a theory more comprehensive than general relativity. The ideas that occupied him almost completely from the 1930s on were a consummation of his life work, a generalisation of all the things that had occupied his mind since boyhood.

Most biographies and analyses, however, treat the Princeton period as one of futile search. The only positive result they see of this period is in the derivation of the equations of motion from the field equations. This approach has given rise to grave misinterpretations concerning the evolution of Einstein's scientific career. His aloofness, which at the time when relativity was in the making was regarded as the attitude of a thinker far ahead of his time, was later interpreted as the aloneness of a scientist who had lost his way and was unable to keep up with the general advance of science.

Now the latest gains in the investigation of ultra-relativistic effects offer a new basis for an evaluation of Einstein's work during the 1930s-1950s. This means a reappraisal of his life and work as a whole. As concerns Einstein, the only appraisal that matters consists in an answer to the question as to what part of his "merely personal" experiences, thoughts and findings contributed to the "extra-personal" content of scientific progress. To answer this question it is necessary to assess the real progress of science, and this can usually be done only in retrospect, from the positions of a more general and exact theory.

Einstein took practically no part in the specific investigations which contributed to the accumulation of knowledge about elementary particles and their transmutations. The road of progress for the theory of elementary particles was a long one and in effect it did not concern a man devoted to the elaboration of a theory having "internal perfection". During that period the "external confirmation" of physical theories seemed impressive indeed. Theoretical predictions were confirmed by experiments to the ninth decimal. Yet this did not prevent theoretical constructions from rapidly giving way to new ones, which were equally short-lived. The reason for this was that most of them were advanced *ad hoc*. The most important upshot of this abundance of hasty, short-lived *ad hoc* hypotheses was to revive the interest of physicists in a natural general theory of elementary particles possessing "inner perfection". The evolution can be illustrated on the following example.

Photons represent particles of electromagnetic radiation which can be emitted or absorbed by systems of charged particles. Now in vacuum, where there are no other particles, a charged particle emits and absorbs so-called virtual photons. They contribute to the energy, and consequently the mass, of an electron. The smaller the intervals between consecutive emissions and absorptions of virtual photons, the greater their contribution to the electron's energy. The time between the emission of a virtual photon and its absorption can be infinitely small and, correspondingly, the path travelled (which equals the photon's lifetime times the velocity of light) can be equally small.

Hence, the contribution of virtual photons to an electron's energy can be infinitely large. Computations taking account of an electron's interaction with its own emission yield infinite values for the energy and mass of the electron.

This is an absurd situation which contradicts all existing knowledge of physical phenomena. Accordingly, the infinite energy and mass values are removed from the computations. This is achieved by various ingenious methods and approaches. The gap between the "external confirmation" and "inner perfection" of the physical theory has acquired some peculiar forms. There are many ways of getting rid of infinite energy and mass values. They consist in ignoring very high-energy virtual photons which contribute substantially to the particle's energy. This is done "on credit", in the hope that a future theory of elementary particles will provide the necessary grounds to explain the arbitrary cutting out of high energies. Such a theory may be based on concepts of minimum distances and minimum time intervals derived from more general principles. We shall shortly examine this idea. The important thing is that today physicists do not sit back in expectation of unambiguously framed theories. They devise methods of removing infinite energy values in expectation of some future theory.

In this situation the ideas of "pure description" and the conceptual or *a priori* nature of physical notions seem archaic indeed. By themselves phenomenological theories are unable to offer unambiguous descriptions of processes lying at the foundations of contemporary physics. Physics seeks a non-phenomenological, but not *a priori*, picture of such processes; confident in the possibility of such a theory it calculates the energy of electrons, removing infinite values "on credit". All the more valid today is Einstein's scheme of "external confirmation" and "inner perfection".

It should be noted that this scheme bodied forth in the 1930s-1950s during Einstein's attempts to develop a unified field theory and in his criticism of quantum mechanics, on the one hand, and in the elaboration of the theory of elementary particles by other phycisists, on the other hand. The latter led to some remarkably beautiful and harmonious conceptions which, however, did not fit into the overall picture. Moreover, the schemes they presented contradicted one another even within one and the same conception. Relativistic quantum theories of the second third of our century are like the picture of the creation of the world drawn by Empedocles, in which separate organs of animals first appeared on earth and joined together at random.

An indication of the absence of "inner perfection" in the theory of elementary particles was the abundance of empirical quantities. Each empirical constant indicates a point at which the causal explanation breaks down, requiring the introduction of a quantity which cannot be explained. Einstein's ideal was a world picture devoid of empirical constants. The theory of elementary particles retained the fundamental empirical quantities of mass and charge of different kinds of particles. They remain today in spite of the important conclusions of principle derived by Heisenberg when he *computed* the masses of some particles.

On the whole, the theory of elementary particles was characterised by an absence of "inner perfection".

On the other hand, Einstein's constructions during the 1930s-1950s lacked "external confirmation". They did not contradict the known facts, but neither could they boast the *experimentum crucis* which is essential for a revision of the world picture. The theories of elementary particles which rapidly succeeded one another (and sometimes coexisted) on the pages of physical journals were not "mad" enough in respect of their logical paradoxicality, they did not break drastically enough with classical concepts. Einstein's constructions were not "mad" enough in respect of paradoxical experimental confirmation. Paradoxical observables abounded in the "orthodox" theory of elementary particles. There even appeared the concept of "strangeness" to denote a very definite quantity.

Can we expect the diverging paths of scientific progress to intersect? Will a theory be developed which would marry new and even more paradoxical and "mad" general ideas with an unambiguous explanation of the totality of paradoxical facts discovered in the physics of elementary particles?

The road to such a theory is a long one. Theoretical physicists will have occasion to recall Einstein's words, written in February 1955, shortly before his death, in a letter to Max von Laue. It was in reply to an invitation to attend a conference in Berlin devoted to the fiftieth anniversary of relativity.

"Old age and poor health," Einstein wrote, "make such a trip impossible, and I must say that I am not sorry, for anything resembling a personality cult has always been extremely distasteful to me. In the present case, moreover, many people have contributed to the advance of this theory, and it is far from completed.... If many years of search have taught me anything, it is that we are much farther from an understanding of elementary particles than most men realise (yourself excluded), and a festive pageant would hardly befit the present state of affairs."[1]

This letter is a good illustration of the basis of Einstein's stand. He was not the man either to rest content with old, once discovered truths (including the classical concepts of subatomic processes) or to accept new ideas as conclusive. His criticism came actually not from classical but from quantum-relativistic positions. In the quoted letter he speaks of the incompleteness of relativity theory. An elaboration of relativity must substantiate the laws of quantum.

Recognition of the incomplete nature of contemporary ideas makes sense only, of course, if the principle is accepted that a consistent unified theory of elementary processes can be developed.

If the emergence of such a theory derives from apparent tendencies, and the prediction that it is bound to appear is well-grounded, then it is necessary to undertake a principled reappraisal of Einstein's great effort in the last thirty years of his life. Following the example of physics, we may undertake some retrospective evaluations "on credit". In fact, in a biography of Einstein this is necessary, for Einstein's work was consonant not only, and frequently not so much, with contemporary research as with the future of science. Let us analyse the question of Einstein's so-called aloofness from this point of view.

[1] C. Seelig, op. cit., S. 396.

Infeld considers it to be a characteristic feature of Einstein's work, probably the most characteristic. It explains his personality, his immersion in himself even amidst association with others, his failure to respond to many so-called urgent problems which happened to agitate most physicists at a given moment, and the mere ripple of attention to his work in later years.

"For him," Infeld writes, "the isolation was a blessing since it prevented his thought from wandering into conventional channels. This aloofness, this independent thought on problems which Einstein formulated for himself, not marching with the crowd but looking for his own lonely pathways, is the most essential feature of his creation. It is not only originality, it is not only imagination, it is something more, which can be understood by a glimpse at the problems and methods of Einstein's work."[1]

Let us take a look at the special theory of relativity from this aspect. Here we can speak of Einstein's isolation only in a purely environmental sense, in the sense that he had no contacts with physicists in Bern, and that, in his own words, he had never seen a real theoretical physicist until he was almost thirty ("except in the mirror," Infeld comments). The paper "On the Electrodynamics of Moving Bodies", however, dealt with a problem which lay close to the hearts of many physicists. This is seen in the almost simultaneous appearance of two other fundamental works—by Lorentz and Poincaré—designed to explain Michelson's experiment. The Russian mathematician N. N. Luzin once remarked that a young scientist advancing revolutionary conceptions cannot hope to make himself heard if his ideas do not free the scientific community from difficult and often futile searches and if they are of no help in its troubles. "In order to pull scientists out of their beds they must be given answers to the questions that worry them."

Special relativity answered the extremely urgent question concerning the reason for the negative result of Michelson's and similar experiments. That is why it aroused at least as much interest as other outstanding physical works did just after the turn of the century. Why the interest displayed towards Einstein's theory was out of all proportion with other

[1] L. Infeld, op. cit., p. 275.

physical theories has been discussed in the foregoing. The problem posed before classical physics by Michelson's experiment proved fatal; it differed from the Sphinx's riddle which Oedipus had to answer in that death was the reward for the correct answer. Nor need we reiterate that this "death" of classical physics is no more than a figure of speech: one could with equal justification speak of its resurrection. What really died was belief in the validity and immutability of the classical rule of velocity addition and the classical concept of absolute time.

In the 1890s two trends of theoretical thinking, corresponding to two heuristic criteria, converged. One consisted in the search for a theory to explain new experimental data. It sought the "external confirmation" of theories. The other trend was to develop theories which would be rid of arbitrary, *ad hoc* assumptions explaining a comparatively small sphere of phenomena. It sought the "inner perfection" of a theory. Lorentz's *ad hoc* theory was superseded by Einstein's, which explained the results of Michelson's experiment on the basis of a general principle (i.e., one which, in the final analysis, rests on a great number of different facts).

An answer was supplied to a question which troubled many physicists. The experiments had been made, but their results failed to fit into the pattern of existing theories and it was necessary to develop one which would agree with the new observations. Einstein's theory was the only one of several which possessed both "external confirmation" and "inner perfection".

General relativity did not resolve any problems or aporias threatening physics. It explained the results of Galileo's experiments which, of course, hardly troubled 20th-century physicists. At the time when Einstein was battling against tremendous odds to elaborate a new theory of gravitation hardly anyone was interested in it. The eight years of work on general relativity culminating in its enunciation in 1916 and the three more years that passed before its verification by observation were years of great isolation for Einstein. If not for Einstein's remarkable scientific tenacity general relativity would not have been discovered within the first quarter of the 20th century, and maybe even much later on. As Einstein once remarked to Infeld:

"The special relativity theory would have been discovered by now whether I had done it or not. The problem was ripe. But I do not believe that this is true in the case of general relativity theory."

The "external confirmation" of general relativity was actually available 300 years prior to its final enunciation. Elaboration of the theory was based on the known "confirmation"—the equality of gravitational and inertial mass; it sought the second confirmation—the bending of light rays in a gravitational field. The intersection of this line of "external confirmation" with the search for inner harmony passed, however, far away from the bustling cross-roads of science.

Einstein's isolation and aloofness during the whole of his Princeton period was more pronounced than ever. In his work on the unified field theory he remained completely outside the pale of all more or less influential or comprehensive schools of theoretical physics. There was nothing in the theory to attract broad sections of the scientific community in the way of explaining the results of an experiment. There was no point of intersection between the theory's "inner perfection" and its "external confirmation". This time the "inner perfection" was the most comprehensive imaginable. It involved initial assumptions capable of explaining the totality of physical processes, irrespective of the fields responsible for them, without introducing any supplementary hypotheses. These initial assumptions, however, were in no way connected with experiments capable of supporting their trustworthiness.

The fate and historic meaning of the unified field theory, which occupied Einstein for thirty years, resembles the fate and meaning of his criticism of quantum mechanics. Einstein's attitude towards quantum mechanics was not purely negative. He did not oppose it with new conceptions of his own, nor did he seek to develop some non-statistical theory of the microcosm. On the contrary, the unified field theory was enunciated in positive form. Yet it is the positive and specific features of the theory which will probably not enter into the final unified theory. We may define Einstein's unified theory as "erroneous" (in inverted commas), for there is nothing wrong in its general premises, viz., that there exist certain laws which determine the structure of all fields and that all known fields are modifications of a single, unified field. In his paper "Comments on Einstein's Outline of a Unified Field Theory", published in 1959, Werner Heisenberg speaks of the rapid increase in the body of knowledge about elementary particles and fields as the primary reason for Einstein's failure. During the period 1930-1950 there was ample evidence of this and hardly an issue of any leading physical journal appeared without an announcement of the discovery of some new elementary particle or other. Each particle was associated with a field, the particle being regarded as an agent for transmitting the interactions of other particles, just as the photon transmits the electromagnetic interactions of electrons and other electrically charged particles. In this avalanche of new facts it was difficult to find firm ground for a unified field theory.

"At first this truly remarkable attempt seemed to fail," Heisenberg writes. "At the very time when Einstein was engaged in the problem of a unified field theory, new elementary particles and new fields correlated with them were being continuously discovered. As a result, the firm empirical basis which was essential for the fulfilment of Einstein's programme was still lacking, and his attempts yielded no convincing results."

But this difficulty in developing the unified field theory resulted in a gradual accumulation of arguments in favour of Einstein's programme. The discoveries during the 1930s-1950s brought into the world picture particles which change into other particles, and consequently, fields which change into other fields. The unified field theory can now be based on quantum notions: the transformation of one field into another represents a transmutation of a quantum of one field into a quantum of another, into an elementary particle of another type. We find that the idea of the "transquantal" world of ultra-relativistic effects and the unified field theory may come together in the general concept of transmutations of elementary particles as the fundamental processes of the universe. This has not yet been achieved. We can only speak of the possibility in principle of going over from a world picture in which the fundamental concept is the motion of immutable particles in gravitational, electromagnetic, etc., fields, to a world picture in which the fundamental physical image is the transmutation of particles. That such transmutations are possible, and, as a result, such a new world picture is in principle possible, must make us change our attitude towards Einstein's "fruitless" conceptions.

The unified field theory will represent a consummation of the theory of relativity. As Einstein saw it, the "consummation" of a theory means that one discovers certain more general initial concepts and laws which enable one to elaborate a more comprehensive theory from which earlier theories can be derived. Such was the consummation of special relativity. It led to the development of general relativity, from which it can be derived as a special case. A similar consummation of general relativity (the theory of gravitation, that is) can be envisaged: the unified field theory must give the conditions in which the unified field becomes a gravitational field and obeys the relationships of general relativity. In each theory we find limiting concepts and quantities which do not display their nature within the boundaries of the given theory and must be taken as fundamental; they can be substantiated and derived from other concepts and quantities only in the framework of a more general theory. In celestial mechanics, which is a theory of the motions of stars, planets and other heavenly bodies, the initial, given, unexplained quantities are the masses of celestial bodies and the initial distances between them. These quantities can be explained by a cosmogony which deals with the motions and transformations of molecules, atoms and elementary particles. In atomic physics, given are the masses and charges of elementary particles which await explanation and derivation from the more general laws of a unified theory of elementary particles.

Why are the initial distances between celestial bodies what they are, and not something else? When we express them in miles or kilometres or other arbitrary units the problem is obscured: the number denoting the distance between two celestial bodies is an arbitrary convention which depends on the accepted unit: centimetres, miles, kilometres or light-years. The conventionalism of distance is overcome if we use some natural measuring rod, the radius of the solar system, for example. Expressed in terms of this measuring rod, the ratio of, say, the radius of Neptune's orbit to the radius of Mars's orbit should lend itself to causal explanation, it should derive from the theory of the formation of the solar system. Similarly, if the masses of particles are expressed not in grams but as ratios of the mass of an electron, then these masses—the constants of atomic and nuclear physics—must be explicitly derivable from more general laws, that is, from a unified theory of elementary particles and from a picture of particle formation which gives the relationships between the masses of different types of particles.

To Einstein the exclusion of arbitrary constants from physics, their explanation and the derivation of the limiting values of a given theory out of a more general theory represented the pivotal tendency of scientific creation. The exclusion of such arbitrary constants is an expression of the unity and knowability of the universe. In his *Autobiographical Notes* Einstein advanced as an intuitive assumption the postulate that in an ideal world picture there are no arbitrary constants. The speed of light expressed in centimetres per second is tied up with arbitrary units. But, Einstein says, we can introduce instead of the second the time it makes light to travel a unit length, this unit being not the centimetre but, say, the radius of the electron. The gram as a unit of mass can be replaced by the mass of the electron or some other particle. In general, it is possible completely to exclude from physics constants expressed in terms of centimetres, grams or seconds and to take "natural" units in their stead.

"If one considers this done, then only 'dimensionless' constants could occur in the basic equations of physics. Concerning this I would like to state a theorem which at present cannot be based upon anything more than upon a faith in the simplicity, i.e., intelligibility, of nature: there are no *arbitrary* constants of this kind; that is to say, nature is so constituted that it is possible logically to lay down such strongly determined laws that within these laws only rationally completely determined constants occur (not constants, therefore, whose numerical value could be changed without destroying the theory)."[1]

Thus, according to Einstein, every dimensionless constant—the ratio of a speed to another speed, a mass to another mass (say, the mass of some particle to that of the electron), a length (a wavelength, or the radius of a particle, or the radius of the universe) to another length (say, the radius of the electron)—can always be explained within a theory; in the ideal it is always possible to answer questions concerning

[1] *Philosopher-Scientist*, pp. 62-63.

the whys and wherefores of such a constant, a different theory giving a different magnitude for the constant. This stems from "a faith in the simplicity, e.g., intelligibility, of nature". We are by now sufficiently familiar with Einstein's general ideas to comprehend the meaning of these words. Knowledge of the external world means knowledge of the laws it obeys, of the causal ties embracing and uniting the world.

Ernst Strauss, Einstein's assistant in Princeton in 1944-1948, quotes in his reminiscences a very important remark made by his teacher: "What interests me is: could God have made the world different, does the requirement of logical simplicity leave any latitude?"[1]

We already know that Einstein's "God" is a pseudonym for the rational causality of natural processes. We also know that this causality finds expression in logical simplicity, in a minimum number of independent postulates, in a natural theory most truly reflecting the world picture. The question is whether the criterion of logical simplicity leads to an unambiguous world picture. Are two physically different, but logically equally simple, schemes possible? Einstein, it seems, was inclined to believe that "God could not have made the world differently", that the requirement of logical simplicity uniquely determines the physical world picture. In its progress towards objective truth science increasingly gains in logical simplicity (thanks to the exclusion of empirical constants which are not logically derivable and consequently lack causal links with other constants) and offers an increasingly faithful description of reality. The world pictures succeeding one another form a converging series.

Thus, when Einstein speaks of logical requirements he has in mind the real objective connections between the laws of nature. Each law is linked with others and a single chain of cause and effect embraces the macrocosm and the microcosm. This makes it possible logically to derive one law from another, the single chain including both quantitative laws and constants. Phenomenological constants—the radii of planetary orbits, the masses of particles, etc.—do not satisfy Einstein's criteria of the worth of a scientific theory. There is nothing purely phenomenological in the world picture, just

[1] *Helle Zeit*, S. 72.

as there is nothing purely *a priori*. A causal explanation may be stalled at the boundaries of a given theory; it cannot be halted, and sooner or later it will overstep those boundaries.

Johannes Kepler, one of the greatest prophets of modern causal thinking, asked of the quantitative relationships of the universe—the distances between the planets of the solar system—"Why are they what they are and not otherwise?" Unable to get an answer, he immersed into a mysticism of numbers. The causal thinking characteristic of modern science reached its zenith in the work of Einstein. Yet he too was unable to offer a concrete causal explanation of all physical constants, he was unable to evolve a theory in which all constants would derive from physical conditions. The initial relationships of relativity will remain of a phenomenological nature as long as they are not derived from more general properties of moving matter. To such properties may belong its discontinuous nature, its microscopic structure, and the quantitative relationships of the microcosm, i.e., the data with which quantum physics operates. Relativity treats as basic relationships the contraction of moving measuring rods and the dilation of time in moving systems. From the point of view of quantum theory, measuring rods and clocks are compound bodies.

"Generally speaking, they are made up of many elementary particles," Heisenberg writes. "They are subject to complex actions of various fields of force. It is therefore hard to understand why their behaviour should be described by an especially simple law."

Einstein fully realised that the initial relationships of relativity theory which define the behaviour of measuring rods and clocks could be derived from more general relationships written down as equations. He writes in his *Autobiographical Notes*:

"...a remark concerning the theory as it is characterised above. One is struck [by the fact] that the theory (except for the four-dimensional space) introduces two kinds of physical things, i.e., (1) measuring rods and clocks, (2) all other things, e.g., the electromagnetic field, the material point, etc. This, in a certain sense, is inconsistent; strictly speaking, measuring rods and clocks would have to be represented as solutions of the basic equations (objects consisting of moving

313

atomic configurations), not, as it were, as theoretically self-sufficient entities."[1]

Of course, when we speak of the "behaviour of measuring rods and clocks" we understand this figuratively. There was once a time, to be sure, when such expressions were understood literally. In the 2nd century B.C. Syracusans might have seriously thought that the lever with which Archimedes would move the world lay in some back yard ready to be produced as soon as he was provided with a suitable fulcrum. Others, disbelieving the existence of such a lever, might be prone to accuse Archimedes of falsehood. It would be just about as naive to imagine that "the behaviour of measuring rods and clocks" makes sense only in the presence of rulers, measuring tape, chronometers and observers to use them. Our concern is with things which existed billions of years before observers with their measuring gadgets ever came into being. We have noted that Einstein described objective processes with the aid of "measuring rods" and "clocks", viz., rigid rods and periodically recurring motions, and "observers", which may be instruments recording clock readings (the number of revolutions or line segments covered by a body from an initial instant) and the number of rigid rods laid off between two points. It is very easy to remove the subjective understanding of the formula "the behaviour of measuring rods and clocks". The real difficulty (which Einstein did not and *could not* overcome) is to reveal the microscopic processes explaining the relationships between spatial and temporal measurements (the "behaviour of measuring rods and clocks") in systems moving relative to each other. Even today we are unable to demonstrate unambiguously and for certain how the microscopic structure of matter (and possibly the discontinuity of space and time) lead to the relationships of Einstein's relativity theory. They govern all processes in the world of galaxies, planets, molecules and atoms. Do they govern the behaviour of elementary particles in infinitely small domains of space-time? This we do not know. If they do, then it is impossible to explain the behaviour of measuring rods and clocks in terms of their atomic structure: we cannot explain the nature of relativity relationships in terms of processes subject to them. We can

[1] *Philosopher-Scientist*, p. 59.

expect, however, that in very small, submicroscopic domains relationships are to be found from which the relationships of relativity develop in going over to larger spatial domains and larger time intervals.

We find a transition to relationships and concepts based on new principles in Einstein's works on thermodynamics and in 19th-century classical thermodynamics. It is a transition from microscopic *motions* of individual molecules to *states* of macroscopic bodies. Now we have motions subject to Einsteinian relationships. The problem may consist of going over to these *motions* from submicroscopic *states*. In some respects this point of view ascends to Einstein's ideas. Recall that out of relativity sprang the new relativistic electron theory based on the transmutation of electron-positron pairs into photons and the breeding of electron-positron pairs out of photons. Recall also what has been said in connection with quantum mechanics and Einstein's position: in the thirty years that passed since the initial discoveries, transmutations of elementary particles, transformations of particles of one kind into particles of another kind, provided explanations for a wide range of facts. In this period there appeared and developed the notion of particles of one kind emitting particles of another kind and their subsequent absorption. We know that a particle which macroscopically exists continually, actually (in the submicroscopic domain) changes into other particles and then back again.

It seems therefore natural to view transmutations as the basis of the discontinuous structure of space-time. A particle of a specific type jumps from one elementary, indivisible spatial cell into another in the course of an elementary, indivisible time interval, turning into another kind of particle in the process. Such an assumption concerning the indivisibility of elementary transmutations and elementary transitions enables one to visualise the discontinuity of space-time. If a particle disappears from one cell and reappears in a neighbouring one no signal can be sent over a distance smaller than the elementary one or in a time interval less than the elementary one. Two events—the occurrence of a particle at point x at time t, and its occurrence at point x' at time t', cannot be separated by a distance smaller than the elementary distance or by a time interval less than the elementary interval.

The assumption concerning the discrete nature of space-time seems justified if only because it has been voiced at every stage in development of science. Already Epicurus spoke of "kinemas"—microscopic displacements of atoms "in instants that can be perceived by the imagination alone", and always with the same speed. Bodies consisting of atoms may move with smaller speeds; they can even remain motionless if the number of "kinemas" moving one way is approximately the same as the number directed the other way.

The world of contemporary analogues of Epicurus's "kinemas"—the world of elementary transmutation-displacements —can serve as a conceptual illustration of the laws which Einstein sought behind the rules for quantum-mechanical relationships. We cannot get beyond these relationships by considering the result of a large number of transmutation-displacements, ignoring individual displacements and taking into account the macroscopic motions of particles: knowing a particle's position at a given time, we can determine only the probability of its velocity. A particle moves in a certain direction, and its macroscopic trajectory has a definite direction if the probability of elementary displacements in that direction is greater than the probability of elementary displacements in the opposite direction. In this case, after a great number of transitions, the particle will have traversed its macroscopic path along which a sharp position is incompatible with a sharp velocity. Here everything is subject to the statistical laws of quantum mechanics, and there is nothing to suggest the laws that are behind the rules of quantum mechanics. It is not a question of "hidden parameters", of unknown processes making possible an exact determination, within one experiment, of the position and velocity of a moving particle, a determination of the law of motion of that particle which would define for certain its occurrence at a given point and not merely the probability of such an occurrence. There are no such "hidden parameters", and the motion of a particle (an immutable particle which travels without disappearing and reappearing) is determined by the statistical laws of quantum mechanics. But such motion may represent merely the statistical result of a large number of elementary processes to which the concept of determinate or indeterminate dynamic variables is not applicable.

Such schemes are nothing more than conceptual illustrations of a consideration which is of special importance for an understanding and historical appraisal of Einstein's "fruitless" ideas. In no ways did these ideas tend to pull physics back from quantum-statistical causality to classical causality. The suggested scheme illustrates the possibility in principle of a development of the microcosmic theory which goes *further* from classical notions than quantum mechanics, to ideas which, from the point of view of classical physics, would be even more paradoxical and "mad". As Einstein saw it, the process of cognition can never encounter absolute limits in the shape of ultimately conclusive theories, and it never turns back. It may repeat past cycles, but always on a new basis.

In the early 'forties Einstein had already approached ideas that are maturing in relativistic quantum physics only today, in the 'sixties, in connection with the properties of elementary particles and field interactions. At the beginning of this chapter we quoted a passage from a letter to Mühsam written in 1944, in which Einstein speaks of "an agony of mathematical torment". This passage is preceded by a paragraph outlining the general concept of the unified theory:

"The goal is a relativistic characteristic of physical space, but without introducing differential equations. The latter do not offer a reasonable understanding of quanta and matter. In a sense this is a rejection of the principle of near action in which we have been so confident since Hertz's time. In principle this is possible without resorting to the statistical method, which I have always thought to be a poor way out."[1]

"A relativistic characteristic of physical space" means a conception of space in which the nature of the physical processes taking place in it is derived from its properties. Such a conception must, in Einstein's view, employ a mathematical apparatus of a different kind than the conventional differential equations of physics.

We have spoken before of the physical meaning of differential equations. Given in them are the ratios of infinitesimal increments of particle velocities and the forces acting on the particles to infinitesimal space and time increments. The physical meaning of these equations is that events are always

---

[1] *Helle Zeit*, S. 51.

occurring, no matter how small the spatial domain and time interval, in which they are investigated and these "events" are subject to the laws of physics as expressed by the equations. In other words, their meaning consists in the continuity of physical space and time, in the possibility of infinitely dividing space and time so that they remain physical in the sense that their structure determines the nature of physical processes. Does this assumption agree with the atomistic structure of matter and the discrete structure of fields, i.e., with the existence of field quanta as indivisible portions of energy? No, Einstein replies, it does not. It may therefore be necessary to give up the principle of close-quarter action, i.e., the notion of the continuity of physical processes, the notion that every process develops from instant to instant and from point to point.

It is more difficult to get to the root of Einstein's comments concerning the statistical method. It is highly improbable that he considered statistical ideas to be a "poor way out" in all cases. Einstein is the author of fundamental works on statistics in classical and quantum physics in which he solves important problems by applying and developing statistical methods. The comment, therefore, probably refers to the notion that the statistical laws of quantum mechanics are ultimate laws of physical reality. Einstein's idea was that there exist deeper laws of a non-statistical nature.

Strangely enough, this expectation does not in essence contradict Max Born's ideas of the statistical nature of both quantum and classical mechanics. It is apparent from the letter to Mühsam (and from many other statements) that Einstein was far from regarding "transquantal" processes as being classical or, even more so, mechanical. These processes do not consist in "classical" motion with a sharp position and velocity for every instant of time—otherwise differential equations could be applied and they could be traced with infinite accuracy down to the smallest domains. But neither do they consist in "quantised" motion with a sharp position *or* a sharp velocity. They simply do not consist in mechanical motion, in displacements of physical objects. Beyond the relative boundaries embracing a given form of causality which once seemed paradoxical lie other forms of causality, also paradoxical: beyond Laplace's classical determinism there is quantum-mechanical determinism, and beyond the latter is the determinism of sub-microscopic processes which departs still more drastically from classical processes. Eternal is only the general principle of causality; it is eternal as knowledge itself, for knowledge is a continuous process in which our causal conceptions of the surrounding world are modified, characterised, clarified, and generally grow more complex.

Sub-microscopic laws may possibly make for a generalisation of the basic laws of relativity. The behaviour of measuring rods and clocks may well be dependent on relationships between elementary distances and elementary time intervals. The following can be offered as a conceptual illustration. The minimum length lies in the neighbourhood of 10^{-13} cm. This, evidently, is the minimum distance over which a signal can be sent, the minimal possible displacement of a particle. Now suppose that time consists of minimal intervals of the order of $3x10^{-24}$ sec. This, evidently, is the minimum propagation time of a signal, the minimum time in the course of which a particle can suffer a displacement in space. Our final assumption is that a particle undergoes the minimum diplacement of 10^{-13} cm in the minimum time of $3x10^{-24}$ sec. In other words, a particle's motion comprises jumps of 10^{-13} cm lasting $3x10^{-24}$ sec each. The velocity of these jumps equals the quotient of the distance divided by the time, i.e., $10^{-13}/3x10^{-24} \approx 3x10^{10}$ cm/sec, or 300,000 km/sec, which is the velocity of light. The particle cannot travel any faster, and neither can a body consisting of particles. If we track all the microscopic elementary displacements (of 10^{-13} cm in $3x10^{-24}$ sec) we will have a *microscopic path*, which in the general case will represent a broken line: the displacements take place with the same speed but in various directions. If we neglect the individual microscopic displacements and take account only of the result of a great number of them, we have a countinuous *macroscopic path*. It can be much shorter than the microscopic path consisting of elementary displacements. For example, if a particle suffered an approximately equal number of displacements in opposite directions it will remain at approximately the same point, and its macroscopic path will be negligible. Correspondingly, the macroscopic velocity (the velocity on the macroscopic path) will also be negligible. If the number of displacements is much greater in one direction the macroscopic path will be longer. Finally, in the event of all the elementary displacements being in the same direction the macroscopic path will coincide with the microscopic one, and the macroscopic speed will be the speed of light. This will be the maximum possible speed for any body, and from this can be derived certain laws governing the behaviour of measuring rods and clock–the relationships of Einstein's relativity theory.

We assumed the elementary spatial displacements and the elementary time intervals as such that the velocity of the displacements from one spatial cell to another be equal to the speed of light. If there were no other reasons for the choice of these constants, i.e., if they were chosen *ad hoc*, the assumption as a whole would be typical of an arbitrary construction agreeing with observations yet lacking in authenticity. The general assumption concerning the existence of atoms of space and time–the smallest elementary, further indivisible distances and time intervals–was not introduced *ad hoc*. The same is true of the order of the quantities presented above: 10^{-13} cm and 3×10^{-24} sec. These numbers appear fairly naturally in a number of physical problems. It is therefore possible to assume that physics will some day arrive at a quantum-atomistic substantiation of relativity theory as a macroscopic theory and that in this substantiation there will figure natural constants: the minimum distances and time intervals.

Thus only now, in the light of the apparent prospects of the theory of elementary particles and in connection with more or less definite forecasts in this sphere, can we revise the traditionally purely negative evaluation of Einstein's latter thirty years. Even before this it seemed unnatural to drop from the history of science such a long period of intense work by one of the greatest minds it can boast. One might suspect that Einstein had in mind some vague contours of a new world picture. These contours have not yet been unambiguously defined, but we are already in a position to offer a more concrete illustration of them. The objective meaning of Einstein's "grumbling", to use Born's remark concerning his attitude towards quantum mechanics, never consisted–and this is quite clear today–in attempts to get back to classical conceptions. Einstein had no sympathy for explanations of quantum mechanics made from the classical position of "hidden parameters". Today we are in a position more specifically to illustrate a different line of revision of quantum

Einstein on his seventieth birthday

mechanics which involves a more radical rejection of the classical concept of an immutable moving particle as the basic image of the world picture.

Such a rejection, it would seem, is implicitly present in Einstein's rejection of *Mach's principle*. Mach's principle reduces the universe to the motions and force interactions of bodies. It is most apparently at variance with the breeding and absorption of particles, which violates the principle of the immutability of objects underlying the world picture. Such processes do not fit into the "classical ideal", into a world picture "of the type of Newton's mechanics". In its synthesis with quantum mechanics, relativity has approached the line beyond which this world picture ends. Einstein, too, found himself at the outposts of the initial conception, in spite of the tremendous appeal of the "classical ideal".

This is a sign of scientific genius. Einstein's interests were centred on the *fundaments* of science, on the general principles determining all world events. As he wrote to Solovine in 1924:

"For me interest in science is restricted to the study of principles, and this offers the best explanation of my work. That I have published so few papers derives from the same circumstance: a consequence of my ardent desire to understand the principles is that much of my time has been spent on fruitless efforts."[1]

This was written in 1924, just when the relativity theory was being brilliantly confirmed. Already then Einstein was engaged in the search for more general fundaments of the universal world harmony. He did not find them, and at times he was prone to regard his quest as being quite futile. Neither were they found subsequently. Furthermore, interest in the primary fundaments of the world picture did not agree with the mode of scientific creativity which prevailed in physics in the 'thirties and 'forties. The situation changed in the 'fifties and 'sixties. In order to substitute an unambiguous unified conception possessing "inner perfection" for the purely conceptual methods of quantum electrodynamics and the general theory of elementary particles it was necessary to get back to thoughts concerning the general fundaments of physics. And here it was found that Einstein's ideas, to

[1] *Solovine*, p. 49.

which he had devoted thirty years of work, were not fruitless. The latter half of Einstein's life has left an indelible imprint on the ways of science in the second half of the 20th century, not so much in the results achieved as in the problems posed.

We have said before that quantum-relativistic conceptions did not represent a tragedy for Einstein. This, however, does not mean that the evolution of his ideas was smooth and did not include some difficult, frequently agonising and futile, search.

Einstein's letters reveal the deep marks left in his mind by this search. To future generations it is the *problems* raised by a scholar that are of greatest interest; to himself it is the *answers* that matter, and a lack of answers is a source of dissatisfaction and doubt concerning the correctness of the chosen road.

Why have Einstein's answers to the questions he posed failed to enter modern science?

First of all, no positive and unambiguous solution of the unified field problem has yet been found. This, however, does not explain why Einstein was reluctant to depart from the "classical ideal" in pursuance of which he developed the relativity theory.

Einstein's ideas were a consummation of the three-century rule of the "classical ideal" which found embodiment in the rationalism of Descartes and Spinoza, Newtonian mechanics, and 19th-century physics. Today science is on the threshold of a new period. Einstein, however, did not become the herald of its positive tendencies. His genius displayed itself in a realisation of the limitations of the "classical ideal", in his search for a new causal harmony which, as we now know, transcended this ideal. He went no further.

Leaving aside other considerations, the new causal harmony did not body forth in the same shapely bronze-cast forms in which the "classical ideal" appeared to Einstein. The new ideal of science will attain a harmonious structure. The search for a consistent, unified, general theory is already forming the content of physical thought and science is coming closer to Einstein's mode of thinking. The positive solutions, however, will be different.

Einstein's mode of thinking is characterised, among other things, by an affinity, and in some cases a merger, of physical and philosophical problems. This derives from his quest for "inner perfection", from the task of building up physical theories which would derive naturally from the general pattern of reality.

This idea is finding growing confirmation in the current development of theoretical physics. In the early 'forties Einstein pointed out that the difficulties of physical thinking could be overcome only through a deeper and closer union of physical analysis with philosophical analysis. He wrote in 1944: "The present difficulties of his science force the physicist to come to grips with philosophical problems to a greater degree than was the case with earlier generations."[1]

Einstein speaks of the fundamental problem of concern to the physicist: the relationship between "pure thought" and the empirical foundations of knowledge. He finds that through the chaos of different opinions there is visible a systematic trend, "an increasing skepticism concerning every attempt by means of pure thought to learn something about the 'objective world', about the world of 'things'. . . ."

Einstein takes the words "objective world" and "things" in quotation marks in order, as he writes, to introduce concepts which are "suspect in the eyes of the philosophical police". He writes that since Galileo the conviction gradually gained recognition that all knowledge about things is exclusively a working-over of the raw material furnished by the senses. Einstein agrees with this conception, but he cannot accept phenomenalism as its conclusion.

We are already familiar with this train of thought, which Einstein repeats in all his epistemological excursions. The empirical origin of knowledge does not prevent "pure thought" from constructing hypothetical conclusions deriving from the general scheme of the universe and not from a given series of experiments. In principle these conclusions should be subject to experimental verification, but they must also possess "inner perfection" in the sense that they derive most naturally from the general conceptions of physical reality.

Approaching this idea—the most general in Einstein's epistemological statements—are the demands, which have become the vogue of the sixties, for a consistent theory

[1] *Ideas and Opinions*, p. 19.

deriving from the totality of world knowledge which would substantiate the conceptual *ad hoc* methods. They were accepted "on credit", in the expectation of a theory possessing "inner perfection". The time has now come to pay the bill, and this necessity urges physical thinking in the direction of general problems embracing the whole of the universe, and correspondingly, to a new synthesis of integral philosophical analysis of the universe with concrete physical conceptions.

Recalling the excellent characteristic of the current situation in theoretical physics given by Niels Bohr, today we can be satisfied only by the very "maddest" physical theory. This essentially is Einstein's "wonder", which invites paradoxical theories. With Einstein the "flight from wonder" consisted in the advancement of a new and paradoxical theory which made paradoxical phenomena seem quite natural. Today it is no longer a question of individual phenomena but of paradoxical conceptions. Science is at the threshold of a unified theory embracing the whole of the universe; its fundamental premises differ radically from the "classical ideal", since it is the "maddest" of all. It removes the "madness" from individual physical conceptions, just as relativity theory removed the "wonder" from Michelson's findings. Einstein's "flight from wonder", his explanation of a wonderful fact by means of a wonderful theory is a prototype of the contemporary "flight from madness", of the transition from a wonderful special theory to a wonderful general picture of physical reality. The degree of "madness" is determined by the scope and historical stability of the revised conceptions. Bohr's requirement for a higher degree of "madness" means that today physics is in need of a revision of very general and stable principles.

It would be natural to assume that the revision must affect the "classical ideal" which had guided Einstein in his search and to the restriction of which he came towards the end of his life.

Chapter 26

"THE EVOLUTION OF PHYSICS"

*Without the belief that it is possible to grasp
the reality with our theoretical constructions
and without the belief in the inner harmony
of our world, there could be no science. This
belief is and always will remain the fundamental motive for all scientific creation.
Throughout all our efforts, in every dramatic
struggle between old and new views, we
recognise the eternal longing for understanding,
the ever-firm belief in the harmony of our
world. . . .*

A. E i n s t e i n,
L. I n f e l d
"The Evolution of Physics" (1938)

In 1936 reactionary forces were gaining ground in the
universities of Poland, and Leopold Infeld, the Polish student
who had visited Einstein in 1920, now a lecturer at the
University of Lvov, felt that he would probably soon be
forced to leave the university. He wrote to Einstein, who
invited him to Princeton. Infeld received a small fellowship
which enabled him to engage in theoretical research under
Einstein. In due time he arrived in Princeton and was
knocking on the door of room No. 209 in Fine Hall, where
the institute of mathematics and theoretical physics was
located. Sixteen years had passed since Infeld had seen Einstein, and he found that Einstein had aged more than
warranted by the time lapse. Einstein's eyes, however, were
deep and radiant as ever.

Infeld expected a brief private conversation, questions
about his crossing from Europe, etc. Instead, Einstein began at
once to speak of the problems on which he was working.
This was not the indifference of a superior, and Infeld knew
it, for he had had adequate proof of Einstein's good will
and friendly concern. Once again he felt the charm of Ein-

stein's personality. Einstein was completely immersed in the "extra-personal", and the readiness and open-mindedness with which he shared his problems with others was part of his charm. At their first meeting Einstein outlined to Infeld the results to date of his work on the unified field theory. At that moment Levi-Cività, one of the authors of the mathematical methods employed by Einstein in developing general relativity, entered the room. Levi-Cività was about sixty at the time. He was a small, thin man, and had left Italy because he had refused to swear the fascist oath designed for university professors. Seeing that Einstein was engaged Levi-Cività turned to leave. He indicated his intention by gestures rather than by words (feeling that his Italian gesticulation was more understandable than his English). Einstein asked him to remain and take part in the discussion. He briefly described the preceding conversation. Levi-Cività's Anglo-Italian could be comprehended only because it consisted mainly of mathematical formulas. Einstein's command of English was not much better, but as he spoke in unhurried, expressive tones and formulated his ideas with utmost clarity and precision one had no difficulty in understanding him.

"I watched the calm, impressive Einstein and the small, thin, broadly gesticulating Levi-Cività as they pointed out formulae on the blackboard and talked a language which they thought to be English," Infeld writes. "The picture they made, and the sight of Einstein pulling up his baggy trousers every few seconds, was a scene, impressive and at the same time comic, which I shall never forget. I tried to restrain myself from laughing by saying to myself:

" 'Here you are talking and discussing physics with the most famous scientist in the world and you want to laugh because he does not wear suspenders!' The persuasion worked and I managed to control myself just as Einstein began to talk about his latest, still unpublished, paper concerning the work done during the preceding year with his assistant Rosen."[1]

This amusing scene is of definite interest for Einstein's biography. At the beginning of this book it was noted that the story of Einstein's life could not be restricted to a

[1] L. Infeld, op. cit., p. 260.

chronicle of commonplace events and personal details. Purely personal details serve to stress the characteristic tendency of Einstein's life, his flight from the daily commonplace. His refusal to wear suspenders might be amusing, but it is not ridiculous. It might cause a smile, but it was an expression of the intense intellectual life which was not concerned with the superficial manifestations of respectability. Once an acquaintance of Infeld's asked him why Einstein wore long hair, a funny leather jacket, no socks, no suspenders, no collars.

"The answer," Infeld says, "is simple and can easily be deduced from his aloofness and desire to loosen his ties with the outside world. The idea is to restrict his needs and, by this restriction, increase his freedom. We are slaves of millions of things, and our slavery progresses steadily.... We are slaves of bathrooms, Frigidaires, cars, radios and millions of other things. Einstein tried to reduce them to the absolute minimum. Long hair minimises the need for the barber. Socks can be done without. One leather jacket solves the coat problem for many years. Suspenders are superfluous, as are night-shirts and pyjamas. It is a minimum problem which Einstein has solved, and shoes, trousers, shirt, jacket are the very necessary things; it would be difficult to reduce them further."[1]

In one of his stories Maxim Gorky describes a man struggling unsuccessfully against a brisk wind to keep the flap of his coat down. "I looked at him and thought of the amount of energy which people spend in fighting petty annoyances. If we were not so worried by the nasty little worms of petty daily evils we could easily crush the terrible serpents of our misfortunes."

An important aspect in Einstein's desire to simplify and restrict his requirements was his sharpened sense of social justice. He writes in "The World as I See It":

"A hundred times every day I remind myself that my inner and outer life are based on the labours of other men, living and dead, and that I must exert myself in order to give in the same measure as I have received and am still receiving. I am strongly drawn to a frugal life and am often

[1] L. Infeld, op. cit., p. 293.

oppressively aware that I am engrossing an undue amount of the labour of my fellow-men."[1]

Thus Einstein's more than modest dress was in some logical and emotional way linked with the basic traits of his inner life. In general this is very characteristic of Einstein: every detail of his life, habits, inclinations is in the final analysis linked (usually quite simply and apparently) with his basic ideals. This contributes to the impression of remarkable integrity which his image carries.

When Levi-Cività left, Einstein asked Infeld to accompany him home. They discussed quantum mechanics and Einstein explained why he did not find it aesthetically satisfactory. "He took me to his study," Infeld writes, "with its great window overlooking the bright autumn colours of his lovely garden, and his first and only remark which did not concern physics was:

" 'There is a beautiful view from this window.' "[2]

The remark did not concern physics, but neither was it quite unrelated. To Einstein the beauty of a scientific theory was a reflection of the beauty of nature. Einstein had just been speaking of the aesthetic shortcomings of quantum mechanics. We know that his criticism of quantum mechanics was largely intuitive ("I can only call on my little finger as a witness"); we also know how closely he linked scientific intuition with aesthetic criteria in the choice of a scientific theory. This gives us an insight into the meaning of his remark about the aesthetic shortcomings of quantum mechanics.

Einstein worked with Infeld on the equations of motion. In classical physics there exist field equations with which, knowing the sources of the field, one can determine its intensity at any point, that is, the force with which the field would act on a unit charge at that point. For example, knowing the configuration of electrically charged bodies one can calculate with the aid of the electromagnetic field equations the force with which a charge will be attracted or repulsed at a given point. Similarly, the classical gravitational field equations enable one to determine the force of gravity at any point if the configuration of the gravitating masses is known. In classical physics, alongside

[1] *Ideas and Opinions,* p. 8.
[2] L. Infeld, op. cit., p. 262.

the field equations there exist the equations of motion in which field intensity enters as a given quantity. Knowing it one can use the equations of motion to determine a body's position at any instant. In classical physics the field equations and the equations of motion are mutually independent. In Einstein's theory of gravitation, on the other hand, the equations of field and motion cannot be considered independently. The equations of motion can be derived from the field equations. This very difficult task was solved in the late 'thirties by Einstein in co-operation with Infeld, and independently by V. A. Fock in the Soviet Union.

The derivation of the equations of motion from the field equations was a difficult mathematical problem. Essential in overcoming the mathematical difficulties was a certain physical intuition, a vague, glimmering idea of the problem important to the primary concepts of the physical world picture.

General relativity treats gravitational field, or space-time curvature, as being subject to the spatio-temporal existence of material bodies responsible for the field or curvature. The field equations give the space-time curvature or (what is the same thing) the field intensity when the sources responsible for it are supplied. Consider a particle moving in a gravitational field. If its law (equation) of motion is independent of the field equations, we have two realities: 1) the field, and 2) bodies moving in the field and responsible for it. If the equations are not independent and are contained in the given field equations, then the only reality in hand is the field. If particle motions are in the final analysis determined by, and only by, the field equations, then we can treat the particles as field foci.

This mode of thinking is not immediately connected with the problem of deriving the equations of motion from the field equations, though with Einstein this derivation probably carried some such meaning. It was connected with the evolution of Einstein's ideas in the "fruitless" period.

As Hermann Weyl once wrote, classical science treated space as a kind of tenement which is not affected by the events taking place in it. Non-Euclidean geometry demonstrated that space could possess a variety of properties, and general relativity showed their dependence on the presence of bodies—centres of gravitation—in space. The "tenement" was being continuously reconstructed by its tenants. Weyl's analogy is no longer suitable to illustrate the new approach to space and bodies: it is hard to picture the tenants of a building as being part of its architectural embellishments.

During 1936 and 1937, Infeld met with Einstein almost daily and they walked a lot in and around Princeton. Infeld's memoirs of the period add new traits and colours to the portrait of Einstein familiar to us from reminiscences of the 1920s. To Infeld belongs one very unusual comparison designed to characterise the tremendous intensity of Einstein's continuous mental effort.

"In America," Infeld writes, "I saw for the first time in my life Negro dances and plays which were full of fire and vital force. The Savoy dance hall in Harlem changes into an African jungle with burning sun and richly growing vegetation. The air is full of vibration. Vital force emanates from the loud music and the passionate dancing until the whole atmosphere becomes unreal. In contrast the white people look half alive, ridiculous and humiliated. They help to form the background against which the primitive, unbounded vitality of the Negroes shines more brightly. One feels that any pause, any interval is unnecessary, that this intensive motion could go on forever.

"I often had this picture in mind while watching Einstein work. There is a most vital mechanism which constantly turns his brain. It is the sublimated vital force. Sometimes it is even painful to watch. Einstein may speak about politics, listen kindly to requests and answer questions properly, but one feels behind this external activity the calm, watchful contemplation of scientific problems, that the mechanism of his brain works without interruption. It is a constant motion which nothing can stop."[1]

Einstein's contemplation of the universe was a stream which could be halted or diverted neither by comparatively insignificant episodes nor by the most tragic personal or social events. This is not an indication of personal or social indifference. Einstein was acutely aware of the experiences of his next of kin. With him social upheavals took on the dimensions of personal tragedies, yet he always pursued his work with undivided devotion. Infeld recalls Einstein's life

[1] L. Infeld, op. cit., 271-72.

and work at the time when Elsa was in her death-bed. The ground floor of their Princeton home had become a hospital. Einstein worked in his study above. He was deeply afflicted by the imminent parting with the dearest person in his life, but he continued to work with the same intensity as before. A few days after Elsa's death Einstein resumed his work at Fine Hall. He looked tired and his complexion was more sallow than ever. He immediately began to discuss the difficulties in developing the equations of motion. Thinking was as essential to Einstein as breathing.

Infeld in his memoirs deals with the very important question of the intellectual, "mental" sources of Einstein's human kindness. We have already had occasion to observe that Einstein's moral qualities were in profound, though not immediately apparent, harmony with the traits of his intellect. Rarely can a scientist be found whose mind would be so permeated with feeling, so emotionally coloured and devoted to serving the "extra-personal" and to aesthetic admiration of nature. And on the other hand, rarely can a person be found in whom kindness, love, and a sense of responsibility towards people would derive so directly from his mode of thinking.

Infeld offers a very accurate characteristic of this trait of Einstein's.

"I learned much from Einstein in the realm of physics. But what I value most is what I was taught by my contact with him in the human rather than the scientific domain. Einstein is the kindest, most understanding and helpful man in the world. But again this somewhat commonplace statement must not be taken literally.

"The feeling of pity is one of the sources of human kindness. Pity for the fate of our fellow-men, for the misery around us, for the suffering of human beings, stirs our emotions by the resonance of sympathy. Our own attachments to life and people, the ties which bind us to the outside world, awaken our emotional response to the struggle and suffering outside ourselves. But there is also another entirely different source of human kindness. It is the detached feeling of duty based on aloof, clear reasoning. Good, clear thinking leads to kindness and loyalty because this is what makes life simpler, fuller, richer, diminishes friction and unhappiness in our environment and therefore also in our lives. A sound social attitude, helpfulness, friendliness, kindness, may come from both these different sources; to express it anatomically, from heart and brain. As the years passed I learned to value more and more the second kind of decency that arises from clear thinking. Too often I have seen how emotions unsupported by clear thought are useless if not destructive."[1]

Many people who knew Einstein would ask, what is greater in him: his brain, with its capacity of probing the structure of the universe, or his heart, with its ready response to human grief and every manifestation of social injustice. This question is embodied in many of the memoirs pertaining to Einstein's life in Princeton. Gustav Bucky, his physician, writes that, irrespective of the impression created by the depth and unconformity of Einstein's ideas, "his human kindness remained the greatest and most moving wonder."[2] Bucky relates that, although Einstein hated sitting for portraits, there was one argument which could be relied upon to persuade him. All an artist had to do was to say that the portrait would help to improve his financial affairs, and Einstein would forthwith submit to hours of sitting for the poor artist. Bucky writes that the very sight of Einstein in the street was enough to bring a good-natured smile to the faces of passers-by.

"Even in Princeton everyone looks with hungry, astonished eyes on Einstein," Infeld writes. "During our walks we avoided the more crowded streets to walk through fields and long forgotten byways. Once a car stopped us and a middle-aged woman got out with a camera and said, blushing and excited:

" 'Professor Einstein, will you allow me to take a picture of you?'

" 'Yes, sure.'

"He stood quiet for a second, then continued his argument. The scene did not exist for him, and I am sure after a few minutes he forgot that it had ever happened.

"Once we went to a movie in Princeton to see the *Life of Émile Zola*. After we had bought our tickets we went to a crowded waiting room and found that we should have to

[1] L. Infeld, op. cit., pp. 286-87.
[2] *Helle Zeit*, S. 61.

wait fifteen minutes longer. Einstein suggested that we go for a walk. When we went out I said to the doorman:

" 'We shall return in a few minutes.'

"But Einstein became seriously concerned and added in all innocence:

" 'We haven't our tickets any more. Will you recognise us?'

"The doorman thought we were joking and said, laughing:

" 'Yes, Professor Einstein, I will.' "[1]

In the beginning of 1937 Infeld was faced with the dilemma of how to continue his work with Einstein. His Princeton fellowship was for only one year, and even though Einstein intervened urgently on his behalf it was not prolonged. Infeld finally thought of a way out of his predicament, which was to write a popular science book together with Einstein. A prospective publisher would be only too glad to be offered a book with Einstein's name on it as author. Half of an advance on royalties would suffice for Infeld to spend another year in Princeton. After a good deal of hesitation Infeld finally put the proposition to Einstein. The latter listened calmly and then said: " 'This is not at all a stupid idea. Not stupid at all.' Then he got up, stretched out his hand to [Infeld] and said: 'We shall do it.' "[2]

Einstein did not want to write a popular book on relativity. His idea was to present the principal ideas of physics in their logical development. Physical ideas alone, without the mathematical apparatus. An historical exposition would help to show how physical pictures are born and evolve before they are clothed in the mathematical formalism. An historical presentation brings out the adventure of search and the battle of ideas.

"It is a drama, a drama of ideas," Einstein said of the future book. "It ought to be absorbing and highly interesting for everyone who likes science."[3]

Einstein's interest in the intuitive and semi-intuitive pictures which precede a rigid exposition, his treatment of physical pictures as a "drama of ideas" derives directly from his epistemological principles. If a picture can be

[1] L. Infeld, op. cit., p. 290.
[2] Ibid., p. 311.
[3] Ibid., p. 313.

visualised then it should be possible in principle to verify a theory experimentally, making *a priori* statements unnecessary. If science were the outcome of an unambiguous logical development of *a priori* assumptions inherent in knowledge (Kant), or of free conventions (Poincaré), it would be anything but a drama. If it were a collection of phenomenological statements, "pure description", the result of subjective "experience" (Mach), it would not be a "flight from self-evidence", it would contain no paradoxes, no conflict of ideas, nothing of that which makes science a drama and leaves a trace in history.

Einstein's ideas of the book were embodied in its presentation. The idea was to remove all effects and embellishments superficial to the subject matter. They did not seek to stagger the imagination by comparing the gigantic dimensions of the universe and intergallactic distances of millions of light years with sub-atomic dimensions. Furthermore, Einstein and Infeld did not want their book to create the impression that science has departed in any way from plain common sense. If science represents the unfolding of *a priori* conceptual schemes it can have nothing in common with conceptions arising from daily experience. Einstein's epistemological positions were based on the assumption that scientific thinking follows the same road as daily common sense: only it delves much farther into domains governed by new laws which (at least initially) seem paradoxical to daily common sense.

The Evolution of Physics was first published in 1938. The authors write in the preface:

"Whilst writing the book we had long discussions as to the characteristics of our idealised reader and worried a good deal about him. We had him making up for a complete lack of any concrete knowledge of physics and mathematics by quite a great number of virtues. We found him interested in physical and philosophical ideas and we were forced to admire the patience with which he struggled through the less interesting and more difficult passages"[1].

This reader, it must be said, was not so much idealised as to be non-existent. *The Evolution of Physics* does not

[1] A. Einstein, L. Infeld, *The Evolution of Physics*, Simon and Schuster, New York, 1954, p. x.

require special knowledge, though it does impose rigid demands on intelligence, an ability for abstract reasoning and consistency. Primarily, however, it requires a deep interest in the ideological evolution of mankind. It is significant of our time that there exist so many real people in the world of whom this idealised reader is a prototype. A great many people are today seeking the answers to contemporary problems in the history of science. The fundamental answer—the harmony and knowability of the world —is expressed in the epigraph to this chapter. This passage is preceded in *The Evolution of Physics* by a brief characteristic of the development of the scientific world picture from which follows the idea of its harmony and knowability.

The primary concepts are mass, force and motion under no forces, which does not affect the course of events in a moving system. These concepts are used in formulating the mechanical world picture: between particles there act forces depending only on the distance. "A courageous scientific imagination was needed to realise fully that not the behaviour of bodies, but the behaviour of something between them, that is, the field, may be essential for ordering and understanding events."[1] Later absolute time was abandoned, and then the restriction of relative motion to intertial systems was overcome. Events in all systems are reduced to the relative displacements of bodies. The background for events is no longer the one-dimensional time and three-dimensional space continuums but the four-dimensional space-time continuum. Finally, "the quantum theory again created new and essential features of our reality. Discontinuity replaced continuity." The goal of physics remained the same at every stage: discovery of the objective harmony in the maze of observed facts. The results of scientific history lie in the existence and the understanding of this harmony. "We want the observed facts to follow logically from our concept of reality."[2]

This was the goal on which were centred the scientific, and hence the life interests of Einstein. Rationalism linked by a continuity of succession with the philosophy of Spinoza

[1] A. Einstein, L. Infeld, *The Evolution of Physics*, Simon and Schuster, New York, 1954, p. 312.
[2] Ibid., p. 312.

and enriched by three centuries of progress in science and practice acquires its most general form: in the ideal the logic of scientific thinking leads to the totality of empirically observable physical relationships. The fact that in its advance science is steadily approaching this ideal is testimony to the reign of determinism in the world: the logic of scientific thinking reflects the real causal links embracing the universe.

The greatest concentration of interests and mental powers on this pivotal idea constitutes the main feature of Einstein's life and work.

Einstein's attitude towards the book was characteristic enough. He took active part in all the preparatory work, but as soon as the manuscript was ready he lost all interest in it; he never even looked at the proofs of the book. Not wanting to upset the publishers, Infeld told them that Einstein had liked the finished copy very much. Actually he hadn't even opened the book.

Chapter 27

THE A-BOMB TRAGEDY

*The atom M is a rich miser who, during his
life, gives away no money (energy). But in his
will he bequeaths his fortune to his sons M'
and M'', on condition that they give to the
community a small amount, less than one-
thousandth of the whole estate (energy or
mass). The sons together have somewhat less
than the father had (the mass sum M'+M" is
somewhat smaller than the mass M of the
radioactive atom). But the part given to the
community, though relatively small, is still so
enormously large (considered as kinetic
energy) that it brings with it a great threat
of evil. Averting that threat has become the
most urgent problem of our time.*

E i n s t e i n

Since the beginning of civilisation, and up until the mid-
20th century industrial power production has been based on
processes involving the regrouping of atoms—the chemical
reactions of burning in which the released energy is infinitesimal in comparison with the internal energy of bodies.
The use of atomic piles brought in processes in which the
liberated energy is compatible with the mass of the bodies
involved multiplied by the velocity of light. These were
peaceful installations. When a thermal engine was devised
in which the piston was ejected from the cylinder after the
very first cycle (firearms, in other words), this did not
mark a new era in power production. The new era began
with the first thermal engines in which the expansion of gas
or steam was utilised to turn the shafts of working machines. Similarly, the atomic era was ushered in not by the
first A-bomb but by the first atom-powered electric station.

The liberation of atomic energy is based on laws discovered
through the application of relativity theory to the physics of

the atomic nucleus. It was found experimentally that the mass of an atomic nucleus is less than the sum of the masses of its component particles, protons and neutrons. This so-called mass defect is explained on the basis of the mass-energy equivalence discovered by Einstein. The particles of different nuclei are either closely or loosely packed together, and accordingly different energies are needed to pull them apart. The binding energy of particles in the nucleus varies from element to element along the series of Mendeleyev's Periodic Table. According to Einstein's equivalence principle, the differences in energy correspond to differences in mass.

The transformation of nuclei of one type into nuclei of another type—whether through the fission of heavy or the fusion of light nuclei—results in a change in the packing density. In such reactions the mass of the resultant nuclei may be less than that of the initial ones. This reduction in mass corresponds to a release of energy, the liberated energy being equal to the reduction in mass times the square of the velocity of light.

Calculations based on these corollaries of relativity theory indicate that the energy release is greatest in nuclear reactions involving the heaviest and lightest atomic nuclei.

The nuclei of the heavier elements (those with higher atomic weights) at the end of the Periodic Table, are looser than the nuclei of elements in the middle of the table. Hence, in transformations from heavy into medium nuclei, or in other words, in the disintegration of heavy nuclei consisting of a great number of protons and neutrons into smaller ones, energy is liberated. The principle is expressed in Einstein's parable of the rich miser sharing his estate between his sons presented in the epigraph.

At the other extreme, with the light nuclei at the beginning of the Periodic Table, fusion into larger nuclei results in an increase in packing density. The fusion of hydrogen nuclei into helium is accompanied by the liberation of enormous quantities of energy.

Thus, relativity applied to nuclear physics predicted two types of reaction, fission and fusion. In both reactions energy is liberated, and the net mass of the resultant nuclei is less than that of the initial ones. The energy liberated in these reactions, which equals the reduction in mass multiplied by the square of the velocity of light, is tremendous, hundreds of thousands of times more than in the combustion of the same amount of matter.

The reaction of fission of uranium nuclei was discovered in the late 1930s. When bombarded with neutrons these heavy nuclei split into two nuclei of elements occupying the middle of the Periodic Table. Soon it was found that in the process of uranium fission neutrons are emitted which are themselves capable of splitting neighbouring nuclei. The process thus develops into a chain reaction which, once it has been triggered, involves the whole mass of the uranium in which it takes place. These were the results obtained by Frédéric Joliot-Curie in France and by Enrico Fermi, who had begun his work on uranium fission in Italy. Later he escaped from the Mussolini regime to the United States, where Leo Szilard and others were working on the problem.

The dawn of the atomic age began to break at a time when the political horizon was overcast with clouds. Germany under the nazis was rapidly building up its war potential. Einstein was more than ever apprehensive of the possible applications of physical research. He realised that a world war was not far off. Infeld writes that Einstein was well aware of the importance of events in Spain: the attack against the Republic was a dress rehearsal for all-out fascist aggression. He hoped for the success of the Republic.

"I remember the gleam that came into his eyes when I told him that the afternoon papers carried news of a Loyalist victory," Infeld writes.

" 'That sounds like an angel's song,' he said with an excitement which I had hardly ever noticed before."[1]

Less than two years later the war had begun. In the summer of 1939, Einstein was confronted with a problem of tremendous importance and urgency.

In July of that year the physicists Wigner and Szilard went to visit Einstein at a place on the north coast of Long Island where he usually spent the hot time of the year. Robert Jungk writes of the two men's mission in his book *Brighter Than a Thousand Suns*.[2]

[1] L. Infeld, op. cit., p. 292.
[2] R. Jungk, *Brighter Than a Thousand Suns*, New York, 1958, p. 78. For Szilard's Memoirs see also *Helle Zeit*, S. 98-104.

They drove around for a long time in search of Einstein's house. "Suddenly Szilard exclaimed: 'Let's give it up and go home. Perhaps fate never intended it. We should probably be making a frightful mistake by enlisting Einstein's help in applying to any public authority in a matter like this. Once a government gets hold of something it never lets go.'

" 'But it's our duty to take this step,' Wigner objected. 'It must be our contribution to the prevention of a terrible calamity.' "

The "terrible calamity" which the two men hoped to prevent was the manufacture of a uranium bomb by nazi Germany. Information had leaked out which suggested to Szilard and other physicists that nuclear weapons might soon be placed in the hands of the nazi armies. Szilard knocked at every door in an attempt to rouse the United States government to the danger. But he was an unknown person with no connections among the powers that be. Besides, words like "nuclear binding energy" or "nuclear fission" seemed hardly related to practical tasks. Szilard finally decided that the best course would be to enlist Einstein's help and appeal to Queen Elizabeth of Belgium. Belgium possessed large reserves of uranium and Szilard hoped to keep them out of German hands. He had also hoped that Einstein would be more successful in drawing the attention of U.S. government authorities to the problem of the uranium bomb. The responsibility which Szilard was undertaking was tremendous. He viewed all minor obstacles to his purpose as something of a finger of fate. Every detail of the fated trip remained impressed in his mind.

Finally, a seven-year boy showed Szilard and Wigner where Einstein lived, he said he knew him well.

"The possibility of a chain reaction in uranium had not occurred to Einstein," Szilard relates. "But almost as soon as I began to tell him about it he realised what the consequences might be and immediately signified his readiness to help us.... But it seemed desirable, before approaching the Belgian government, to inform the State Department at Washington of the step contemplated.... Such was the position when Wigner and I left Einstein's place on .Long Island."[1]

---

[1] R. Jungk, op. cit., p. 84.

After consulting several friends, Szilard finally met with Alexander Sachs, financier, friend and unofficial adviser to President Roosevelt. Sachs readily appreciated the importance of the information. It was decided that Einstein should forward a letter directly to the President, and a draft was duly prepared.

On August 2, Szilard, accompanied this time by Edward Teller, again visited Einstein. Later, when the participants in the undertaking realised the burden of their responsibility, they tried to reconstruct all the details and, in particular, to determine who had drafted the final wording of the letter.

Szilard observes: "So far as I remember, Einstein dictated a letter to Teller in German and I used the text of that letter as a basis for two more drafts, one comparatively short and one rather long, both addressed to the President. I left it to Einstein to decide which he preferred. He chose the longer draft. I also prepared a memorandum as an enclosure to Einstein's letter."[1]

Teller, on the other hand, claims that Einstein merely signed the letter they had brought him. This is also Einstein's version.

Here is the letter the consequences of which were so great:

Albert Einstein
Old Grove Road
Nassau Point
Peconic, Long Island
August 2, 1939

F. D. Roosevelt
President of the United States
White House
Washington, D.C.

Sir:

Some recent work by E. Fermi and L. Szilard, which has been communicated to me in manuscript, leads me to expect that the element uranium may be turned into

[1] R. Jungk, op. cit., p. 80.

a new and important source of energy in the immediate future. Certain aspects of the situation seem to call for watchfulness and, if necessary, quick action on the part of the Administration. I believe, therefore, that it is my duty to bring to your attention the following facts and recommendations.

In the course of the last four months it has been made probable—through the work of Joliot in France and Fermi and Szilard in America—that it may become possible to set up nuclear chain reactions in a large mass of uranium by which vast amounts of power and large quantities of new radium-like elements would be generated. Now it appears almost certain that this could be achieved in the immediate future.

This new phenomenon would also lead to the construction of bombs, and it is conceivable—though much less certain—that extremely powerful bombs of a new type may thus be constructed. A single bomb of this type, carried by boat or exploded in a port, might very well destroy the whole port together with some of the surrounding territory. However, such bombs might very well prove to be too heavy for transportation by air.

The United States has only very poor ores of uranium in moderate quantities. There is some good ore in Canada and the former Czechoslovakia, while the most important source of uranium is the Belgian Congo.

In view of this situation you may think it desirable to have some permanent contact maintained between the Administration and the group of physicists working on chain reactions in America. One possible way of achieving this might be for you to entrust with this task a person who has your confidence and who could perhaps serve in an unofficial capacity. His task might comprise the following:

a) To approach Government Departments, keep them informed of the further developments, and put forward recommendations for Government action, giving particular attention to the problem of securing a supply of uranium ore for the United States.

b) To speed up the experimental work which is at present being carried on within the limits of the budgets of University laboratories, by providing funds, if such funds be required, through his contacts with private persons who are willing to make contributions for this cause, and perhaps also by obtaining the co-operation of industrial laboratories which have the necessary equipment.

I understand that Germany has actually stopped the sale of uranium from the Czechoslovakian mines which she has taken over. That she should have taken such early action might perhaps be understood on the ground that the son of the German Under-Secretary of State, von Weizsäcker, is attached to the Kaiser Wilhelm Institute in Berlin, where some of the American work on uranium is now being repeated.

Yours very truly,

A. EINSTEIN[1]

Einstein's interference was the sequel to a long evolution in his attitude towards the outside world. At the same time, his action is characteristic of the beginning of the atomic era.

To what type of scholar does Einstein belong, the one in the ivory tower or the active participant in the march of history? Ernst Kuno Fischer once compared two great philosophers. Spinoza never turned to the powers that be, was independent of them and chose to grind diamonds so as to be free to meditate in seclusion. Leibnitz was an adviser to kings, author of innumerable political and administrative projects, a man whose epistolary heritage numbers some 15,000 letters. The difference between them lies not only in their personal likes and dislikes but also in the difference of the requirements imposed on the scholar at various periods, and the difference in general conceptions which lead, in the one case, to escape from the daily turmoil of life and, in the other, to active participation in public affairs.

[1] *Einstein on Peace*, edited by Otto Nathan and Heinz Norden, Simon and Schuster, New York, 1960, pp. 294-96.

Einstein's attitude was closer to that of Spinoza. He frequently remarked that the ideal social position for a scholar would have been that of a labourer, artisan or lighthouse keeper. For a long time he stubbornly refused to be drawn into the affairs of others, take part in public meetings or attempt in any way to actively influence events in his university, city, country, or in the world. His calling, dream and devotion was science, pure—in all senses of the word—science.

And yet hardly any other natural scientist has ever participated so actively and effectively in mundane affairs as Einstein. This began not in 1939, but almost twenty-five years earlier, during the First World War. With the mounting of his fame, in his travels, in the fight against nazism—all through his life he increasingly identified himself with world affairs. And now the time had come when he was destined to pave the way for the interference of science in the affairs of man to a degree without precedent in world history.

Of course, no one, and least of all Einstein himself, can be blamed for the events that followed. His signature on the letter to Roosevelt was not a key to Pandora's box. But his participation, to whatever extent, in the launching of the experimental work on uranium fission and his subsequent active struggle against the military applications of atomic energy were a sign of the time. Not only because the credit goes to Einstein for the formula connecting energy with mass. There was a time when relativity, though in the full glare of the public limelight, was a symbol of something extremely remote from human affairs and interests.

Now the intuitive feeling that there was something more than pure theory in Einstein's work was being justified. Mankind had approached the historic landmark beyond which science became the source of man's greatest hopes and worst fears. Refusal to lend one's weight to the struggle at this juncture would be tantamount to a betrayal of science. For the very being, objectivity, rational nature and truth of science demanded that the hopes of people be justified and their fears be dispelled.

Einstein had before him the spectre of Hitler with the atom bomb in its hand. But neither was he wholly confident in American ruling circles.

344

This lack of confidence was so great that already in September 1940 Einstein spoke of his letter to Roosevelt as the most unfortunate thing in his life. His only justification was the fear that Germany might build the bomb.

As a matter of fact, Hitler would never have been able to get atomic weapons into his hands before the end of the war. For one, the time leased to him by history was too short. Starting with the autumn of 1942 the advance of the Soviet Army and massive air raids made the construction of installations like an atomic pile in Germany a practical impossibility. Furthermore, the purge of the scientific community in Germany and the escape of many leading scientists sharply lowered the level of research work in the country. Besides, many of the physicists who remained in Germany were concerned not so much with making discoveries as with preventing them from falling into nazi hands. Fritz Houtermans, who was working on nuclear chain reaction in uranium fission, kept his results secret: when he was alarmed by news that Heisenberg and Weizsäker were engaged in similar studies Max von Laue reassured him: "My dear colleague, no one ever invents anything he doesn't really want to invent." To this it should be added that Hitler and his circle were highly suspicious of theoretical physics as a source of practically applicable discoveries: its rationalist, objective nature was much too alien to the Führer's mystical inspirations.

Such considerations, however, could not absolutely rule out the possibility of the atom bomb appearing in Germany. At best they served to delay the necessary research work. The real obstacle was the turn in the war in 1942. This question was settled along with others on the banks of the Volga. The defeat of nazi Germany rid the globe of the terrible menace of the atom bomb in Hitler's hands.

In 1939 Einstein could neither know nor foresee all this, and the spectre of a nazi atom bomb continued to loom over him much later.

Einstein's letter was delivered to Alexander Sachs, who handed it to Roosevelt only on October 11. It did not impress the President. But on the following day, at breakfast, Sachs told Roosevelt the story according to which Napoleon had sent Robert Fulton away when he came to the French Emperor with an offer to build a fleet of steamships for landing in England. "Had Napoleon shown more imagination and humility at that time," Sachs added, "the history of the 19th century would have taken a very different course."

After listening to the story Roosevelt wrote a note and handed it to the footman serving breakfast, who returned shortly with a bottle of French brandy of Napoleonic vintage and filled their glasses. Roosevelt summoned his military aide General Watson, and the gears of the machine for creating the atom bomb started turning. They were slow in gathering momentum, and in March of the following year (1940) Einstein sent another letter to the President in which he again spoke of the heightened interest which nazi Germany seemed to be displaying towards uranium. In spite of Roosevelt's support, however, the works were continually bogged down in government authorities and business circles. Judging from the reminiscences of Szilard and other participants in the project, these circles did not place great stock in theoretical thinking. The project owed its success mainly to the enthusiasm of the physicists and engineers assigned to it, for they shared with the original sponsors their confidence in the theoretical calculations and their fear of a nazi bomb.

The defeat of Germany removed that fear, but a new and much more tangible danger appeared.

"In 1945, when we ceased worrying about what the Germans might do to us, we began to worry about what the government of the United States might do to other countries," Szilard wrote later.[1]

Once again he goes to Einstein—this time to enlist his support in passing on to Roosevelt a memorandum aimed at preventing the atom bomb from being dropped on Japanese cities. Einstein dispatched the letter, but it never reached its addressee. On April 12, 1945, the day of Roosevelt's sudden death, it lay unopened on his desk.

The tragedy of Hiroshima and Nagasaki was a grave trial for Einstein. Antonina Vallentin writes of her conversation with Einstein in which he discussed the subject:

" 'My actual role was that of a mailbox,' Einstein remarked. 'The letter was written and brought to me; all I had to do

[1] R. Jungk, op. cit., p. 178.

346

was sign it.' We were sitting in his study at his Princeton home. A greyish light streamed through the big window and fell on his wrinkled cheeks and on his eyes, which seemed to burn in his head. A silence laden with mute questions ensued. His eyes, sparkling as always, were turned to me. I said: 'And yet you pressed the button.' He turned away quickly and looked out of the window at the deserted valley and the bright-green lawn with a clump of old trees that hid the horizon. Then, as if answering the tree top where his glance lingered, Einstein said, quietly, thoughtfully, punctuating each word: 'Yes, I pressed the button.' "[1]

This "Yes, I pressed the button", could be interpreted to mean that Einstein regarded his letter to Roosevelt as having been the cause of the catastrophe which struck Hiroshima and Nagasaki in 1945, and which continues to hover over the world. At least, that seems to be Antonina Vallentin's impression. Hellen Dukas, however, who for many years was party to Einstein's inner thoughts, says that the words, "Yes, I pressed the button", do not accord with his idea of the role of personalities and their actions in the destinies of mankind. Einstein completely rejected the idea that major historic upheavals are in any way subject to the will and whim of outstanding personalities or "makers of history". And in any case he did not rank himself among such makers—the very idea of ranking himself as such, and his role in science and history, could never have occurred to him. Tolstoi's "green wand" was his for the asking, for with him disengagement from the momentary and "merely personal" was an intrinsic quality of his inner world.

To this it should be added that in the eyes of anyone familiar with the history of nuclear research, the letter to Roosevelt could in no way be equated to the idea "I pressed the button". It was not this episode that was responsible for Einstein's deep tragedy, which oppressed him from 1945 to the end of his days.

The tragedy of the atom bomb was but an extreme expression of a thing which had troubled him for many years. With his characteristic feeling of personal responsi-

[1] A. Vallentin, op. cit., p. 215.

bility for all the evil in the world, he felt very deeply the great, age-old tragedy of irrational, destructive exploitation of the achievements of the human mind. The mind seeks harmony in nature and by its inner trends guides society to harmony, to a rational organisation of the community. In antagonistic societies, however, the fruits of reason may turn poisonous and every scientific idea, every discovery of the inner *ratio* of the world may become a weapon in the hands of irrational forces. These were sentiments which Einstein had frequently voiced before. The present occasion, to be sure, involved the application of one of the fundamental corollaries of relativity. Einstein, however, felt his responsibility for the nature of this application not as the creator of relativity theory—he never thought of himself in that capacity and his very mode of thinking precluded such kind of self-appraisal. Einstein identified himself with the collective reason of mankind, he had an acute sense of responsibility for science as a whole—and this was what served to aggravate so greatly the last act in the lengthy tragedy of scientific creation in an antagonistic society. This burden did not undermine his confidence in mankind's ability to remove the threat of atomic warfare and utilise the fruits of science for creative purposes. Atomic energy as such carries no inherent threat to humanity; the threat lies in the misuse of the new forces of nature. "The discovery of atomic chain reaction," Einstein wrote, "in itself presents no greater danger of the annihilation of humanity than the invention of matches; the thing to do is to remove the possibilities of abusing the power it presents."

Einstein pointed out that atomic energy led to a quantitative increase in the urgency and importance of an old problem. "The release of atomic energy has not created a new problem. It has merely made more urgent the necessity of solving an existing one," he wrote in November 1945. The problem lies in the possibility of applying scientific discoveries for aggressive and destructive purposes. Einstein believed that the time would come when the old problem would be resolved, society would be remodelled on a rational basis and scientific discoveries would be utilised only for the benefit of people.

This belief, however, did not remove the tragedy; it could not make Einstein forget the fate of Hiroshima nor to underestimate the possibility of it being repeated in some other city. It did not relieve Einstein of the sense of moral responsibility for the ways in which science was being exploited. All his life he refused to be reconciled with social contradictions, he could never forget them and relapse into social and ethical indifference or compromise.

Uncompromising social and moral integrity is characteristic of most genuine scientists. The servicing of science demands such independence, consistency, integrity and courage which are incompatible with moral compromise. Personal or public opportunism are frequently a prologue to ideological opportunism in science and a complete or partial renunciation of genuinely scientific investigation. Scientific and ethical criteria are intertwined in all scientists. In Einstein they were fused.

He was deeply aware, more than any other scientist of his generation, of the tragedy of aggressive military applications of science. "Deeply" is the word, for the immediate participants in the manufacturing of the atomic bomb may have felt the tragedy of Hiroshima more poignantly and painfully. For Einstein, however, the question was not one of a series of nuclear investigations, in which he actually took no part, but of science as a whole. On the other hand, the work of atomic authorities in the United States presented a most graphic testimony to the dependence of science on irrational forces. The selfsame demon of irrationality could be seen peering out of reports of all kinds of meetings and conferences, whether they took place in the War Department, in industrial corporations or in universities and institutes dependent on them. This demon no longer anathematised science; it made a servant of it. From the heights of speculative thinking Einstein could see that science as a whole had fallen into a terrible dependence on circles alien and hostile to the idea of unselfish service to truth. To Einstein science was synonymic with freedom of thought serving an "extra-personal", rational cause. Science serves practical interests without betraying its rational essence; this essence bodies forth most fully when practical interests are aimed at the reshaping of society and nature along rational lines based on reason and science, and hence on truth and justice. A rational, harmonious social system provides the basis for free and harmonious development and rational thinking. The interests of an antagonistic social system are opposed to truth and are extraneous, compulsory conditions for science.

The militarisation of science and aggressive foreign policies induced Einstein to come out in February 1950 and appear in a television programme with the following evaluation of the postwar situation in the United States:

"Every single act in [American] foreign policy is governed exclusively by one viewpoint: how do we have to act in order to achieve utmost superiority over the opponent in case of war? Establishing military bases at all possible strategically important points on the globe. Arming and economic strengthening of potential allies. Within the country: concentration of tremendous financial power in the hands of the military; militarisation of the youth; close supervision of the loyalty of citizens, in particular of the civil servants, by a police force growing more conspicuous every day. Intimidation of people of independent thinking. Subtle indoctrination of the public by radio, press, and schools."[1]

Einstein repeatedly voiced his opposition to "loyalty tests" of all kinds. In May 1953, William Frauenglass, a teacher in Brooklyn, N. Y., wrote to Einstein. He had been summoned before a Congressional Committee for coming out in support of international cultural contacts. Frauenglass had refused to testify concerning his political views, an act fraught with all kinds of trouble. Einstein's reply, dated May 16, was published in the *New York Times* on June 12, 1953. Stripped of the preliminaries, it reads:

"The problem with which the intellectuals of this country are confronted is very serious. The reactionary politicians have managed to instil suspicion of all intellectual efforts into the public by dangling before their eyes a danger from without. Having succeeded so far, they are now proceeding to suppress the freedom of teaching and to deprive of their positions all those who do not prove submissive, i.e., to starve them.

"What ought the minority of intellectuals to do against this evil? Frankly, I can only see the revolutionary way of non-co-operation in the sense of Gandhi's. Every intellectual

[1] *Ideas and Opinions*, p. 159.

350

Den damals Ordnung, für Ihre Ausführungen – habe den neunte Punkt
meinte ich als theoretischen Grundlagen des Aufgabe. –

Das Problem, von welches wohl die Intelligenz dieses
Landes gestellt sieht, daß nur sehr einseits, Es ist nur
erschöpfenden politischer Maßnahmen-zu-gelungen darüber
Verzögerung einer äußeren Gefahr des Entstehen gegen
die intellektuellen Bemühungen wiederum wäre zu
mochte, statt der Basis stets Erfolgreich auch wie
darauf, die freie Lehre zu unterschätzen und
sie nicht Gefangenen aus allen Stellungen zu verdrängen,

d. h. zu verhindern.

Was soll die Mehrheit der Intellektuellen tun
gegen den Willen? Ich sehe nur offene wehrhaften aus den
verzweiflenden Weg der Nun – cooperation der Gewalt gehorchend i.
Jeder Intellektuelle, der vor einem Zwang der damalis Gelladen
wird, müßte jede Aussage verweigern, d. h. haupt wünschen.

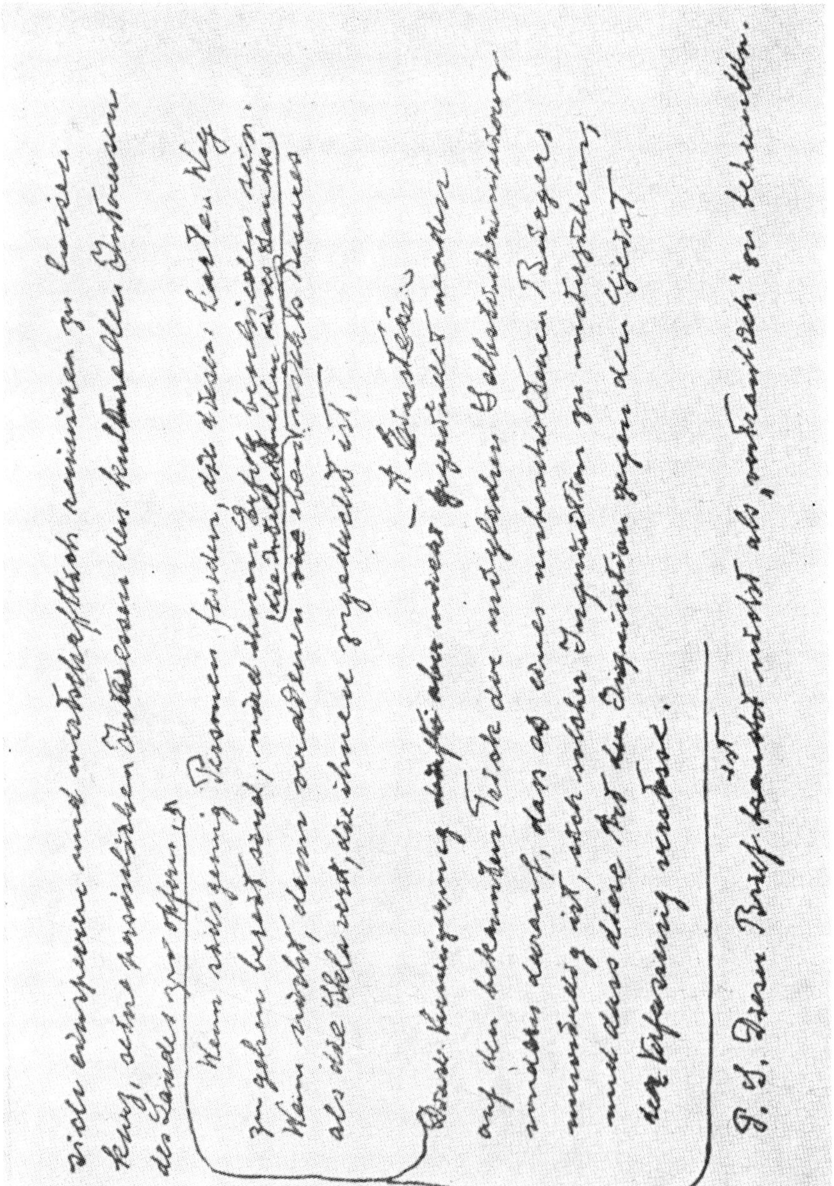

Einstein's letter to William Frauenglass. May 16, 1953

who is called before one of the committees ought to refuse to testify, i.e., he must be prepared for jail and economic ruin, in short, for the sacrifice of his personal welfare in the interest of the cultural welfare of his country.

"However, this refusal to testify must not be based on the well-known subterfuge of invoking the Fifth Amendment against possible self-incrimination, but on the assertion that it is shameful for a blameless citizen to submit to such an inquisition and that this kind of inquisition violates the spirit of the Constitution.

"If enough people are ready to take this grave step they will be successful. If not, then the intellectuals of this country deserve nothing better than the slavery which is intended for them."[1]

---

[1] *Ideas and Opinions*, pp. 33-34.

Chapter 28

DEATH

The search for truth is more precious than its possession.

L e s s i n g

A recurring theme in letters written by Einstein in the 1950s is that of tiredness, a general tiredness with life. These remarks, whether expressed in a jocular or serious vein, are an expression of a tranquil, reconciled sadness, like the mood that sometimes grips a person on a quiet evening. In no way did this mood affect Einstein's humour, optimism or passion for work. It had nothing to do with summing up the results of a lifetime. Einstein's thoughts remained concentrated on the varying fortunes of the unified field theory. It would be hard to find in Einstein's writings a summing up of his life work.

One piece, which could be regarded as a summing up, is his *Autobiographical Sketch,* a few pages written in March 1955, his last spring, for an anniversary publication devoted to the centenary of the Zurich Polytechnic.[1] In it Einstein writes of his first attempt to enter the Polytechnic, his year at the cantonal school in Aarau, and the atmosphere of freedom at the school. He also recalls the "thought experiment" which occupied him there: what will happen if a man tries to catch a light ray? For such a man the waves of light would seem to stand still. The incompatibility of this picture with the principle of relativity marked the beginning of his meditations, which led to the ideas set forth in 1905 in the famous paper, *On the Electrodynamics of Moving Bodies.*

Einstein then goes on to describe his student days and his attitude towards mathematical knowledge. He pays warm tribute to the memory of Marcel Grossmann. Einstein recalls his work at the Bern Patent Office, where conditions were so favourable for his scientific investigations.

[1] *Helle Zeit,* S. 9-17.

After a very cursory mention of special relativity, Einstein dwells in comparative detail—three pages—on the general theory of relativity. He offers an extremely vivid and original characteristic of the search which culminated in 1916 in the formulation of the general theory. It is probably the most monumental exposition of the theory ever made.

The autobiography ends with the following words on the unified field theory:

"Forty years have passed since the theory of gravitation was completed. They were devoted entirely to the single purpose of generalising the gravitational theory and developing a field theory capable of becoming the basis for the whole of physics. Many men have sought the same goal. Many ideas which had first seemed hopeful had to be rejected. Yet the last ten years have led to a theory which seems to me natural and promising, although I am still unable to say whether it will prove of value to physics or not. This uncertainty is due to insurmountable mathematical difficulties, which, however, are inevitable in any non-linear field theory. Furthermore it remains doubtful whether it will be possible to derive the atomistic structure of matter and radiation, as well as quantum phenomena, from the field theory. Most physicists unhesitatingly respond with a decisive 'No', for they think that in principle quantum problems must be solved in some other way."[1] This passage is followed by Lessing's words quoted in the epigraph: "The search for truth is more precious than its possession."

We are by now sufficiently well acquainted with Einstein's life and world outlook to perceive the sense in which he uses the words "the search for truth" and "the possession of truth", and why they conclude his ideas on the unified field theory, as well as the autobiography as a whole.

To Einstein "truth" is the truth of the real world, the world picture. This picture infinitely approaches the original, gradually ridding itself of arbitrary assumptions and coinciding to an ever greater degree with the ideal of science—a picture in which there would be no empirical physical constants lacking causal explanation. In its eternal approach to the ideal, science possesses at every stage of its development a certain relative truth, a relative, approximate

---

[1] *Helle Zeit*, S. 16-17.

conception of physical reality which is subject to further modification. "Possession of the truth" means possession of a certain determinate world picture.

But science not only possesses the truth in the sense that it presents a specific scheme of the universe (within the limits of the current state of knowledge). Every such scheme, even though it is superseded by new ones and perishes, still retains for the newly developing conception of reality an historically invariant content which is not subject to revision. More so, at every stage of development science carries certain inner forces of development, the problems which it bequeaths to the following epoch. This inner energy of science is not usually embodied in firm, positive forms. The contradictions which may have passed unobserved in one age and emerge in another, hypotheses which await their confirmation—are the links connecting the scientific theories of a given age with the further development of science. The speed of scientific progress is dependent on them to a large degree. These potentialities of science become apparent when a specific theory is replaced by another, having bequeathed to the latter its unsolved problems. To regard science from this aspect—as an infinite series of more and more exact and comprehensive conceptions—we must accept as the truth of science its continuous, ever developing and expanding problems, problems for which new and more and more exact and general solutions are found, solutions which serve as the basis for the immutability of science, as the basis for the immortality of science. The "search for truth" means that new theories must come to replace the old ones which have prepared the ground for them. This is the fate of theories and their makers.

Einstein did not consider that the unified field theory presented an unambiguous explanation of the world structures. He was well aware of the tentative nature of his theory, and he said as much in the cited passage (not for the first time, either). He was not in possession of the truth. But the unified field theory brought a powerful trend into science. It pushed theoretical physics to a synthesis of relativistic and quantum ideas, to a synthesis of different, and as yet unrelated and even contradictory, conceptions pertaining to different kinds of fields of force. In this sense the unified field theory was in the mainstream of science. Its specific form, as enunciated by Einstein in the 1940s-1950s, might go with its maker. But its underlying tendency will always remain a legacy—and we can see this today with special clarity thanks to the development of quantum-relativistic conceptions of particle transmutations as expressions of the interactions of different kinds of fields. To imbue science with such a tendency is a manifestation of the "search for the truth", if not "its possession".

The uphill search for the unified field theory which failed to yield unambiguous positive results was the calvary of a genius who (and this is especially apparent in the 1960s) opened the road to the new truth, to new links in the eternal approach to objective reality.

Einstein sensed very deeply the living ties between the eternal, continuous content of science and its passing values. This conception of the development of science forms the underlying text of his interview with Bernard Cohen, author of books on Franklin and Newton. Cohen visited Einstein two weeks before Einstein died.[1]

Cohen arrived at the small framed house with green shutters on Sunday morning in April 1955. He was greeted by Helen Dukas, who conducted him to Einstein's study on the second floor. We have already seen this room before. Cohen writes of the large table at the window laden with pads of paper, pencils, trinkets, books and a collection of well-worn pipes.

Einstein entered the room and Miss Dukas introduced Cohen. Einstein left the room for a moment and returned with his pipe. He sat in his easy-chair with a blanket tucked around his feet. He wore an open shirt, a blue sweat shirt, gray flannel trousers and leather slippers.

"His face," Cohen writes, "was contemplatively tragic and deeply lined, and yet his sparkling eyes made him seem ageless. His eyes watered almost continually, even in moments of laughter he would wipe away a tear with the back of his hand."

Cohen found Einstein's command of English remarkable— he had lived in America for twenty years by then—and was struck by the contrast between his soft speech and his ringing laughter.

---

[1] B. Cohen, op. cit., p. 73.

Much of the interview was devoted to the history and philosophy of science. Einstein spoke of the essential difference between his positions and those of Mach and described in considerable detail his meeting with Mach in Vienna and their discussion concerning the existence of molecules and atoms. Einstein commented on the fact that "today physicists are almost all philosophers, although 'they are apt to be bad philosophers' ". As an example he cited "logical positivism", supported by a group of Mach's pupils, especially the "Vienna circle" (Philipp Frank, Moritz Schlick, R. Carnap, O. Neurath, and others). Unlike Mach, they allowed for logical constructions in science that were not directly related to sense-impressions, but in the basic epistemological question they followed Mach and denied the objective reality behind sense-impressions and observations. Einstein seems to have been well aware that there was not much difference between "logical positivism" and orthodox "Machism" or between other schools of positivism.

A large part of the interview was devoted to Newton and his work. Cohen notes a peculiar aspect in Einstein's approach to the history of science, which can be related to the basic features of his attitude towards science. "As Einstein saw it," he writes, "there is an inner or intuitional history and an external or documentary history. The latter is more objective, but the former is more interesting."

Einstein sought to illustrate the importance of historical intuition by analysing the chain of logical, subconscious, purely psychological motives which led Newton to the ether concept from the idea of action at a distance through empty space. Newton's process of thought could be visualised, but, as Einstein declared, "the question arises as to whether—or perhaps, to what extent—one can document such intuition." Einstein believed that the historian is likely to have a better insight into the thought processes of a scientist than the scientist himself.

Physical intuition, as we have mentioned in connection with *The Evolution of Physics*, leads to conceptions which anticipate, and sometimes interpret, strict mathematical relationships. The clash of such conceptions gives rise to the "drama of ideas".

In Einstein's view, the important thing is to *preserve* such ideas and their struggle in science. Even when the historical episodes of the "drama of ideas" do not produce epical results or develop into indubitable, historically invariant forms and remain without a sequel, even so they continue to live on in science.

Einstein discussed with Cohen the problem of how often in the history of science great questions seem to be resolved, only to reappear in new form. He expressed the view that perhaps this was a characteristic of physics, and suggested that some of the fundamental problems might always be with us.

Einstein speaks not of solutions, but of problems, collisions, conflicts, contradictions—of all that makes history a drama of ideas. When a problem remains *even though it has been solved in a given epoch,* it is an indication of the approximate, temporal, relative nature of the solution. It introduces a positive, historically invariant content into the world picture, but it does not remove the problem; it expands and modernises the problem and prepares it for its reappearance in science.

One is reminded of Lenin's remarks on Aristotle, of the contradictions, searchings, approaches, the living that could not be destroyed by the desiccating genius of medieval Aristotelianism.

In order to judge a particle's state of motion one must know not only its position at a given instant but also the derivative of its coordinates with respect to time, its velocity. In order to judge the advance of scientific thinking one must know not only the point which it has reached and the answers it has supplied to the problems confronting it but also its speed, its gradient. And this includes, together with answers, new questions, the modification and expansion of old questions, everything projected into the future, which lives on after science has found a certain answer and attained a certain point. True, the analogy with the moving particle is inadequate, as science advances not only under the action of an external force but to a considerable degree spontaneously, as a result of internal collisions. But then, for all we know, particles may be moving in the same way.

If the history of science—even its most stable, apparently self-evident and *basically* unshakable conceptions—is viewed as a process of accumulation, expansion and variation of questions recurrently addressed to the future, historic retrospection becomes a discussion with scholars of the past, each of whom as it were, addresses us over the ages.

However restricted by primitive knowledge was the outlook of Aristotle, Democritus or Epicurus, Aristotle's problem of φθορά (annihilation) and γένησις (production) in connection with motion, nevertheless, remains alive to this day; Democritus's problem of "real non-being"—vacuum—cannot become obsolete; the problem of the transformation of Epicurus's "kinemas" into continuous motion remains a problem to this day. These *living* collisions of the past, addressed to us and conjugate with the direction, speed and gradient of scientific development, are found to be immortal.

Thus did Einstein approach the old scholars, and especially Newton. This point of view does not obviate historical interest in things which tended to restrict the positive answers of science. As Einstein wrote, addressing himself to Newton: "You found the only way which, in your age, was just about possible. . . ." But these words follow several pages of quite contemporary discussion with Newton on quite contemporary problems, and it begins with the personal address: "Newton, forgive me."

Einstein saw Newton as a scholar of the 17th century. His positive solutions belonged to him, as well as to the next two centuries. The unsolved questions, the contradictions and problems of the 17th century belong also to the future. These problems contribute to Newton's immortality and make it possible for one to discuss with him problems of the universe as if he were alive.

One capable of conversing with an immortal achieves immortality himself. Einstein's sense of living collaboration with the past and future generations of explorers of the world was responsible for his peculiar indifference towards the specific form which the scheme of the basic laws of reality might take under his pen. He knew that as a specific solution the unified field theory could disappear without achieving the status of an unambiguous physical theory. Despite the unparalleled intensity of his search, Einstein took a tranquil view of the problematical nature of his finds. He knew that the problem would be solved, only to gain in complexity and reappear in science. A specific solution might disappear, but the truth would remain and expand forever.

358

Science was so much part and parcel of Einstein's life that his attitude towards his own fate, his life and death, was inseparable from his attitude towards science. His 1955 *Autobiographical Sketch* at the end of his life and his 1949 "obituary" were not so much a summing-up as prophesies for the future. Einstein, as has been said before, never cared for a summing-up of his life. Once an intrusive visitor—of whom he had so many—asked him: "How, on your death-bed, would you answer the question whether your life was successful or in vain?" As usual Einstein paid no attention to the tactlessness of the question and replied with characteristic simple sincerity: "I would not be interested in such a question either on my death-bed or at any other time. After all I am only a tiny particle of nature."[1]

Einstein's attitude towards death can be found in many memoirs. In 1916 Einstein fell seriously ill and his life was in real danger. If not for the care of Elsa, who kept constant watch over his sick-bed, he might never have pulled through. Hedwig Born (Max Born's wife), who called on Einstein during his illness, found him discussing the possibility of his own death. He spoke in such a detached, tranquil manner that Mrs. Born decided to ask him whether he feared death. "No," he replied, "I feel myself so much a part of everything living, that I am not in the least concerned with the beginning or termination of the concrete existence of any person in this eternal flow."[2]

These, of course, were not just words. Mrs. Born, who was so familiar with Einstein's humour and practical jokes, realised their utter seriousness. She adds several profound remarks of her own. Einstein's words, she says, express his identification with humanity, towards which he aspired all his life in his quest for the laws of nature.

Hedwig Born demonstrates a wonderful keenness of observation in her approach to the very essence of Einstein's scientific exploit and his attitude towards people. Emergence into the "extra-personal", interest in the objective laws of the universe gave rise to a sense of identity with the cosmos, with life in all its manifestations, with mankind, with people who in the succession of generations expand their knowledge

[1] *Helle Zeit*, S. 87.
[2] Ibid., S. 36.

of nature, their power over nature, and approach a rational organisation of the human community. What in his attitude towards people seemed to emanate from his brain instead of his heart represented an expression of the absolute harmony of his heart and his brain. He once said in a chat with Infeld:

"Life is an exciting show. I enjoy it. It is wonderful. But if I knew that I should have to die in three hours it would impress me very little. I should think how best to use the last three hours, then quietly order my papers and lie peacefully down."[1] Two thousand years before Einstein, a philosopher whose fate it has been to be regarded as an advocate of personal pleasures also spoke of his attitude towards death. In his famous letter to Menekius, Epicurus advanced his argument against fear of death, which was to be repeated so many times: when we are, death is not; when death is, we are no more. Men whose life is imbued with extra-personal content understand, and to one degree or another accept, the convincing force of this argument. Epicurus himself, when he was dying ordered a hot bath and undiluted wine; in his last letter he calls the day of his death the happiest in his life because it was filled with memories of philosophical discourses. It would be hard to find a person more remote from Epicureanism or farther removed from thoughts of Epicurus's bath and wine than Einstein. But it would be hard to find a person closer to the Hellenic harmony of outlook and life.

At the time of Cohen's visit in April 1955, Einstein felt quite well. Several days later a Princeton friend (Cohen doesn't mention his name) went with Einstein to the hospital to see Einstein's stepdaughter Margot, who was ill with sciatica. After they left the hospital they had a long walk during which they talked about death. Einstein's companion commented that to him death was both a fact and a mystery. "And also a relief," Einstein added.

This was nothing new. Einstein loved life, yet many years before, he had ended a letter to Solovine with the words: "death is not so bad, either".[2] This was not indifference to life. On the contrary, it was the greatest love of life and the "extra-personal", it was an attitude towards life atuned to the Hellenic harmony but belonging to the great age in which

[1] L. Infeld, op. cit., p. 294.
[2] *Solovine*, p. 71.

Albert Einstein. *Epstein*

the human race is confronted with the most important "extra-personal" problems in history.

A week later, on April 13, Einstein came down with a sharp pain in the right-hand side of the abdomen. The doctors diagnosed inflammation of the gallbladder. At the hospital they suggested an operation, which Einstein refused. It was the same hospital where Margot was staying. In the evening of April 17 Margot was brought to Einstein's bedside in her wheel-chair. He felt well, chatted with Margot and bid her good night. Helen Dukas had left the hospital earlier. Shortly after midnight Nurse Alberta Rozsel, noticed that Einstein was breathing heavily in his sleep. She hurried to the door to summon a doctor. Suddenly Einstein muttered several words in German. Nurse Rozsel did not understand them and hurried to the bed. It was 1.25 a.m., and Einstein was no more. The post mortem revealed an aortic haemorrhage of the abdomen.

Einstein's will was read in the morning. His request was that his funeral be held without religious rites or official ceremony. The time and place of the funeral was to be kept secret from all except a few close friends, who saw his body to the crematorium.

Einstein's death was deeply felt by ordinary people all over the world. As Leonid Andreyev wrote in his parable *Gulliver's Death* (on the occasion of the death of Leo Tolstoi), while Gulliver was alive the Lilliputians could always hear the beating of his heart at night. This can be truly said of Einstein. The knowledge that such a man lived among them imbued people with confidence in the power and immortality of reason. Now the giant's heart had ceased to beat. Such a sense of irretrievable loss afflicting all men had formerly been felt only with the passing away of outstanding statesmen or great writers. Now for the first time people had this feeling with the death of a natural scientist.

Chapter 29

IMMORTALITY

Death is that you fear? Would you rather be immortal? Live in totality! Though you may die, life will continue forever.

Schiller

To live means to change, and the posthumous life of our ideas recorded on paper obeys the same law: they live on, changing continuously, growing less and less like what they were when they issued from our hearts and saw light.

Anatole France

The fundamental unsolved problem which Einstein bequeathed to 20th-century physics is the unified field theory and associated "transquantum" laws governing ultrarelativistic effects in the interactions of different fields. Science will not part with this inheritance; the searches, approaches and difficulties of Einstein's conception will recur in science again and again, just as the searches and difficulties of the old scholars of bygone ages have recurred. But along with unsolved problems Einstein's heritage includes the tangible assets of unambiguous physical theories, relativity in the first place.

In respect of every scholar who has sought to present a unified world picture it is possible to delineate in retrospect the boundaries of that picture, and thus the boundaries of his creative exploit. For Newton these boundaries were determined by the transition from motions incompatible in speed with the propagation of light to motions compatible with it. In the world of these motions Newton's laws, the classical rule of velocity addition in the first place, cease to be sufficiently accurate. Here we pass the boundary of Newtonian mechanics. Einsteinian mechanics also has its boundaries. But it would be wrong to reduce the historical exploits of

Einstein and Newton to the development of positive physical systems which, like everything in the world, appear, mature, and die. The geniuses of science create immortal values. To these belong, first of all, the generalisations which always retain their validity for a specific domain of phenomena, can be further generalised, specified and elaborated in going over to other phenomena, but can never be cast aside. Newton's theory will always be valid in the world of bodies moving slowly in comparison with the velocity of light. Special relativity will always be a true reflection of the world of moving bodies in negligible gravitational fields. General relativity will always present a true picture of the world of immutable bodies in continuous motion in a gravitational field.

In going over from one world picture to another some specific variants of the overall content of science are left behind, but as such it is immutable and undying. The process of innovation never dies. In nature it consists in the eternal evolution of matter from one form to another. In science it consists in the eternal evolution of positive views around a certain pivotal idea. The most general of such ideas is that of the causality of natural processes, and it is a reflection of the eternal evolution of matter. It never disappears and yet never acquires exhaustive, final form, but takes on new aspects and shades in every new world picture. The enrichment and elaboration of the unified, immutable idea of causality is the eternal contribution of natural scientists to science.

Such a contribution may be made without a clear idea of the specific domain to which it belongs. Many scientists develop, specify and enrich the principle of casuality without a clear realisation of the impact of their discoveries. Einstein did not belong to this category. He knew that the apotheosis of the causal explanation of nature as a whole consisted in the contribution of each scientific theory to the basic, historically invariant, immutable foundation of science.

Not that every new experimentally verified and applied theory automatically joins the ranks of previously established theories. Nor are the "tangible assets" of science isolated from the unsolved problems. Every new positive theory, every positive solution breeds a vast number of new questions, in fact more than the number of questions it has solved. It takes a dogmatic interpretation of a new theory to prevent new questions, difficulties and contradictions from arising. It is these newly arising problems which contribute to the inevitable further evolution of the theory, to the living immortality inherent in every living organism, which is so different from the immortality of a marble statue.

Relativity belongs to the "tangible assets" of science: special relativity is as complete and unambiguous as classical thermodynamics, for example. General relativity, although it has not as yet attained similar completeness, represents a logical sequel to the theory of gravitation. But relativity has posed to science the problem of particle transmutations, the problem of field interactions, the problem of deriving the postulates of relativity (the statements concerning variations in the behaviour of measuring rods and clocks) from the atomistic structure of matter and radiation (and possibly also from the atomistic structure of space-time). These problems are more numerous, difficult and acute than the problems once raised by Michelson's experiment (recall but the infinite energies obtained in the continual description of quantum processes taking into account relativistic laws).

The following is characteristic of these quantum-relativistic problems.

In the 1960s one can no longer question the need for a radical revision of the world picture in order to overcome the current predicaments of theoretical physics. In fact, in our time the very meaning of the words "a radical revision of the world picture" is changing.

For three centuries or so the heliocentric revolution was regarded as the most sweeping revision of the universal scheme. Actually it was a prologue to a more general change in the world picture—a revision of its primary image. In the 17th century scholars began to regard the Aristotelian categories of "being", "not being" and "qualitative motion" as capable of a purely mechanistic explanation, as secondary effects of a simple displacement of immutable bodies. There is nothing in the world which could not, in the final analysis, be explained by the configurations and reciprocal displacements of analogous bodies.

Electrodynamics brought about a crisis in this "classical ideal" and it was saved only by the paradoxical concept of the constancy of the velocity of light in systems moving relative to one another.

In the 19th century an idea was advanced which seemed to break even more drastically with its precursors. Non-Euclidean geometry encroached on relationships which had seemed self-evident not only in the elementary empirical sense in which people once spoke of the "self-evident" fixedness of the earth. The theorems of Euclidean geometry had seemed intrinsic to reason and logically self-evident. As the Russian mathematician V. F. Kagan put it at a session of the University of Kazan celebrating the centenary of Lobachevsky's non-Euclidean geometry, "it seemed easier to move the earth than to reduce the sum of the angles in a triangle, make parallel lines converge or perpendiculars to the same line diverge".

Lobachevsky and Riemann spoke of the real nature of non-Euclidean relationships; before Einstein, however, there existed no logically closed theory which would treat these relationships as specific and indubitable physical statements. When Einstein discovered an unambiguous physical equivalent for non-Euclidean relationships he changed the very meaning lying behind the words "a new world picture". Today such change means not just going over to a new kinematic scheme of bodies moving in space, but going over to a new geometrical interpretation of space itself.

Relativity also carried the germ of an even more radical interpretation of the words "a new world picture". In order to develop a world picture in which the fundamental concept is that of the transmutation of elementary particles within the cells of a discrete space-time, one must develop a new logic, new norms of logical speculative reasoning. Today a revision of the world picture means more than just a new kinematics of moving bodies, more than just a new geometry; it means a new logic. This is an even greater "madness", an even more sweeping rejection of traditional norms and a new principle.

The progress of science is not limited to the development of more precise conceptions of the world, it is not reduced to such developments, nor to the greater thoroughness or comprehensiveness of such developments. The progress of science is not fully measured by the level of knowledge, nor even by the first or second derivative of that level with respect to time. What changes is the "qualitative" degree to which a transition to new conceptions is more drastic, general, paradoxical, "mad"—the very meaning of these epithets changes. From the kinetic "madness" of a moving earth to the physico-geometrical "madness" of a non-Euclidean universe, and on to the logical paradoxes of contemporary quantum-relativistic field theory. However habitual and "self-evident" any new link in the chain of scientific progress might become, it leaves its indelible imprint of courage and freedom. When science departed from the anthropomorphic self-evidence of the Ptolemaic system it also learned the lesson of relinquishing other "self-evident" absolutes. It could never turn back. Once science had begun to operate with different geometries in describing the universe it could no longer go back to the idea of an absolute, *a priori* geometry. Now that various systems of logical reasoning are applied to different physical conditions in quantum field theory, science will never revert to an absolute logic. In the drive for truth science acquires both new trophies and new types of weapons.

In this respect Einstein's works gave impetus to a sweeping rearmament of science. After Einstein, not only did people get to know more about the universe but the very mode of scientific cognition changed. Einstein's ideas represented a great synthesis of experimental and mathematical paradoxes, a rejection, within the framework of a single theory, of empirical self-evidence (in continuance of the Copernican tradition) and habitual, seemingly *a priori* mathematical (in relativity theory) and logical (in quantum theory) norms. This impact on the mode of scientific thinking is irreversible and its imprint will remain for ever. Einstein's ideas are immortal as links in the irreversible approximation of science to the truth because they have led to an irreversible change in the methods of scientific thinking.

The immortality of a scientific theory derives not only from the answers it provides, the new problems it poses, and its influence on the mode of scientific cognition. Science develops in the living intertwining of internal motive forces and public thinking, on which it in turn exerts a profound influence. A scientific theory acquires historical importance by its impact on historical circumstances, on the life, work and self-consciousness of people.

Recall once again Engels's remarkably exact and comprehensive formula in which he characterises the social impact of natural science in the 17th and 18th centuries. In the final analysis, the upshot of the merger of natural science and philosophy was the Great French Revolution. What is the upshot of philosophical generalisations of Einstein's theory? An answer to a similar question with regard to the whole of the new physics was given in 1908 by Lenin: modern physics is giving birth to dialectical materialism.[1] Relativity, with its deliberate and consistent penetration into the material causality of physical phenomena, with its universal understanding of causality and its explicit and sharp anti-dogmatic tendency, fits into this formula.

Before taking over from the old traditional conceptions, the new physical theories appearing in the past had to be spearheaded against specific physical notions: against the absolute nature of "up" and "down", against the fixedness of the earth, against the possibility of *perpetuum mobile*, etc. In order to overthrow the classical concepts of absolute space and time, relativity had to be spearheaded not only against specific physical concepts (the stationary ether, etc.), but also against the dogmatic spirit in science, against dogmatism as such. The principle of the constancy of the velocity of light, the new theory of mass and energy, the principle of the equivalence of acceleration and gravitation, the concept of space-time curvature—this road could not be traversed spontaneously, as a series of consecutive anti-dogmatic, essentially scientific generalisations. This road is so revolutionary, it included such a paradoxical destruction of "self-evident" concepts that it could not be passed without a deliberate and consistent refutation of dogmatism. That is why Einstein's anti-dogmatic ideas are inseparable from the positive content of relativity. This is seen in any systematic exposition of the theory; it is even more apparent in its historical exposition, and it is there for all to see in Einstein's life history. Einstein's anti-dogmatism was directed against both phenomenological "self-evidence", which provides the basis for positivistic "pure description", and the *a priori* logical "self-evidence" of concepts. Such a position, cannot, of course, become "obsolete", for it is an expression

[1] V. I. Lenin, *Collected Works*, Moscow, 1962, Vol. 14, p. 313.

of the continuous renovation of science. Relativity enters naturally into the ideological arsenal of those social forces whose purpose it is to remove all barriers from the road of the ceaseless, infinite expansion of human knowledge and power over nature.

What do we mean by giving practical value to relativity theory?

The practical applications of 17th- and 18th-century physics resulted in the development of machine production and in the new social conditions engendered by it. Practical application of relativity has ushered in the atomic age. Atomic energy and all that accompanies it, from nuclear alchemy to cybernetics, is not just an *application* of science—it is science itself. Applications of science and scientific experiment merge in such fields as space research, the construction and utilisation of atomic reactors, the construction and utilisation of cybernetic systems. Industry's task lies no longer in the manufacture of certain established types of instruments but in the rapid transition to new instruments. Production is measured not by its level but by the rate of scientific and industrial progress. Shops and even instruments (space-research instruments, for example) become laboratories, and reciprocally, laboratories become shops.

Looking ahead and envisaging the broader applications of modern physical ideas, one finds that the atomic age is based on applications of relativity theory to problems of the microscopic and submicroscopic world governing processes inside the atomic nucleus and interactions of elementary particles. This is the aspect of relativity which is turned to the future, to a unified theory of elementary particles and fields and a more consistent unification and generalisation of quantum and relativistic laws.

Facing the future are the most abstract trends in contemporary physics, trends remote from any practical applications, and even from the status of unambiguous physical theory. Trends coinciding in spirit with the aspirations which led Einstein on in his work since the 1930s until the very end.

The embodiment of these tendencies in unambiguous, verified and practically applicable theories will probably correspond to the broadest industrial applications of processes involving the liberation of energies compatible with the internal energy of particles. Utilisation of such concentrated energy sources and energies will require completely automated production to a degree currently achieved in cybernetic systems. Such automation, which in principle includes automatic transition to better systems, has so far been realised in computer systems for processing and transmitting information. When the atomic age emerges from its primary stage such automation will spread to all the basic industries and to transport.

The restriction of cybernetics to the processing and transmission of information which is characteristic of the present transitional stage of technological progress, corresponds to specific features in the development of physics. Up to a certain time quantum physics dealt with comparatively small energies of radiation and could therefore remain non-relativistic. Then higher energies came to be studied, and relativistic concepts of the microcosm were required, resulting in a deeper generalisation of quantum mechanics and general relativity. Cybernetic systems for the production, transmission, distribution and utilisation of energies of tremendous intensity will represent the embodiment of quantum-relativistic conceptions.

How will such technologies affect the nature of human labour? An answer to this question enables us to appreciate the impact of Einstein's ideas on human destinies. Arranging the components of labour in an ascending scale of reconstructional effect on technology, we obtain a series: utilisation of available equipment, the search for new, more effective structural and technological schemes within the framework of the same physical principles, the search for new physical principles. We can already perceive the extent to which automatic mechanisms have enhanced the reconstructive component of labour by replacing the labourer in the first link of the series. At the next stage, cybernetic systems capable of altering their own design will enable people to concentrate on more ambitious problems. Cybernetics does not replace man, it changes the nature of his creative work. On the example of the most advanced branches of modern engineering we see how labour merges with research—not in special problems but in the basic problems of physical reality, problems of the structure of outer space, elementary particles and fields. Such labour is *incompatible with social exploitation.*

Thus Einstein's work is linked with the spiritual and material emancipation of the human race. Therein lies the immortality of his scientific exploit. Immortal also is the image of Einstein, who renounced the "merely personal" and the daily commonplace, in the name of cognition of the world as an orderly whole united by causal relationships.

The time will come when the man in the street will know more about nature than Einstein did. But he will draw from Einstein's work his aloofness from the "merely personal", he will hear the beating of the giant heart. People reading Einstein's works will always be struck by the loftiness and athletic musculature of his mind (as the intellectual might of Karl Marx's *Capital* was once characterised).

This is Einstein: a man among men, and a man with his thoughts. This is his life: the Luitpold Gymnasium; Italy with its blue Mediterranean coastline, fine old cities and museums; student days in Switzerland; the Bern Patent Office; Professorship; Berlin; the First World War; world fame; travels; a refugee from the nazis; work in the United States; the A-bomb tragedy. This is his work: Brownian movement, photons, special relativity, general relativity, attempts to develop the unified field theory.

Remember the verses about God creating Newton and illuminating the universe, and the Devil who sent Einstein to plunge it back into darkness. To illumine once and for all the absolute laws of reality is truly beyond the possibilities—and the intentions—of man. It might be the Devil's work to reject Newton's illumination of the universe—and with it any light at all. But it takes human inspiration and human genius to replace the light kindled by Newton with a much brighter light, never to regard the picture of the universe in any given light as final, and never to fear that the removal of an old light will result in darkness. This was the achievement of one of the greatest physicists of all times, a man, take him for all in all.

SELECTED REFERENCES

1. *Helle Zeit—Dunkle Zeit. In Memoriam Albert Einstein*, edited by Carl Seelig, Europa Verlag (Zurich 1956).
2. *Albert Einstein: Philosopher-Scientist*, edited by Paul A. Schilpp, Tudor, New York, 1951.
3. A. Einstein. *Ideas and Opinions*, Alvin Redman, London, 1956.
4. A. Einstein. *Out of My Later Years*, Thames and Hudson, London, 1950.
5. A. Einstein. *Lettres à Maurice Solovine*, Paris, 1956.
6. A. Einstein, L. Infeld. *The Evolution of Physics*, Simon & Schuster, New York, 1954.
7. *Einstein on Peace*, edited by O. Nathan and H. Norden. Simon & Schuster, New York, 1960.
8. B. Cohen. *An Interview with Einstein*, Scientific American, Vol. 193, No. 1, July 1955.
9. P. Frank. *Einstein, His Life and Times*, Jonathan Cape, London, 1950.
10. M. B. Freeman. *The Story of Albert Einstein*, Random House, New York, 1958.
11. G. H. Garbedian. *Albert Einstein, Maker of Universes*, Funk & Wagnall, New York, 1939.
12. L. Infeld. *Quest*, Doubleday, Doran, New York, 1941.
13. R. Jungk. *Brighter Than a Thousand Suns*, New York, 1958.
14. A. Moszkowski. *Einstein. Einblicke in Seine Gedankenwelt*, Hamburg-Berlin, 1921.
15. C. Seelig. *Albert Einstein. Leben und Werk Eines Genies Unsere Zeit*, Zurich, 1960.
16. A. Vallentin. *Le drame d'Albert Einstein*, Paris, 1957.

NAME INDEX

A

Adler, Friedrich—172, 174, 234
Afanasyeva-Ehrenfest, Tatyana—234
Ampère, André—38
Andreyev, L. N.—361
Archimedes—314
Aristotle—119, 124, 281, 357, 358
Avenarius, Richard—38
Azef—228

B

Bach, Johann Sebastian—89
Balzac, Honoré de—218
Bamberger, Louis—254
Bargmann, Valentin—256
Beethoven, Ludwig van—21, 90
Beilis, M.—228
Bellarmine, Robert—210
Bergmann, Peter G.—256
Bergson, Henri—239
Berkeley, George—68, 76
Bernstein, Aaron—23
Besso, Michele Angelo—39, 40
Bismark, Otto—70
Boétie, Etienne de la—123
Bohr, Niels—7, 184, 269, 270, 275, 278, 279, 282, 285, 288, 293
Boltzmann, Ludwig—113
Born, Hedwig—359
Born, Max—84, 272, 275, 289, 290, 318
Boyle, Robert—124
Brahe, Tycho—179, 180

Brahms, Johannes—90
Brod, Max—180
Broglie, Louis de—272, 282
Brown, Robert—133
Brüning, Heinrich—249
Bruno, Giordano—10
Büchner, Ludwig—23
Bucky, Gustav—332
Byland, Hans—83

C

Calvin, Johann—172
Carnap, R.—356
Carnot, Sadi—130
Cervantes, Miguel—38, 84
Chavan, Lucien—40
Chicherin, G. V.—228
Clifford, W. K.—38
Cohen, Bernard—191, 355, 360
Copernicus, Nicolaus—10, 108, 149, 210
Curie-Sklodowska, Marie—186, 220, 221, 264

D

D'Alembert, Jean—252
Darwin, Charles—134
Debussy, Claude—90
Dedekind, Richard—38
Democritus—78, 358
Descartes, René—54, 56, 104, 107, 271, 281, 322
Dickens, Charles—38
Dickson, Eugenia—228

Lucretius – 83
Lunacharsky, A. V. – 228, 229
Luzin, N. N. – 306

M

Mach, Ernst – 38, 50, 72, 79, 126, 128, 132, 136, 137, 153, 158, 174, 177, 184, 190, 239, 321, 334, 356
Maier, Gustav – 30
Malebranche, Nicolas de – 59
Mann, Heinrich – 18
Maritsch, Mileva (see Einstein, Mileva)
Marx, Karl – 71, 216
Maupertuis, Pierre-Louis – 252
Mayer, Julius Robert – 281
Mayer, Walter – 256
Maxwell, James Clerk – 145, 159, 281
Meitner, Lise – 195
Mendeleyev, D. I. – 206, 258
Meyerson, Emile – 239
Michelson, Albert Abraham – 146, 156, 216, 233, 306
Millikan, R. A. – 255
Milyukov, P. N. – 228
Minkowski, Hermann – 28, 164, 165
Moszkowski, Alexander – 21, 22, 89, 167, 168
Mozart, Wolfgang Amadeus – 24, 90
Mühsam, Hans – 295, 317

N

Napoleon, Bonaparte – 345
Nernst, Walter – 175, 180, 186, 193, 194, 252
Neurath, K. – 356
Newton, Isaac – 9, 35, 61, 68, 71, 115, 120, 126, 127, 135, 138, 180, 206, 209, 271, 281, 322, 356, 358, 362
Noether, Emma – 164
Nordmann, Charles – 238
Nüesch, Jakob – 32

O

Olschki, Leonardo – 55
Osiander, Andreas – 210
Ostwald, Wilhelm – 132, 136, 137, 198

P

Painlevé, Paul – 239
Pearson, Charles – 38
Pernet, Johann – 28 fn., 31
Perrin, Jean – 186
Pick, Georg – 185, 188
Planck, Max – 43, 86, 139, 142, 147, 163, 171, 174, 178, 186, 193, 198, 252, 253, 278
Platter, Julius – 28 fn.
Podolsky, B. – 286, 288
Poincaré, Henri – 38, 72, 74, 77, 105, 112, 113, 153, 157, 158, 165, 186, 306, 334
Pope, Alexander – 9

R

Racine, Jean-Baptiste – 38
Rathenau, Walther – 237
Rebstein, Jakob – 28 fn.
Ricci, C. G. – 184
Riemann, Bernhard – 38, 109, 164, 165, 365
Rolland, Romain – 199
Roosevelt, Franklin Delano – 341, 345
Rosen, Nathan – 256, 286, 288, 326
Rousseau, Jean-Jacques – 18, 59
Rozsel, Alberta – 361
Rudio, Ferdinand – 28 fn.
Ruess – 22, 23
Russell, Bertrand – 81, 105
Rust, Bernard – 248
Rutherford, Ernest – 186, 269

S

Sachs, Alexander – 341, 345
Saitschik, Robert – 28 fn.
Samuel, Sir Herbert – 241

Printed in U.S.A.
GROSS BROS. Printing Co. Inc.